HOW HUMANS
EVOLVED

Robert Boyd • Joan B. Silk

University of California, Los Angeles

W. W. Norton & Company has been independent since its founding in 1923, when William Warder Norton and Mary D. Herter Norton first published lectures delivered at the People's Institute, the adult education division of New York City's Cooper Union. The Nortons soon expanded their program beyond the Institute, publishing books by celebrated academics from America and abroad. By mid-century, the two major pillars of Norton's publishing program—trade books and college texts—were firmly established. In the 1950s, the Norton family transferred control of their company to its employees, and today—with a staff of four hundred and a comparable number of trade, college, and professional titles published each year—W. W. Norton & Company stands as the largest and oldest publishing house owned wholly by its employees.

For Sam and Ruby

Manufacturing by Courier, Kendallville
Book design by Mary McDonnell
Cover design: Mary McDonnell
Page Layout: Brad Walrod/High Text Graphics, Inc

Library of Congress Cataloging-in-Publication Data
    Boyd, Robert, Ph.D.
        How humans evolved / Robert Boyd and Joan B. Silk,—4th ed.
            p.   cm.
    Includes bibliographical references and index
    ISBN 0-393-17915-X (pbk)
    ISBN 978-0-3931791-5-6 (pbk)

    1. Human evolution. I. Silk, Joan B. II. Title.

GN281.B66 2005
599.93'8—dc22   2005053918

W. W. Norton & Company, Inc., 500 Fifth Avenue, New York, N.Y. 10110
www.wwnorton.com
W. W. Norton & Company, Ltd., Castle House, 75/76 Wells Street, London W1T 3QT

2 3 4 5 6 7 8 9 0

PART THREE: THE HISTORY OF THE HUMAN LINEAGE

PART FOUR: EVOLUTION AND MODERN HUMANS

THE HISTORY OF THE
HUMAN LINEAGE

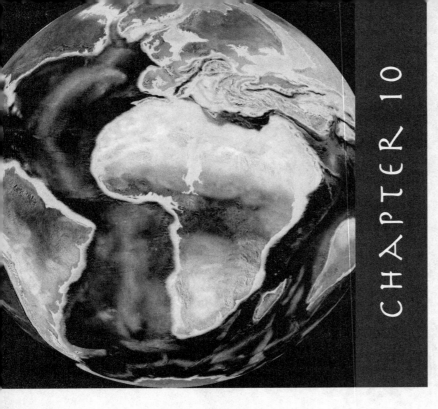

FROM TREE SHREW TO APE

During the Permian and early Triassic periods (Table 10.1), much of the world's fauna was dominated by therapsids, a diverse group of reptiles that possessed traits, such as being warm-blooded and covered with hair (Figure 10.1), that linked them to the mammals that evolved later. At the end of the Triassic, most therapsid groups disappeared, and dinosaurs radiated to fill all of the niches for large, terrestrial animals. One therapsid lineage, however, evolved and diversified to become the first true mammals. These early mammals were probably mouse-sized, nocturnal creatures that fed mainly on seeds and insects. They had internal fertilization but still laid eggs. By the end of the Mesozoic era, 65 million years

242

TABLE 10.1   The geological timescale.

Era	Period	Epoch	Period Begins (mya)	Notable Events
Cenozoic	Quarternary	Recent	0.012	Origins of agriculture and complex societies
		Pleistocene	1.8	Appearance of Homo sapiens
	Tertiary	Pliocene	5	Dominance of land by angiosperms, mammals, birds, and insects
		Miocene	23	
		Oligocene	34	
		Eocene	54	
		Paleocene	65	
Mesozoic	Cretaceous		136	Rise of angiosperms, disappearance of dinosaurs, second great radiation of insects
	Jurassic		190	Abundance of dinosaurs, appearance of first birds
	Triassic		225	Appearance of first mammals and dinosaurs
Paleozoic	Permian		280	Great expansion of reptiles, decline of amphibians, last of trilobites
	Carboniferous		345	Age of Amphibians; first reptiles, first great insect radiation
	Devonian		395	Age of Fishes; first amphibians and insects
	Silurian		430	Land invaded by a few arthropods
	Ordovician		500	First vertebrates
	Cambrian		570	Abundance of marine invertebrates
Precambrian				Primitive marine life

ago (mya), placental and marsupial mammals that bore live young had evolved. With the extinction of the dinosaurs at the beginning of the next era (the Cenozoic) came the spectacular radiation of the mammals. All of the modern descendants of this radiation—including horses, bats, whales, elephants, lions, and primates—evolved from creatures something like a contemporary shrew (Figure 10.2).

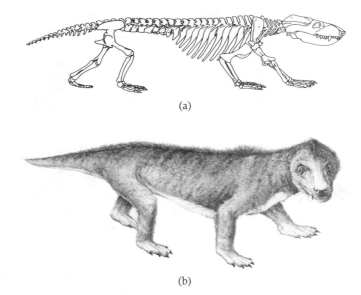

(a)

(b)

FIGURE 10.1 Therapsids dominated the Earth about 250 mya, before dinosaurs became common. The therapsids were reptiles, but they may have been warm-blooded and they had hair instead of scales. The therapsid *Thrinaxodon*, whose skeleton (a) and reconstruction (b) are shown here, was about 30 cm (12 in.) long and had teeth suited for a broad, carnivorous diet.

In order to have a complete understanding of human evolution, we need to know how the transition from a shrewlike creature to modern humans took place. Remember that, according to Darwin's theory, complex adaptations are assembled gradually, in many small steps—each step favored by natural selection. Modern humans have many complex adaptations, like grasping hands, **bipedal** locomotion (walking upright on two legs), toolmaking abilities, language, and large-scale cooperation. To understand evolution fully, we have to consider each of the steps in the lengthy process that transformed a small, solitary, shrewlike insectivore scurrying through the leaf litter of a dark Cretaceous forest into someone more or less like you. Moreover, it is not enough to chronicle the steps in this transition. We also need to understand why each step was favored by natural selection. We want to know, for example, why claws were traded for flat nails, why quadrupedal locomotion gave way to upright bipedal locomotion, and why brains were so greatly enlarged.

In this part of the text, we trace the history of the human lineage. We begin in this chapter by describing the emergence of creatures that resemble modern lemurs and tarsiers; then we document the transformation into monkeylike creatures, and finally into

FIGURE 10.2 The first mammals probably resembled the modern-day Belanger's tree shrew.

animals something like present-day apes. In later chapters, we recount the transformation from hominoid to hominin. We will introduce the first members of the human tribe, Hominini; and then the first members of our own genus, *Homo*; and finally the first known representatives of our own species, *Homo sapiens*. We know something about each step in this process, although far more is known about recent periods than about periods in the most distant past. We will see, however, that there is still a great deal left to be discovered and understood.

CONTINENTAL DRIFT AND CLIMATE CHANGE

To understand the evolution of our species, it is important to understand the geological, climatic, and biological conditions under which these evolutionary changes occurred.

When we think about the evolution of modern humans, we usually picture early humans wandering over open grasslands dotted with acacia trees—the same breathtaking scenery that we see in wildlife documentaries. As we shift the time frame forward through millions of years, the creatures are altered but the backdrop is unchanged. Our mental image of this process is misleading, however, because the scenery has changed along with the cast of characters (Figure 10.3).

It is important to keep this fact in mind because it alters our interpretation of the fossil record. Remember that evolution produces adaptation, but what is adaptive in one environment may not be adaptive in another environment. If the environment remained the same over the course of human evolution, then the kinds of evolutionary changes observed in the hominin fossil record (such as increases in brain size, bipedalism, and prolonged juvenile dependence) would have to be seen as steady improvements in the perfection of human adaptations: evolution would progress toward a fixed goal. But if the environment varied through time, then evolution would have to track a moving target. In this scenario, new characteristics seen in fossils would not have to represent progress in a single direction. Instead, these changes might have been adaptations to changing environmental conditions. As we will see, the world has become much colder and drier in the last 20 million years and particularly variable in the last 800,000 years, and these changes likely altered the course of human evolution. If the world had become warmer rather than colder during this period, then our human ancestors would probably have remained in the safety of the trees and would not have become terrestrial or bipedal. We would probably be stellar rock climbers but poor marathon runners.

The positions of the continents have changed relative to each other and to the poles.

The world has changed a lot in the last 200 million years. One of the factors that has contributed to this change is the movement of the continents, or

FIGURE 10.3 Today, East African savannas look much like this. In the past, the scenery is likely to have been quite different.

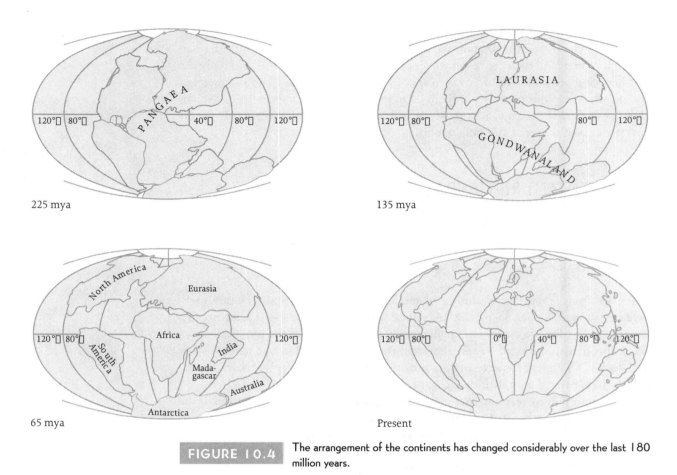

225 mya

135 mya

65 mya

Present

FIGURE 10.4 The arrangement of the continents has changed considerably over the last 180 million years.

continental drift. The continents are not fixed in place; instead, the enormous, relatively light plates of rock that make up the continents slowly wander around the globe, floating on the denser rock that forms the floor of the deep ocean. About 200 mya, all of the land making up the present-day continents was joined together in a single, huge landmass called **Pangaea**. About 125 mya, Pangaea began to break apart into separate pieces (Figure 10.4). The northern half, called **Laurasia**, included what is now North America and Eurasia minus India; the southern half, **Gondwanaland**, consisted of the rest. By the time the dinosaurs became extinct 65 mya, Gondwanaland had broken up into several smaller pieces. Africa and India separated, and India headed north, eventually crashing into Eurasia, while the remainder of Gondwanaland stayed in the south. Eventually, Gondwanaland separated into South America, Antarctica, and Australia, and these continents remained isolated from each other for many millions of years. South America did not drift north to join North America until about 5 mya.

Continental drift is important to the history of the human lineage for two reasons: First, oceans serve as barriers that isolate certain species from others, so the position of the continents plays an important role in the evolution of species. As we will see, the long isolation of South America creates one of the biggest puzzles in our knowledge of primate evolution. Second, continental drift is one of the engines of climate change, and climate change has fundamentally influenced human evolution.

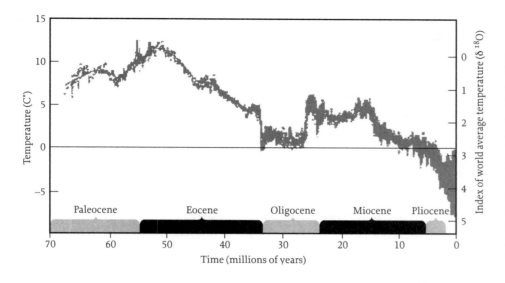

FIGURE 10.5 The gray points are estimates of average world temperature based on the ratio of ^{16}O to ^{18}O taken from deep-sea cores. The red line plots a statistically "smoothed" average value. The variability around the line represents both measurement error and rapid temperature fluctuations that last less than a million years. As we will see (Figure 13.1) most variability in the last several million years has been the result of fluctuations in world temperature, some lasting only a few centuries.

The climate has changed substantially during the last 65 million years—first becoming warmer and less variable, then cooling, and finally fluctuating widely in temperature.

The size and orientation of the continents have important effects on climate. Very large continents tend to have severe weather. This is why Chicago has much colder winters than London, even though London is much farther north. Pangaea was much larger than Asia and is likely to have had very cold weather in winter. When continents restrict the circulation of water from the tropics to the poles, world climates seem to become cooler. These changes, along with other, poorly understood factors, have led to substantial climate change. Figure 10.5 summarizes changes in global temperature during the Cenozoic era. Box 10.1 explains how climatologists reconstruct ancient climates.

To give you some idea of what these changes in temperature mean, consider that during the period of peak warmth in the early Miocene, palm trees grew as far north as what is now Alaska, rich temperate forests (like those in the eastern United States today) extended as far north as Oslo (Norway), and only the tallest peaks in Antarctica were glaciated.

THE METHODS OF PALEONTOLOGY

Much of our knowledge of the history of life comes from the study of fossils, the mineralized bones of dead organisms.

In certain kinds of geological settings, the bones of dead organisms may be preserved long enough for the organic material in the bones to be replaced by minerals (**mineralized**) from the surrounding rock. Such natural copies of bones are called **fossils**. Scientists who recover, describe, and interpret fossil remains are called **paleontologists**.

A great deal of what we know about the history of the human lineage comes from the study of fossils. Careful study of the shapes of different bones tells us about what

BOX 10.1

Using Deep-Sea Cores to Reconstruct Ancient Climates

Beginning about 35 years ago, oceanographers began a program of extracting long cores from the sediments that lie on the floor of the deep sea (about 6000 m, or 20,000 feet, below the surface). Data from these cores have allowed scientists to make much more detailed and accurate reconstructions of ancient climates. Figure 10.5 shows the ratio

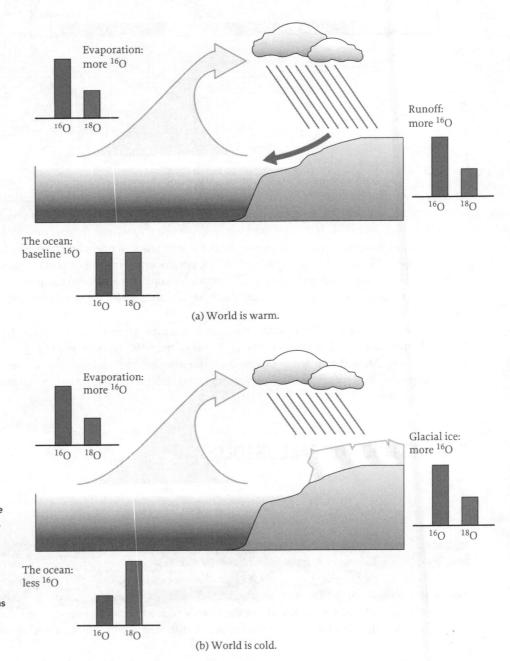

FIGURE 10.6 Water evaporating from the sea is enriched in ^{16}O, and therefore so is precipitation. (a) When the world is warm, this water returns rapidly to the sea, and the concentration of ^{16}O in seawater is unchanged. (b) When the world is cold, much precipitation remains on land as glacial ice, and so the sea becomes depleted in ^{16}O.

Evaporation: more ^{16}O

^{16}O ^{18}O

Runoff: more ^{16}O

^{16}O ^{18}O

The ocean: baseline ^{16}O

^{16}O ^{18}O

(a) World is warm.

Evaporation: more ^{16}O

^{16}O ^{18}O

Glacial ice: more ^{16}O

^{16}O ^{18}O

The ocean: less ^{16}O

^{16}O ^{18}O

(b) World is cold.

of two isotopes of oxygen, $^{16}O{:}^{18}O$, derived from different layers of a deep-sea cores extracted . Because different layers of the cores were deposited at different times over the last 65 million years and have remained nearly undisturbed ever since, they give us a snapshot of the relative amounts of ^{16}O and ^{18}O in the sea when the layer was deposited on the ocean floor.

These ratios allow us to estimate ocean temperatures in the past. Water molecules containing the lighter isotope of oxygen, ^{16}O, evaporate more readily than molecules containing the heavier isotope, ^{18}O, do. Snow and rain have a higher concentration of ^{16}O than the sea does because the water in clouds evaporates from the sea. When the world is warm enough that few glaciers form at high latitudes, the precipitation that falls on the land returns to the sea, and the ratio of the two isotopes of oxygen remains unchanged (Figure 10.6a). When the world is colder, however, much of the snow falling at high latitudes is stored in immense continental glaciers like those now covering Antarctica (Figure 10.6b). Because the water locked in glaciers contains more ^{16}O than the ocean does, the proportion of ^{18}O in the ocean becomes greater. Therefore, the concentration of ^{18}O in seawater increases when the world is cold and decreases when it is warm. This means that scientists can estimate the temperature of the oceans in the past by measuring the ratio of ^{16}O to ^{18}O in different layers of deep-sea cores.

early hominins were like—how big they were, what they ate, where they lived, how they moved, and even something about how they lived. When the methods of systematics described in Chapter 4 are applied to these materials, they also can tell us something about the phylogenetic history of long-extinct creatures. The kinds of plant and animal fossils found in association with the fossils of our ancestors tell us what the environment was like—whether it was forested or open, how much it rained, and whether rainfall was seasonal.

There are several radiometric methods for estimating the age of fossils.

In order to assign a fossil to a particular position in a phylogeny, we must know how old it is. As we will see in later chapters, the date that we assign to particular specimens can profoundly influence our understanding of the evolutionary history of certain lineages or traits.

Radiometric methods provide one of the most important ways to date fossils. To understand how radiometric techniques work, we need to review a little chemistry. All of the atoms of a particular element have the same number of protons in their nucleus. For example, all carbon atoms have six protons. However, different **isotopes** of a particular element have different numbers of neutrons in their nucleus. Carbon-12, the most common isotope of carbon, has six neutrons; and carbon-14 has eight. Radiometric methods are based on the fact that the isotopes of certain elements are unstable. This means that they change spontaneously from one isotope to another of the same element, or to an entirely different element. For example, carbon-14 changes to nitrogen-14, and potassium-40 changes spontaneously to argon-40. For any particular isotope, such changes (or **radioactive decay**) occur at a constant, clocklike rate that can be measured with precision in the laboratory. There are several different radiometric methods:

1. **Potassium–argon dating** is used to date the age of volcanic rocks found in association with fossil material. Molten rock emerges from a volcano at a very high temperature. As a result, all of the argon gas is boiled out of the rock. After this, any argon present in the rock must be due to the decay of potassium. Because

this occurs at a known and constant rate, the ratio of potassium to argon can be used to date volcanic rock. Then, if a fossil is discovered in a geological **stratum** ("layer"; plural *strata*) lying under the stratum that contains the volcanic rock, paleontologists can be confident that the fossil is older than the rock. A new variant of this technique, called **argon–argon dating** because the potassium in the sample is converted to an isotope of argon before it is measured, allows more accurate dating of single rock crystals.

2. **Carbon-14 dating** (or **radiocarbon dating**) is based on an unstable isotope of carbon that living animals and plants incorporate into their cells. As long as the organism is alive, the ratio of the unstable isotope (carbon-14) to the stable isotope (carbon-12) is the same as the ratio of the two isotopes in the atmosphere. Once the animal dies, carbon-14 starts to decay into carbon-12 at a constant rate. By measuring the ratio of carbon-12 to carbon-14, paleontologists can estimate the amount of time that has passed since the organism died.

3. **Thermoluminescence dating** is based on an effect of high-energy nuclear particles traveling through rock. These particles come from the decay of radioactive material in and around the rock and from cosmic rays that bombard the Earth from outer space. When they pass through rock, these particles dislodge electrons from atoms, so the electrons become trapped elsewhere in the rock's crystal lattice. Heating a rock relaxes the bonds holding the atoms in the crystal lattice together. All of the trapped electrons are then recaptured by their respective atoms—a process that gives off light. Researchers often find flints at archaeological sites that were burnt in ancient campfires. It is possible to estimate the number of trapped electrons in these flints by heating them in the laboratory and measuring the amount of light given off. If the density of high-energy particles currently flowing through the site is also known, scientists can estimate the length of time that has elapsed since the flint was burned.

4. **Electron-spin-resonance dating** is used to determine the age of **apatite crystals**, an inorganic component of tooth enamel, according to the presence of trapped electrons. Apatite crystals form as teeth grow, and initially they contain no trapped electrons. These crystals are preserved in fossil teeth and, like the burnt flints, are bombarded by a flow of high-energy particles that generate trapped electrons in the crystal lattice. Scientists estimate the number of trapped electrons by subjecting the teeth to a variable magnetic field—a technique called "electron spin resonance." To estimate the number of years since the tooth was formed, paleontologists must once again measure the flow of radiation at the site where the tooth was found.

Different radiometric techniques are used for different time periods. Methods based on isotopes that decay very slowly, such as potassium-40, work well for fossils from the distant past. However, they are not useful for more recent fossils, because their "clock" doesn't run fast enough. When slow clocks are used to date recent events, large errors can result. For this reason, potassium–argon dating usually cannot be used to date samples less than about 500,000 years old. Conversely, isotopes that decay quickly, such as carbon-14, are useful only for recent periods, because all of the unstable isotopes decay in a relatively short period of time. Thus, carbon-14 can be used only to date sites that are less than about 40,000 years old. The development of thermoluminescence dating and electron-spin-resonance dating is important because these methods allow us to date sites that are too old for carbon-14 dating, but too young for potassium–argon dating.

Absolute radiometric dating is supplemented by relative dating methods based on magnetic reversals and comparison with other fossil assemblages.

Radiometric dating methods are problematic for two reasons. First, a particular site may not always contain material that is appropriate for radiometric dating. Second, radiometric methods have relatively large margins for error. These drawbacks have led scientists to supplement these absolute methods with other, relative methods for dating fossil sites.

One such relative method is based on the remarkable fact that, every once in a while, the Earth's magnetic field reverses itself. This means, for example, that compasses now pointing north would at various times in the past have pointed south (if compasses had been around then, that is). The pattern of magnetic reversals is not the same throughout time, so for any given time period the pattern is unique. But the pattern for a given time *is* the same throughout the world. We know what the pattern is because when certain rocks are formed, they record the direction of the Earth's magnetic field at that time. Thus, by matching up the pattern of magnetic reversals at a particular site with the well-dated sequence of reversals from the rest of the world, scientists are able to date sites.

Another approach is to make use of the fact that sometimes the fossils of interest are found in association with fossils of other organisms that existed for only a limited period of time. For example, during the last 20 million years or so there has been a sequence of distinct pig species in East Africa. Each pig species lived for a known period of time (according to securely dated sites). This means that some East African materials can be accurately dated from their association with fossilized pig teeth.

THE EVOLUTION OF THE EARLY PRIMATES

The evolution of flowering plants created a new set of ecological niches. Primates were among the animals that evolved to fill these niches.

During the first two-thirds of the Mesozoic, the forests of the world were dominated by the **gymnosperms,** trees like contemporary redwood, pine, and fir. With the breakup of Pangaea during the Cretaceous, a revolution in the plant world occurred. Flowering plants, called **angiosperms,** appeared and spread. The evolution of the angiosperms created a new set of ecological niches for animals. Many angiosperms depend on animals to pollinate them, and they produce showy flowers with sugary nectar to attract pollinators. Some angiosperms also entice animals to disperse their seeds by providing nutritious and easily digestible fruits. Arboreal animals that could find, manipulate, chew, and digest these fruits could exploit these new niches. Primates were one of the taxonomic groups that evolved to take advantage of these opportunities. Tropical birds, bats, insects, and some small rodentlike animals probably competed with early primates for the bounty of the angiosperms.

The ancestors of modern primates were small-bodied nocturnal quadrupeds much like contemporary shrews.

To understand the evolutionary forces that shaped the early radiation of the primates, we need to consider two related questions. First, what kind of animal did

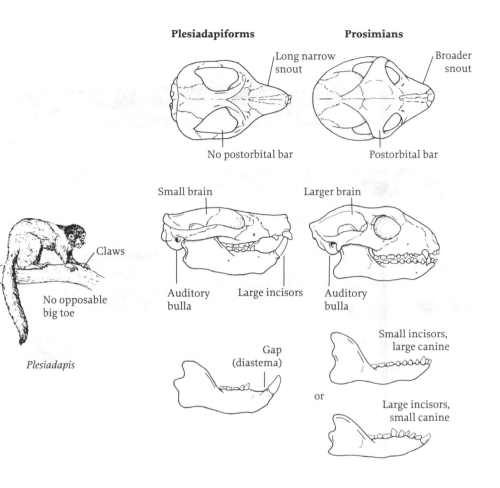

FIGURE 10.7 Plesiadapi-forms were once thought to be primates, but closer analysis indicates they lack many of the defining characteristics of early modern primates. For example, they had claws instead of nails; their eye orbits were not fully encased in bone; their eyes were placed on the sides of the head, so the fields of vision of the two eyes did not converge; and in some species the big toe was not opposable.

natural selection have to work with? Second, what were the selective pressures that favored this suite of traits in ancient primates?

The **plesiadapiforms,** a group of fossil animals found in what is now Montana, Colorado, New Mexico, and Wyoming, give us some clue about what the earliest primates were like. Plesiadapiforms are found at sites that date from the Paleocene epoch, 65 to 54 mya, a time so warm and wet that broadleaf, evergreen forests extended to 60°N (latitude 60° north, near present-day Anchorage in Alaska). The plesiadapiforms varied from tiny, shrew-sized creatures to animals as big as a marmot (Figure 10.7). It seems likely that they were solitary quadrupeds with a well-developed sense of smell. The teeth of these animals are quite variable, suggesting that they had a wide range of dietary specializations. Some members of this group were probably terrestial, some were arboreal quadrupeds, and others may have been adaped for gliding. Most of the plesiadapiforms had claws on their hands and feet, and they did not have binocular vision.

The recent discovery of a 56-million-year-old plesiadapiform by Jonathan Bloch and Doug Boyer of the University of Michigan provides important clues about primate origins. *Carpolestes simpsoni* (Figure 10.8) had an opposable big toe with a flat nail, but claws on its other digits. The claws on its feet and hands probably helped it climb large-diameter tree trunks, but it was also able to grasp small supports. *C. simpsoni* had low-crowned molars, which are suited for eating fruit. Its eyes were on the sides of the head, and the fields of vision did not overlap. These creatures probably used

FIGURE 10.8 An artist's reconstruction of the recently discovered plesiadapiform *Carpolestes simpsoni*. This creature, which lived about 56 mya, had grasping hands and feet.

their hands and feet to grasp small branches as they climbed around in the terminal branches of fruiting trees, and used their hands to handle fruit as they were feeding.

Experts disagree about whether plesiadapiforms ought to be included within the primate order. They possess some but not all of the suite of traits that characterize modern primates, and the decision about how to classify these creatures depends on a relatively arbitrary assessment of how similar they are to other primates. The plesiadapiforms are important to know about, however, because they provide some information about the traits that characterized the common ancestor of modern primates.

The discovery of C. simpsoni helps explain why natural selection favored the basic features of primate morphology.

There are several different theories about why the traits that are diagnostic of primates evolved in early members of the primate order. Matt Cartmill, a Duke University anthropologist, has argued that forward-facing eyes (orbital convergence) that provide binocular stereoscopic vision, grasping hands and feet, and nails on the toes and fingers all evolved together to enhance visually directed predation on insects in the terminal branches of trees. This idea is supported by the fact that many arboreal predators, including owls and ocelots, have eyes in the front of the head. However, the discovery that grasping hands and feet evolved in a frugivorous plesiadapiform species before the eyes were shifted forward presents problems for this hypothesis.

Fred Szalay of Hunter College and Marian Dagosto of Northwestern University have suggested that grasping hands and feet and flat nails on the fingers and toes all coevolved to facilitate a form of leaping locomotion. *C. simpsoni* poses a problem for this hypothesis, too, because it had grasping hands and feet but evidently didn't leap from branch to branch.

Robert Sussman of Washington University hypothesized that the suite of traits that characterize primates may have been favored because they enhanced the ability of early primates to exploit a new array of plant resources—including fruit, nectar, flowers, and gum—as well as insects. The early primates may have foraged and handled small food items in the dimness of the forest night, and this nocturnal behavior may have

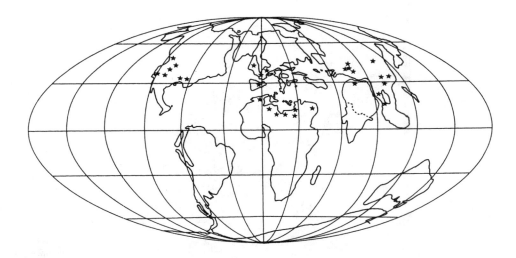

FIGURE 10.9 Sites where Eocene prosimian fossils have been found. The continents are arranged as they were during the early Eocene.

favored good vision, precise eye–hand coordination, and grasping hands and feet. However, *C. simpsoni* foraged on fruit before orbital convergence evolved.

Finally, Tab Rasmussen, also of Washington University, has proposed that grasping hands and feet allowed early primates to forage on fruit, flowers, and nectar in the terminal branches of angiosperms. Later the eyes were shifted forward to facilitate visually directed predation on insects. The idea that the evolution of grasping hands and feet preceded the movement of the eyes to the front of the face fits with the evidence from *C. simpsoni*.

Primates with modern features appeared in the Eocene epoch.

The Eocene epoch (54 to 34 mya) was even wetter and warmer than the preceding Paleocene, with great tropical forests covering much of the globe. At the beginning of the Eocene, North America and Europe were connected, but then the two continents separated and grew farther apart. The animals within these continents evolved in isolation and became progressively more different. There was some contact between Europe and Asia and between India and Asia during this period, but South America was completely isolated. Primate fossils from this period have been found in North America, Europe, Asia, and Africa (Figure 10.9). More than 200 species of fossil prosimians have now been identified. The Eocene primates were a highly successful and diverse group, occupying a range of ecological niches.

It is in these Eocene primates that we see at least the beginnings of all the features that define modern primates (see Chapter 5). They had grasping hands and feet with nails instead of claws, hindlimb-dominated posture, shorter snouts, eyes moved forward in the head and encased in a bony orbit, and relatively large brains.

The Eocene primates are classified into two families: Omomyidae and Adapidae (Figure 10.10). Although their affinities to modern primates are not known, most researchers compare the omomyids to galagos and tarsiers and the adapids to living lemurs (Figure 10.11). Some of the omomyids had huge eye orbits, like modern tarsiers. This feature suggests that they were nocturnal because nocturnal primates who do not have tapeta (singular *tapetum*), such as owl monkeys and tarsiers, have extremely large orbits. (The **tapetum** is a reflecting layer behind the retina that increases the light-capturing capacity of the eye.) Omomyid dentition was quite variable: some seem to have been adapted for frugivory, and others for more insectivorous

FIGURE 10.10 Adapids were larger than omomyids, and they had longer snouts and smaller orbits than the omomyids had. (a) The size of the orbits suggests that the adapids were active during the day, and the shape of their teeth suggests that they fed on fruit or leaves. (b) Omomyids were small primates that fed mainly on insects, fruit, or gum. The large orbits suggest that they may have been nocturnal. They are similar in some ways to modern tarsiers.

(a) Adapids (*Notharctus*)   (b) Omomyids (*Tetonius*)

diets. Some omomyids have elongated calcaneus bones in their feet, much like those of modern dwarf lemurs, and they may have been able to leap from branch to branch.

The adapids had smaller eye orbits and were likely diurnal. They resemble living lemurs in many aspects of their teeth, skull, nasal, and auditory regions. However, the adapids do not display some of the unique derived traits that are characteristic of modern lemurs, including the tooth comb, a specialized formation of incisors used for grooming. They had a range of dietary adaptations, including insectivorous, folivorous, and frugivorous diets. They were generally larger than the omomyids, and their **postcranial** bones (the bones that make up the skeleton below the neck) indicate that some were active arboreal quadrupeds like modern lemurs, while others were slow quadrupeds similar to contemporary lorises. At least one species showed substantial sexual dimorphism, a feature that points to life in nonmonogamous social groups.

Paleontologists are uncertain whether the modern anthropoids evolved from the omomyids or from the adapids.

The more we learn about the primate lineages of the Eocene and early Oligocene, the clearer it becomes that these early monkeys were extremely diverse and quite successful. We are not entirely sure how these fossil primates are related to modern prosimians or which of them gave rise to the first anthropoid primates.

THE FIRST ANTHROPOIDS

During the Oligocene epoch, many parts of the world became colder and drier.

By the end of the Eocene epoch, 34 mya, the continents were more or less positioned on the globe as they are today. However, South America and North America were not

The behavior of adapids and omomyids probably differed. (a) Adapids were probably diurnal. Here a group forages for leaves. (b) Omomyids were probably nocturnal. Several species are shown here.

yet connected by Central America; Africa and Arabia were separated from Eurasia by the Tethys Sea, a body of water that connected the Mediterranean Sea and the Persian Gulf. South America and Australia had completed their separation from Antarctica, creating deep, cold currents around Antarctica (see Figure 10.4). Some climatologists believe that these cold currents reduced the transfer of heat from the equator to Antarctic regions, and may have been responsible for the major drop in global temperatures that occurred during this period. During the Oligocene epoch, 34 to 23 mya, temperatures dropped, and the range in temperature variation over the course of the year increased. Throughout North America and Europe, tropical broadleaf evergreen forests were replaced by broadleaf deciduous forests. Africa and South America remained mainly warm and tropical.

Primates similar to modern monkeys may have first evolved during the Eocene, but they radiated during the Oligocene.

The origins of the anthropoids may extend back into the Eocene epoch. *Algeripithecus minutus*, known from fragmentary fossils in North Africa, possessed some cranial features that we find in modern anthropoids, but it was otherwise quite primitive. These finds are dated to about 50 mya. *Eosimias*, a tiny primate with small incisors, large canines, and broad premolars, lived in southern China during the middle of the Eocene epoch.

The earliest unambiguous anthropoid fossils are found at a site in the Fayum (also spelled "Faiyûm") Depression of Egypt. The Fayum deposits straddle the Eocene–Oligocene boundary, 36 to 33 mya. The Fayum is now one of the driest places on Earth, but it was very different at the beginning of the Oligocene. Sediments of soil recovered from the Fayum tell us that it was a warm, wet, and somewhat seasonal habitat then. The plants were most like those now found in the tropical forests of Southeast Asia. The soil sediments contain the remnants of the roots of plants that grow in swampy areas, like mangroves, and the sediments suggest that there were periods of standing water at the site. There are also many fossils of waterbirds. All this suggests that the Fayum was a swamp during the Oligocene (Figure 10.12). Among the mammalian fauna at the Fayum are representatives of the suborder that includes porcupines and guinea pigs, opossums, insectivores, bats, primitive carnivores, and an archaic member of the hippopotamus family.

The Fayum contains one of the most diverse primate communities ever documented. This community included at least five groups of prosimians, one group of omomyids, and three groups of anthropoid primates: the oligopithecids, parapithecids, and propliopithecids (Figure 10.13). To introduce a theme that will become familiar in the chapters that follow, the more that paleontologists learn about early primates from the Fayum, the more complicated the primate family tree becomes. Instead of a neat tree with a few heavy branches that connect ancient fossils with living species, we have a messy bush with many fine branches and only the most tenuous connections between most living and extinct forms. Nevertheless, we can detect certain trends in the primate fossil record at the Fayum that provide insight about the selective pressures that shaped adaptation within the primate lineage.

The parapithecids were a very diverse group; currently they are divided into four genera and eight species. The largest parapithecids were the size of guenons (3 kg, or about 6½ lb) and the smallest were the size of marmosets (150 g,

FIGURE 10.12   Although the Fayum Depression is now a desert, it was a swampy forest during the Oligocene.

FIGURE 10.13   The Fayum was home to a diverse group of primates, including propliopithecids like *Aegyptopithecus zeuxis* (upper left) and *Propliopithecus chirobates* (upper right), and parapithecids like *Apidium phiomense* (bottom).

BOX 10.2

Facts That Teeth Can Reveal

Much of what we know about the long-dead early primates comes from their teeth. Fortunately, teeth are more durable than other bones, and they are also the most common elements in the fossil record. If paleontologists had to choose only one part of the skeleton to study, most would choose teeth. There are several reasons for this choice. First, teeth are complex structures with many independent features, which makes them very useful for phylogenetic reconstruction. Second, tooth enamel is not remodeled during an animal's life, and it carries an indelible record of an individual's life history. Third, teeth show a precise developmental sequence that allows paleontologists to make inferences about the growth and development of long-dead organisms. Finally, as we saw in Chapter 6, each of the major dietary specializations (frugivory, folivory, insectivory) is associated with characteristic dental features.

Figure 10.14 diagrams one side of the upper jaw of three modern species of primates: an insectivore, a folivore,

and a frugivore. The insectivorous tarsier (Figure 10.14a) has relatively large, sharp incisors and canines, which are used to bite through the tough external skeletons of insects. In contrast, the folivorous indri (Figure 10.14b) has relatively small incisors, and large premolars with sharp crests that allow it to shred tough leaves. Finally, the frugivorous mangabey (Figure 10.14c) has large incisors that are used to peel the rinds from fruit. Its molars are small because the soft, nutritious parts of fruit require less grinding than leaves do.

Knowing what an animal eats enables researchers to make sensible guesses about other characteristics as well. For example, there is a good correlation between diet and body size in living primates: insectivores are generally smaller than frugivores, and frugivores are generally smaller than folivores.

(a)   (b)   (c)

 FIGURE 10.14 The right half of the upper jaws of (a) a tarsier (an insectivore), (b) an indri (a folivore), and (c) a mangabey (a frugivore). I = incisor, C = canine, P = premolar, M = molar.

or about 5 oz). These creatures have the primitive dental formula 2.1.3.3/2.1.2.3, which has been retained in New World monkeys but has been modified in Old World monkeys and apes, whose dental formula is 2.1.2.3/2.1.2.3. (Dental formulas were discussed in Chapter 5.) Many aspects of parapithecid teeth and postcranial anatomy are also primitive, suggesting that they may have been the unspecialized ancestors both of more derived Old World monkey lineages and of the New World monkeys (see Box 10.2).

The propliopithecids are represented by two genera and five species. These primates had the same dental formula as modern Old World monkeys, but they lack other derived features associated with Old World monkeys. The largest and most famous of the propliopithecids is named *Aegyptopithecus zeuxis*, who is known from several skulls and a number of postcranial bones (Figure 10.15). *A. zeuxis* was a medium-sized monkey, perhaps as big as a female howler monkey (6 kg, or 13.2 lb). It was a diurnal, arboreal quadruped with a relatively small brain. The shape and size of the teeth suggest that it ate mainly fruit. Males were much larger than females, indicating that they probably lived in nonmonogamous social groups. Other propliopithecoids were smaller than *A. zeuxis*, but their teeth suggest that they also ate fruit, as well as seeds and perhaps gum. They were probably arboreal quadrupeds with strong, grasping feet. Modern Old World monkeys and apes may have been derived from members of this family.

The third group of Fayum anthropoids, the oligopithecids, were among the earliest Fayum monkeys. The oligopithecids, who may have ranged beyond the Fayum through North Africa and the Arabian Peninsula, share many primitive features with the Eocene prosimians. However, they also share some derived features with contemporary anthropoids. For example, the orbits are fully enclosed in bone. The dental formula of some oligopithecids was the same as that of modern Old World monkeys and apes. It is not clear whether the reductions in the number of premolars in oligopithecids and propliopithecids represent independent evolutionary events or common ancestry.

Primates appear in South America for the first time during the Oligocene, but it is unclear where they came from or how they got there.

The earliest New World monkey fossils come from a late-Oligocene site in Bolivia. The monkeys at this site have three premolars like modern New World monkeys and were about the size of owl monkeys. The shape of their molars suggests they were frugivores. Sites in Argentina and Chile contain a number of monkey genera dating to the early and middle Miocene. They were part of a diverse animal population

FIGURE 10.15   In this reconstruction of the skeleton of *Aegyptopithecus*, the postcranial bones that have been found are shown in red.

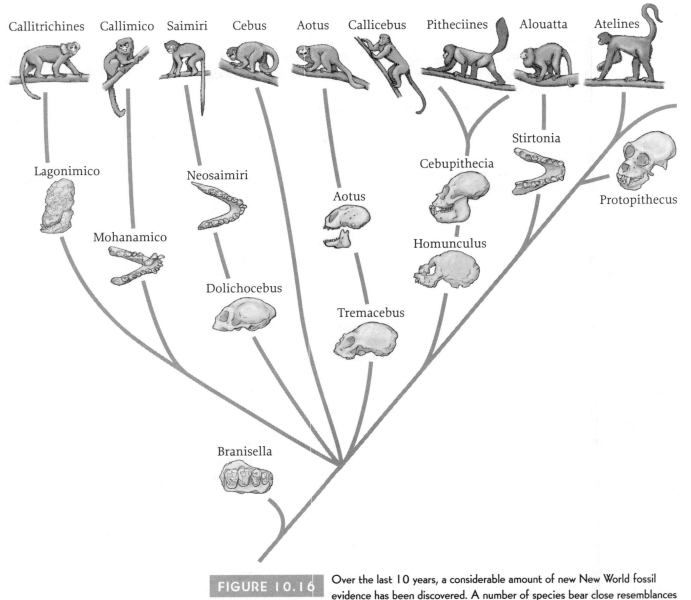

FIGURE 10.16 Over the last 10 years, a considerable amount of new New World fossil evidence has been discovered. A number of species bear close resemblances to modern primate species. There were once many more species of primates than we find in the same areas today.

that included rodents, ungulates, sloths, and marsupial mammals. Most of these Patagonian primates were about the size of squirrel monkeys (800 g, or 1.8 lb), though some may have been as large as sakis (3 kg, or 6.6 lb). In Colombia, Miocene sites dated to 12 to 10 mya contain nearly a dozen species of fossil primates. Many of these species closely resemble modern New World monkeys (Figure 10.16). Pleistocene sites in Brazil and the Carribean islands have yielded a mixture of extinct and extant species. Evidently, several species were considerably larger than any living New World primates. Although there are no indigenous primates in the Carribean now, these islands once housed a diverse community of primates.

The origin of New World primates is a great mystery. It is not clear how monkeys got to South America or how they found their way to the islands of the Carribean. The absence of Oligocene primate fossils in North America and the many similarities between New World monkeys and the Fayum primates suggest to many scientists that the ancestor of the New World monkeys came from Africa. The problem with this idea is that we don't know how they could have gotten from Africa to South America. By the late Oligocene, the two continents were separated by at least 3000 km (about 2000 miles) of open ocean. Some authors have suggested that primates could have rafted across the sea on islands of floating vegetation. Although there are no well-documented examples of primates rafting such distances, fossil rodents appear in South America about the same time and are so similar to those found in Africa that it seems very likely that rodents managed to raft across the Atlantic.

Other researchers suggest that New World monkeys are descended from a North American primate. But there are two problems with this hypothesis. One is that, although there is evidence of Eurasian *prosimians* reaching North America earlier (during the Eocene), there are no known *anthropoid* fossils from North America—for any time period. If we assume that an early anthropoid reached North America at about the same time, then the extensive similarities between Old World and New World monkeys could be readily explained. Otherwise we would have to reach the improbable conclusion that New World monkeys are descended from a prosimian ancestor, and that the many similarities between New World and Old World monkeys are due to convergence.

The second difficulty with this hypothesis is geographic. Because North America did not join South America until 5 mya, this scenario also requires the anthropoid ancestor to have made an ocean voyage, though it may have been possible to break up the voyage by hopping across the islands that dotted the Caribbean. Still other possibilities may exist (Figure 10.17).

The most intriguing hypothesis is that anthropoid primates actually appeared in Africa much earlier, when a transatlantic journey would have been easier to complete. Atlantic sea levels were lowest during the middle of the Oligocene. The Fayum primates with the closest affinities to New World monkeys are considerably younger than this. However, this may not be a fatal liability for the hypothesis. There is good reason to believe that the date of the earliest fossil we have discovered usually underestimates the age of a lineage. The method outlined in Box 10.3 suggests that anthropoids actually originated at least 52 mya.

FIGURE 10.17   Perhaps this is how early monkeys *really* got from Africa to South America.

BOX 10.3

Missing Links

University of Zürich anthropologist Robert Martin has pointed out that most lineages are probably older than the oldest fossils we have discovered. The extent of the discrepancy between the dates of the fossils that we have discovered and the actual origin of the lineage depends on the fraction of fossils that have been discovered. If the primate fossil record were nearly complete, then the fact that no anthropoids living more than 35 mya have been found would mean that they didn't exist that long ago. However, we have reason to believe that the primate fossil record is quite incomplete (Figure 10.18).

Just as not all fossils of a given species are ever found,

FIGURE 10.18 The sparseness of the fossil record virtually guarantees that the oldest fossil found of a particular species underestimates the age of the species. (a) The population size of a hypothetical primate species is plotted here against time. In this case, we imagine that the species becomes somewhat less populous as it approaches extinction. (b) The number of fossils left by this species is less than the population size. It is unlikely that the earliest and latest fossils date to the earliest and latest living individuals. (c) The number of fossils found by paleontologists is less than the total number of fossils.

not all species are known to us either. How many species are missing from our data? Martin's method for answering this question is based on the assumption that the number of species has increased steadily from 65 mya, when the first primates appeared, to the present. This means that there were half as many species 32.5 mya as there are now, three-fourths as many species 16.25 mya as there are now, and so on. Assuming that each species has lived about 1 million years, the average life span of a mammalian species, Martin summed these figures to obtain the number of primate species that have ever lived. Then he took the number of fossil species discovered so far and divided that number by his estimate of the total number of species that have ever lived. According to these calculations, only 3% of all fossil primate species have been found so far.

Next, Martin constructed a phylogenetic tree with the same number of living species that we now find in the primate order. One such tree is shown in Figure 10.19a. He then randomly "found" 3% of the fossil species. In Figure 10.19b the gray lines give the actual pattern of descent, and the red lines show the data that would be available if we knew the characteristics of all the living species but had recovered only 3% of the fossil species. The best phylogeny possible, given these data, is shown in Figure 10.19c.

Then Martin computed the difference between the age of the lineage based on this estimated phylogeny, and the actual age of the lineage based on the original phylogeny. The discrepancy between these values represents the error in the age of the lineage that is due to the incompleteness of the fossil record. By repeating this procedure over and over on the computer, Martin was able to produce an estimate of the average magnitude of error, which turned out to be about 40%. Thus, if Martin is correct, living lineages are, on average, about 40% older than the age of the oldest fossil discovered.

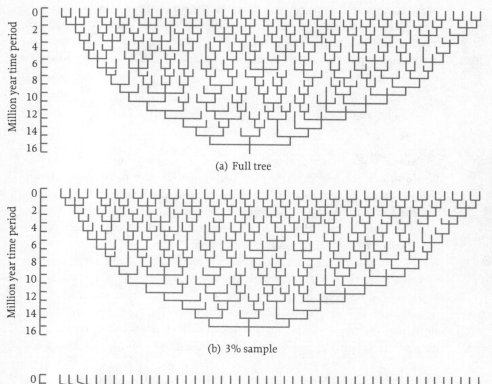

(a) Full tree

(b) 3% sample

(c) Inferred tree

FIGURE 10.19 (a) This tree shows the complete phylogeny of a hypothetical lineage. (b) This tree shows the same phylogeny when only a small percentage of the fossil species have been discovered. The red lines show the species that have been discovered, and the gray lines show the missing species. Note that all *living* species are known, but only 3% of the fossil species have been discovered. (c) The tree we would have to infer from the incomplete data at hand differs from the actual tree in two respects: (1) It links each species to its closest known ancestor, which often means assigning inappropriate ancestors to fossil and modern species, and (2) it frequently underestimates the age of the oldest member of a clade.

THE EMERGENCE OF THE HOMINOIDS

The early Miocene was warm and moist, but by the end of the epoch, the world had become much cooler and more arid.

The Miocene epoch began approximately 23 mya and ended 5 mya. In the early Miocene, the world became warmer, and once again Eurasian forests were dominated by broadleaf evergreens like those in the tropics today. At the end of the Miocene, the world became considerably colder and more arid. The tropical forests of Eurasia retreated southward, and there was more open, woodland habitat. India continued its slow slide into Asia, leading to the uplifting of the Himalayas. Some climatologists believe that the resulting change in atmospheric circulation was responsible for the late-Miocene cooling. About 18 mya, Africa joined Eurasia, splitting the Tethys Sea and creating the Mediterranean Sea. Because the Strait of Gibraltar had not yet opened, the Mediterranean Sea was isolated from the rest of the oceans. At one point, the Mediterranean Sea dried out completely, leaving a desiccated, searing hot valley thousands of feet below sea level. About the same time, the great north–south mountain ranges of the East African Rift began to appear. Because clouds decrease their moisture as they rise in elevation, there is an area of reduced rainfall, called a **rain shadow**, on the lee (downwind) side of mountain ranges. The newly elevated rift mountains caused the tropical forests of East Africa to be replaced by drier woodlands and savannas.

Apes and monkeys differ in some features of their skeletal anatomy, dentiton, brain size, and life history patterns.

Some of the anatomical features that distinguish living apes from Old World monkeys are related to their locomotor behavior. Monkeys climb along on the tops of branches, using their hands and feet to grip branches, and their tails for balance and support. They usually feed in a seated position and have fleshy sitting pads on their bottoms. Apes make much more use of suspensory postures during feeding and locomotion. Although they walk on all fours when they travel on the ground, they swing from branch to branch as they move through the trees and they often hang from branches while feeding (Figure 10.20). Their locomotor behavior is reflected in their skeletons. Compared to monkeys, apes have relatively short trunks, broad chests, long arms, and flexible shoulder joints; they have no tails. Great apes also lack fleshy sitting pads on their bottoms.

FIGURE 10.20 Apes sometimes hang below branches while they feed.

The first evidence of adaptations for suspensory locomotion comes from Miocene fossils collected nearly 40 years ago but overlooked until recently.

Fossils that are now assigned to the species *Morotopithecus bishopi* were first collected at the site of Moroto, in Uganda, in the late 1950s and early 1960s. These finds were dated to about 20 mya and classified as **hominoids**, but they were not officially named until the mid-1990s, when Daniel Gebo of Northern Illinois University, Laura MacLatchy of the University of Michigan, and their colleagues resumed work in

Moroto and collected additional material (Figure 10.21). According to MacLatchy and her colleagues, *M. bishopi* possessed a number of skeletal features that allowed it to move like an ape, not like a monkey. For example, several features of the femur suggest that it might have climbed slowly and cautiously, and the shape of the scapula indicates that it could have hung by its arms and brachiated slowly through the trees. These features are shared with modern apes, but not with the contemporary Miocene apes that we will meet next.

Other early-Miocene apes were similar to Moropithecus in their dentition, but more like monkeys in their postcranial anatomy.

Before *Moropithecus* made its debut in the pages of anthropological journals, most paleontologists believed that the oldest hominoids were members of the family Proconsulidae (Figure 10.22). This family includes 10 genera and 15 species. The smallest **proconsulids** were about the size of capuchin monkeys (3.5 kg, or about 7½ lb) and the largest were the size of female gorillas (50 kg, or a little over 100 lb). The pronconsulids seem to have occupied a range of habitats, including the tropical rain forests in which we find apes today, and open woodlands where we now find only monkeys.

Proconsul is the best-known genus of these early hominoids. The earliest members of this genus were found at a site called Losidok in northern Kenya and date to about 27 mya. The most recent fossils have been found at sites in Africa dated to 17 mya. Plant and animal fossils found with *Proconsul* indicate that they lived in rain-forest environments like those found in tropical Africa today. *Proconsul* species share several derived features with living apes and humans that we don't see in anthropoid primates. For example, *Proconsul* didn't have a tail and did not have the fleshy sitting pads that Old World monkeys and gibbons have. *Proconsul* species also had somewhat larger brains in relationship to body size than similarly sized monkeys had. Otherwise, members of the genus *Proconsul* were similar to *Aegyptopithecus* and the other Oligocene primates. Their teeth had thin enamel, which is consistent with a frugivorous diet. Their postcranial anatomy, including the relative length of their arm and leg bones and narrow and deep shape of their thorax, were much like that of quadrupedal monkeys, but certain features of their feet and lower legs were more apelike. *Proconsul* had an opposable thumb, a feature that we see in humans but not in living apes or monkeys. All of the *Proconsul* species show considerable sexual dimorphism, suggesting that they were not pair-bonded.

Besides *Moropithecus* and *Proconsul*, there were a number of other early-Miocene apes in Africa. These creatures have derived features of apes in their faces and teeth, but not in their postcranial anatomy (Figure 10.23).

The middle Miocene epoch saw a new radiation of hominoids and the expansion of hominoids throughout much of Eurasia.

Exploration of middle-Miocene (15 to 10 mya) deposits has yielded a great abundance of new hominoid species in Africa, Europe, and Asia. Well-known examples include *Kenyapithecus* from East Africa, *Oreopithecus* (Figure 10.24) and *Dryopithecus* from Europe, and *Sivapithecus* from southern Asia. The skulls and teeth of these hominoids typically differ from those of the proconsulids in a number of ways that

FIGURE 10.21 These fossil bones of *Morotopithecus* include parts of the right and left femurs, vertebrae, shoulder socket, and upper jaw. These remains suggest that these creatures moved like apes, not like monkeys. (Photo courtesy of Laura MacLatchy.)

FIGURE 10.22 Members of the genus *Proconsul* were relatively large (15 to 50 kg, or 33 to 110 lb), sexually dimorphic, and frugivorous. The skeleton of *Proconsul africanus*, reconstructed here, shows that it had limb proportions much like those of modern-day quadrupedal monkeys.

⌐⌐ cm

Turkanapithecus   *Micropithecus*   *Afropithecus*   *Proconsul*

FIGURE 10.23 Miocene hominoids exhibit a diverse range of cranial morphology, but they share a number derived characteristics with modern apes.

|10 cm|

FIGURE 10.24 *Oreopithe-cus* had a number of traits that are associated with suspensory locomotion, including a relatively short trunk, long arms, short legs, long and slender fingers, and great mobility in all joints. The phylogenetic affinities of this late-Miocene ape from Italy are not well established.

indicate they ate harder or more fibrous foods than their predecessors. Their molars had thick enamel for longer wear, and rounded cusps, which are better suited to grinding. Their **zygomatic arches** (cheekbones) flared farther outward to make room for larger jaw muscles. And the lower jaw was more robust, to carry the forces produced by those muscles. It seems likely that these features were a response to the climatic shift from a moist, tropical environment to a drier, more seasonal environment with tougher vegetation and harder seeds. Until recently, very little was known about the postcranial skeletons of middle-Miocene apes. In 1996, however, Salvador Moyà-Solà and Meike Köhler of the Institut de Paleontología Miquel Crusafont, Spain, announced the discovery of a 9.5-million-year-old specimen of *Dryopithecus* at a site near Barcelona. This remarkable specimen includes nearly all of one hand, most of the leg and arm bones, some of the vertebrae and ribs, part of the collarbone (or clavicle), and part of a cranium (Figure 10.25). The anatomy of these bones clearly indicates that *Dryopithecus* was an arboreal creature that moved through the canopy by swinging from one branch to another, and did not walk along the top of branches as the quadrupedal proconsulids did.

There are no clear candidates for the ancestors of humans or any modern apes, except perhaps orangutans.

The evolutionary history of the apes of the Miocene is poorly understood. There were many different species, and the phylogenetic relationships among them remain largely a mystery. We have no clear candidates for the ancestors of any modern apes, except for the orangutan, who shares a number of derived skull features with *Sivapithecus* of the middle Miocene. We can establish no clear links between African apes and any of the Miocene apes. Once again, this is not too surprising, given the sparseness of the paleontological record.

We can be almost certain that the earliest hominins evolved from some type of Miocene ape, but we have no idea which one it was. Nonetheless, the study of ape and hominin origins in the Miocene has been very useful for paleontologists. John Fleagle of Stony Brook University points out that, in the process of considering and ultimately rejecting many different candidates for the "missing link" between apes and early hominins, paleoanthropologists have come to realize that the key features distinguishing the earliest hominins from ancestral hominoids were not the features that they had originally been looking for: the big brains and small teeth that characterize modern humans. Instead, it was a suite of skeletal adaptations for bipedalism that marked the primary hominin adaptation.

During the early and middle Miocene, ape species were plentiful and monkey species were not. In the late Miocene and early Pliocene, many ape species became extinct and were replaced by monkeys.

Apes flourished during the Miocene, but all but a few genera and species eventually became extinct. Today there are only gibbons, orangutans, gorillas, and chimpanzees. We don't know why so many ape species disappeared, but it seems likely that many of them were poorly suited to the drier conditions of the late Miocene and early Pliocene.

The fossil record of Old World monkeys is quite different from that of the apes. Monkeys were relatively rare and not particularly variable in the early and middle Miocene, but the number and variety of fossil monkeys increased in the late Miocene and early Pliocene. Thus, although there are many more extinct ape species than living ones, the number of living monkey species greatly exceeds the number of extinct monkey species.

Once again, the fossil record reminds us that evolution does not proceed on a steady and relentless path toward a particular goal. Evolution and progress are not synonymous. During the Miocene, there were dozens of ape species but relatively few species of Old World monkeys. Today there are many monkey species and only a handful of ape species. Despite our tendency to think of ourselves as the pinnacle of evolution, the evidence suggests that, taken as a whole, our lineage was poorly suited to the changing conditions of the Pliocene and Pleistocene.

FIGURE 10.25 Much of the skeleton of *Dryopithecus* was found at a site in Spain dated to 9.5 mya. The characteristics of the skeleton indicate that it was adapted for suspensory postures, much like modern apes are.

FURTHER READING

Conroy, G. C. 1990. *Primate Evolution.* Norton, New York.

Fleagle, J. 1998. *Primate Adaptation and Evolution* (2nd ed.). Academic Press, San Diego, CA.

Klein, R. 1999. *The Human Career* (2nd ed.). University of Chicago Press, Chicago.

MacLatchy, L. 2004. The oldest ape. *Evolutionary Anthropology* 13: 30–103.

Martin, R. 1990. *Primate Origins and Evolution: A Phylogenetic Reconstruction.* Princeton University Press, Princeton, NJ.

Potts, R. 1996. *Humanity's Descent: The Consequences of Ecological Instability.* Morrow, New York.

Simons, E. L., and T. Rasmussen. 1994. A whole new world of ancestors: Eocene Anthropoideans from Africa. *Evolutionary Anthropology* 3: 128–139.

STUDY QUESTIONS

1. Briefly describe the motions of the continents over the last 180 million years. Why are these movements important to the study of human evolution?

2. What has happened to the world's climate since the end of the Age of Dinosaurs? Explain the relationship between climate change and the notion that evolution leads to steady progress.

3. What are angiosperms? What do they have to do with the evolution of the primates?

4. Why are teeth so important for reconstructing the evolution of past animals? Explain how to use teeth to distinguish among insectivores, folivores, and frugivores.

5. Which primate groups first appear during the Eocene? Give two explanations for the selective forces that shaped the morphologies of these groups.

6. Why is there a problem in explaining how primates arrived in the New World?

7. Why does the oldest fossil in a particular lineage underestimate the true age of the lineage? Explain how this problem is affected by the quality and completeness of the fossil record.

8. Explain how potassium–argon dating works. Why can it be used to date only volcanic rocks older than about 500,000 years?

KEY TERMS

bipedal
continental drift
Pangaea
Laurasia
Gondwanaland
mineralized
fossils
paleontologists
radiometric methods
isotopes
radioactive decay
potassium-argon dating
stratum

argon-argon dating
carbon-14 dating/radiocarbon dating
thermoluminescence dating
electron-spin-resonance dating
apatite crystals
gymnosperms
angiosperms
plesiadapiforms
tapetum
rain shadow
hominoids
proconsulids
zygomatic arches

CONTENT FROM *HUMAN EVOLUTION: A MULTI-MEDIA GUIDE TO THE FOSSIL RECORD*

Primate Origins
   Definition of the Primate Order
   Primate Trends
   The Earliest Primates
   Theories of Primate Origins
Prosimians and Anthropoids
   Prosimians vs. Anthropoids

The Tarsier Problem
Eocene Prosimians
Early Anthropoids
Monkeys and Apes
   Old World Monkey Origins
   Early Miocene Apes
   Hominid Connections

CHAPTER 11

FROM HOMINOID TO HOMININ

During the Miocene, the Earth's temperature began to fall. This global cooling caused two important changes in the climate of the African tropics. First, the total amount of rain that fell each year declined. Second, rainfall became more seasonal, so there were several months each year when no rain fell. As the tropical regions of Africa became drier, moist tropical forests shrank and drier woodlands and grasslands expanded. Like other animals, primates responded to these ecological changes. Some species, including many of the Miocene ape lineages, apparently failed to adapt and became extinct. The ancestors of chimpanzees and gorillas remained in the shrinking forests and carried on their lives much as before.

Changes brought about through generations of natural selection allowed a few species eventually to move down from the trees, out of the rain forests, and into the woodlands and savannas. Our ancestors, the earliest **hominins**, were among these pioneering species.

The spread of woodland and savanna led to the evolution of the first hominins about 6 mya.

Beginning about 6 mya, hominins begin to appear in the fossil record. Between 4 and 2 mya, the hominin lineage diversified, becoming community of several hominin species that ranged through eastern and southern Africa. These creatures were different from any of the Miocene apes in two ways: First, and most importantly, they walked upright. This shift to bipedal locomotion led to major morphological changes in their bodies. Second, in the new savanna and woodland habitats, new kinds of food became available. As a result, the hominin chewing apparatus—including many features of the teeth, jaws, and skull—changed. Otherwise, the behavior and life history of the earliest hominins were probably not much different from those of modern apes.

A number of shared derived characters distinguish modern humans from other living hominoids: bipedal locomotion, a larger brain, slower development, several features of dental morphology, and cultural adaptation.

When we say that these creatures were hominins, we mean that they are classified with humans in the "tribe" Hominini. The tribe is a taxonomic unit between the family and the genus. Humans belong to the family Hominidae, which includes all of the great apes and the genus *Homo*.

Five categories of derived traits distinguish modern humans from contemporary apes:

1. We habitually walk bipedally.
2. Our dentition and jaw musculature are different from those of apes in a number of ways. For example, we have a wide parabolic dental arcade, thick enamel, reduced canine teeth, and larger molars in relation to the other teeth.
3. We have much larger brains in relation to our body size.
4. We develop slowly, with a long juvenile period.
5. We depend on an elaborate, highly variable material and symbolic culture, transmitted in part through spoken language.

Because these early hominins were bipedal and shared many dental features with modern humans, they are classified as members of our subfamily. However, because their brains and life history were very similar to those of contemporary chimpanzees, early hominins are not included in the same genus (*Homo*) as modern humans.

In this chapter we describe the species that constituted this early hominin community, and we discuss the selective forces that transformed an ancestral, arboreal ape that was something like an orangutan or chimpanzee into a diverse community of bipedal apes living in the woodlands and savannas of Pliocene Africa. In subsequent chapters we will consider how one of these savanna apes became human.

Many of the morphological features that we focus on in this chapter may seem obscure, and you may wonder why we spend so much time describing them. These features help us identify hominin species and trace the origins of traits that we see in later species. We can also use some of these characteristics to reconstruct aspects of diet, social organization, and behavior.

AT THE BEGINNING

Genetic data indicate that the last common ancestor of humans and chimpanzees lived between 7 and 5 mya. Until recently, we knew very little about the hominin lineage during this period. In the last few years, however, fossil discoveries of three kinds of creatures—*Ardipithecus ramidus*, *Orrorin tugenensis*, and *Sahelanthropus tchadensis*—have begun to shed light on this important period in the history of the human lineage. So far, the materials are fragmentary, and the relationships between them and other hominins are unclear.

Ardipithecus

The genus Ardipithecus *includes two species—*A. ramidus *and* A. kadabba*—and both have similarities to both humans and chimpanzees.*

In 1992, members of an expedition led by Tim White of the University of California Berkeley found the first fossils of a primitive hominin at Aramis, a site in the Middle Awash basin of Ethiopia, just south of Hadar. These fossils, dated to 4.4 mya, include teeth and jaws, the lower part of the skull, and parts of the upper arms. White and his colleagues, Gen Suwa of Tokyo University and Berhane Asfaw of Addis Ababa, named the species *Ardipithecus ramidus*, from the words *ardi* (meaning "ground" or "floor") and *ramis* (meaning "root") in the local Afar language. These fossils date from between 5.8 and 5.2 mya.

Several features suggest that *A. ramidus* was a hominin. The opening on the bottom of the skull through which the spinal cord passes, called the **foramen magnum**, is located forward under the skull, as it is in humans. In apes the foramen magnum is located toward the back of the skull. This is not a definitive indication that these creatures were habitual bipeds, but the forward placement of the foramen magnum is associated with bipedal locomotion in modern humans and may mean that *A. ramidus* was also bipedal. *Ardipithecus ramidus* shares several other derived features with other hominins. These creatures have smaller, more incisorlike canine teeth that are not sharpened by the lower premolar, unlike apes, which have relatively large canines that are sharpened by the first lower premolar. *Ardipithecus ramidus* also resembles humans in several additional features of the teeth and arm bones. Other traits are much more apelike. The molars are smaller in relation to body size than in other early hominins, the enamel is thinner than in other early hominins, and the canines are smaller than in chimpanzees and gorillas but larger than in later hominins. In addition, the deciduous (baby) molars and jaw joint are very similar to those of apes, and the base of the skull is more **pneumatized** (filled with air pockets) than in later hominins.

Ardipithecus ramidus seems to have lived in a forested environment. This conclusion is based on numerous fossils of wood and seeds that were found at the site and come from plant species that grow in woodland habitats. The other animals who lived at Aramis were mainly woodland species. Thus, most of the antelope fossils are of kudus, browsers that typically live in woodlands (Figure 11.1). Moreover, more than 30% of all the mammalian fossils are of colobine monkeys, which are now found mainly in forested areas.

More recently, Yohannes Haile-Selassie, another member of White's team, found 90 more fossil specimens, including bones of the hand, foot, pelvis, arm, leg, and skull. Altogether, these fragments make up about 45% of a complete skeleton. So far,

Haile-Selassie has published descriptions of a partial mandible; a number of teeth; and foot, hand, and arm bones. Haile-Selassie classifies this fossil in a second species, *Ardipithecus kadabba*, because the canine teeth are considerably more chimplike than those of *A. ramidus*.

It is presently unclear whether *Ardipithecus* is related more closely to humans or to chimpanzees. White and his colleagues believe that the reduced canine size and (likely) bipedal locomotion indicate that *A. ramidus* represents the earliest stage of hominin evolution. If so, then this species would be the root of the tree linking the human lineage with that of the apes. Others have suggested that the apelike anatomical features of these two species and their apparent preference for forest environments mean that *Ardipithecus* is related more closely to chimpanzees than to modern humans. We will know much more when the remaining fossil material from Aramis has been described.

Orrorin tugenensis

Orrorin tugenensis is a second early fossil with similarities to humans.

In the spring of 2001, a French–Kenyan team led by Brigitte Senut of the National Museum of Natural History in Paris and Martin Pickford of the Kenya Palaeontology Expedition announced the discovery of 12 hominin fossils in the Tugen Hills in the highlands of Kenya. These fossils, which include parts of thigh and arm bones, a finger bone, two partial mandibles (lower jaws), and several teeth, are securely dated to 6 mya (Figure 11.2). Senut and Pickford assigned their finds to a new species, *Orrorin tugenensis*. The genus name means "original man" in the language of the local people, and it reminded Senut and Pickford of the French word for "dawn," *aurore*.

Like the fossils of *Ardipithecus*, these specimens are similar to chimpanzees in some ways and to humans in others. The incisors, canines, and one of the premolars are more like the teeth of chimpanzees than of later hominins. The molars are smaller than those of *A. ramidus* and later apelike hominins, and they have thick enamel like human molars have. As in chimpanzees and some later hominins, the arm and finger bones have features that are believed to be adaptations for climbing. The thigh bones are more similar to those of later hominins than to those of apes, which Senut and Pickford interpret as evidence that *O. tugenensis* was bipedal. Fossils of forest creatures, such as colobus monkeys, and open-country dwellers, such as impala, were found in the same strata as *O. tugenensis*, indicating that the habitat was a mix of woodland and savanna.

Sahelanthropus tchadensis

Sahelanthropus tchadensis, a third early fossil, has a surprising mix of derived and primitive features.

The first announcements of new hominin fossils sometimes read as though they were written by Hollywood publicists. But like many movies, the discoveries don't always live up to their billing. In July 2002, the discovery of a new hominin fossil was announced, and this time there is a good chance that it deserves all the fanfare.

FIGURE 11.1 *Ardipithecus ramidus* fossils are found in association with the fossils of woodland species like this kudu, suggesting that *A. ramidus* lived in a forested environment.

FIGURE 11.2 The fossils of *Orrorin tugenensis* include parts of the femur, lower jaw, fingers, and teeth.

The fossil consists of a nearly complete cranium, two fragments of the lower jaw, and several teeth found at Toros-Menalla, a site in Chad, by a team of researchers led by Michel Brunet of the University of Poitiers in France (Figure 11.3). Brunet and his colleagues have given the fossil the scientific name *Sahelanthropus tchadensis*. The word *Sahelanthropus* comes from "Sahel," the vast dry region south of the Sahara; and *tchadensis* comes from "Chad," the country where the fossil was found. This fossil has also acquired a nickname, Toumaï, which means "hope of life" in the language of the local people, and is often given to children born during the dry season.

This fossil shook the paleontological community for a number of reasons. First, it comes from an unexpected place. Most work on human evolution has focused on East Africa and South Africa, but this specimen comes from the middle of the African continent. Although Toros-Menalla is now an arid desert, in the late Miocene it was a well-watered woodland. This suggests that early hominins had a much larger range than was previously believed. Second, this fossil is surprisingly old. The geology of the site does not allow radiometric or paleomagnetic dating. However, there is a close match between the other fossil animals found at the site and the fauna found at two sites in East Africa securely dated to between 7 and 6 mya. This makes Toumaï the oldest hominin cranium. *Sahelanthropus tchadensis* may give us a picture of the last common ancestor because genetic data tell us that the hominin lineage diverged from the chimpanzee lineage during this period of time. Third, and most important, is the fact that Toumaï possesses a very surprising mix of anatomical features. The face is relatively flat, and there is a massive browridge over the eyes. These are features associated with hominins who date to later than 2 mya, but not with the hominins who dominate the fossil record between 4 and 2 mya. As in *Ardipithecus*, the foramen magnum is located under the skull (rather than at the back)—a feature that is associated with bipedal locomotion. On the other hand, the braincase is very small [320 to 350 cc (cubic centimeters)], the teeth are primitive, and the back of the skull is very apelike.

Toumaï's very early date and unique mix of derived and primitive features provide yet more evidence that hominin evolution did not follow a simple progression from ape to human. Instead, it seems more and more likely that there were many different hominin species that possessed a variety of different adaptations.

FIGURE 11.3 The cranium of *Sahelanthropus tchadensis* found in Chad dates to between 7 and 6 mya. It has a flat face and large browridge. Australopithecines dated to between 4 and 2 mya have more apelike prognathic faces and lack browridges. (Photograph courtesy of Michel Brunet.)

THE HOMININ COMMUNITY DIVERSIFIES

A number of hominin species lived in Africa between 4 and 2 mya. They are divided into three genera: Australopithecus, Paranthropus, and Kenyanthropus.

Beginning about 4 mya the hominin lineage proliferated, and over the next 2 million years there were between four and seven species of hominins living in Africa at any given time. A number of different taxonomic schemes have been used to classify these creatures. Here we adopt a system advocated by Bernard Wood of George Washington University and Mark Collard of Washington State University. They divide these species into three genera:

1. *Australopithecus* includes six species: *A. anamensis*, *A. afarensis*, *A. africanus*, *A. garhi*, *A. habilis*, and *A. rudolfensis*. The genus name means "southern ape" and was first applied to an *A. africanus* skull found in South Africa. The **australopithecines** were small bipeds with teeth, skull, and jaws adapted to a generalized diet. Wood and Collard's scheme departs from convention; other taxonomic schemes usually place *A. habilis* and *A. rudolfensis* in the same genus as modern humans (*Homo*).

2. *Paranthropus* includes three species: *P. aethiopicus*, *P. robustus*, and *P. boisei*. The genus name means "parallel to man" and was coined by Robert Broom, who discovered the first specimens of *P. robustus*. The paranthropines were similar to the australopithecines from the neck down, but they had massive teeth and jaws adapted to heavy chewing of tough plant materials, and a skull modified to carry the enormous muscles necessary to power this chewing apparatus.

3. *Kenyanthropus* includes only one species: *K. platyops*. The genus name means "Kenyan man" and was given to a specimen recently found in northern Kenya. We do not yet know much about these creatures, but they are distinguished by a flattened face and small teeth.

The sites at which early hominin fossils have been found in Africa are identified on the map in Figure 11.4. In this section we briefly describe the history and characteristics of each of these fossil species and then turn to a discussion of their common features.

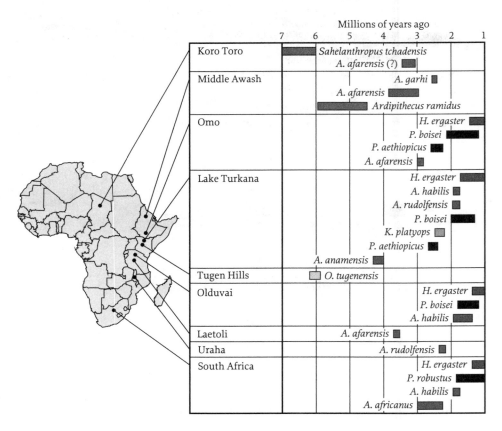

FIGURE 11.4 Hominin fossils have been discovered at a number of sites in eastern and southern Africa. Fossils belonging to each genus have been assigned a different color. Fossils discovered at Bahr el Ghazal in Chad have been provisionally assigned to the species *A. afarensis*, pending more detailed analysis.

You are excused if you feel as though you have mistakenly picked up a Russian novel with a long cast of characters filled with unpronounceable and hard-to-remember names. Keep in mind, however, that the species within each genus are quite similar: the australopithecines are small bipeds with relatively small teeth, the paranthropines are small bipeds with big teeth, and *Kenyanthropus platyops* has small teeth and a flat face.

Australopithecus

A. *ANAMENSIS*

Australopithecus anamensis was bipedal but had a more apelike skull than later australopithecines had.

In 1994, members of an expedition led by Meave Leakey of the National Museums of Kenya found fossils of a new hominin species at Kanapoi and Allia Bay, two sites near Lake Turkana in Kenya (Figure 11.5). Among these specimens are parts of the upper and lower jaw, part of a **tibia** (the larger of the two bones in the lower leg), and numerous teeth. In addition, parts of a **humerus** (the upper arm bone) found at Kanapoi in the early 1970s can now be associated with the new finds. Leakey assigned them to the species *Australopithecus anamensis*. The species name is derived from *anam*, the word for "lake" in the language of the people living around Lake Turkana. Subsequent work has expanded the sample to more than 50 specimens. These fossils are dated to between 4.2 and 3.8 mya.

Several features mark *A. anamensis* as a hominin. It had large molars with thick enamel and smaller canines, and the shapes of the knee and ankle joints strongly indicate that it was bipedal. The arm bones suggest that it retained adaptations for life in the trees. As we will see, these features are shared by later australopithecines as well. However, *A. anamensis* lacks several derived traits seen in later australopithecines. For example, the ear holes are small and shaped like ellipses, as they are in living apes, but the ear holes of later australopithecines are larger and more rounded; the dental arcade is more like the U shape seen in chimpanzees and gorillas, and less like the V-shaped dental arcade seen in later australopithecines; and the chin recedes more sharply than that in other australopithecines does (Figure 11.6). There are also indications that *A. anamensis* sometimes had larger canines than those seen in later hominins. This suite of more primitive characters distinguishes *A. anamensis* from later australopithecines

FIGURE 11.5 *A. anamensis* lived about 4 mya, half a million years before *A. afarensis*. Fragments of limb bones, the upper and lower jaws, and many teeth have been recovered.

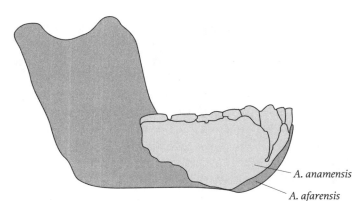

— A. anamensis
— A. afarensis

FIGURE 11.6 *Australopithecus anamensis* had a more receding chin than later australopithecines had, as is evident when side views of the lower jaw of *A. anamensis* (beige) and *A. afarensis* (blue) are superposed.

FIGURE 11.7 The Awash basin in Ethiopia is the site of several important paleontological discoveries, including many specimens of *A. afarensis*.

FIGURE 11.8 A sizable fraction of the skeleton of a single individual was recovered at Hadar. Because the skeleton is bilaterally symmetrical, most of the skeleton of this *A. afarensis* female, popularly known as Lucy, can be reconstructed.

and is consistent with the hypothesis that *A. anamensis* is the ancestor of these species.

Fossils of other animals found at Kanapoi and Allia Bay suggest that *A. anamensis* lived in a mixture of habitats including dry woodlands, gallery forests along rivers, and more open grasslands.

A. *AFARENSIS*

Hominin fossils assigned to the species Australopithecus afarensis *are found at sites in East Africa that date from 4 to 3 mya.* Australopithecus afarensis *is the best-known australopithecine species.*

Australopithecus afarensis is well known from specimens found at several sites in Africa (see Figure 11.4), but the most extensive fossil collections come from several sites in Ethiopia. In the early 1970s a French and American team headed by Maurice Taieb and Don Johanson began searching for hominid fossils at Hadar, in the Afar Depression of northeastern Ethiopia (Figure 11.7). In 1973, this team made a striking discovery: they found the bones of a 3-million-year-old knee joint that showed striking similarities to a modern human knee. The next year the team returned and found a sizable fraction of the skeleton of a single individual, an amazing discovery in a discipline in which an entire species is sometimes named and classified on the basis of a single tooth. They dubbed the skeleton "Lucy," after the Beatles song "Lucy in the Sky with Diamonds" (Figures 11.8 and 11.9). Lucy, who is 3.2 million years old, was not the only remarkable find at Hadar. During the next field season, the team found the remains of 13 more individuals. This collection of fossils is formally identified as material from Afar Locality 333 (AL 333), but it is often called simply the "First Family."

Just after these fossils were discovered, the excavations were interrupted by civil war in Ethiopia, and paleontologists were unable to resume work at Hadar for more than a decade. Then, a team led by Don Johanson returned to Hadar, while a separate team led by Tim White searched for fossils in the nearby Middle Awash basin. Both groups were successful in discovering fossils from many *A. afarensis* individuals, including a nearly complete skull (labeled AL 444-2). In 2001, Ethiopian researcher Zeresenay Alemseged announced the discovery of a very well-preserved, partial skeleton of a child in the Afar region of Ethiopia.

Australopithecus afarensis fossils have also been found at several sites elsewhere in Africa. During the 1970s, members of a team led by Mary Leakey discovered fossils of *A. afarensis* at Laetoli in Tanzania. The Laetoli specimens are 3.5 million years old, several hundred thousand years older than Lucy. In 1995, researchers announced interesting finds from Chad and South Africa. A French team published a description of a lower jaw from Bahr el Ghazal in Chad. This fossil, provisionally identified as *A. afarensis*, is between 3.1 and 3.4 million years old, judging by the age of associated fossils. In South Africa, Ronald Clarke of the Johann Wolfgang Goethe University of Frankfurt, Germany, and Phillip Tobias of the University of the Witwatersrand found several foot bones that may also belong to *A. afarensis*.

Reconstructions of the environments at these sites indicate that *A. afarensis* lived in habitats ranging from woodland to dry savanna. Between 4 and 3 mya, the envi-

ronment at Hadar was a mix of woodland, scrub, and grassland; at Laetoli, it was a
dry grassland sparsely dotted with trees.

*The skulls of A. afarensis share several derived features with modern humans,
but the fossils also display many ancestral traits, including ape-sized brains.*

The cranium (the skull minus the lower jawbone) of *A. afarensis* is quite apelike.
Its **endocranial volume** (the capacity of its brain cavity) is 404 cc—less than a pint.
This is about the same size as the brain of a modern chimpanzee. The cranium of
A. afarensis is also primitive in a number of other details. For example, the base of the
cranium is flared at the bottom and the bone is pneumatized; the front of the face
below the nose is pushed out—a condition known as **subnasal prognathism**; and
the jaw joint is shallow (Figure 11.10). Remember that labeling a trait "primitive"
does not imply that organisms possessing that trait are backward or poorly designed;
it simply means that the organisms resemble earlier forms.

The teeth and jaws of *A. afarensis* are intermediate between those of apes and
humans in a number of ways. Figure 11.11 shows three features that illustrate this
point:

1. The dental arcade of *A. afarensis* has an intermediate V shape, the canines are
   medium-sized, and the **diastema** (the space between the teeth and the jaw; plural *diastemata*) is modest.
2. In its canines, *A. afarensis* displays less sexual dimorphism than chimpanzees but
   more than modern humans.
3. The first lower premolar of *A. afarensis* has a small inner cusp and a larger outer
   cusp. This is intermediate between chimpanzees, who have a single cusp on their
   lower premolars, and modern humans, who have two cusps of approximately
   equal size.

Anatomical evidence indicates that A. afarensis was bipedal.

The transition from a forest ape to a terrestrial biped involves many new adaptations. A number of these changes are reflected in the morphology of the skeleton.

FIGURE 11.9 Here, Lucy's
skeleton (left)
stands beside the skeleton of a modern
human female. The parts of the skeleton
that have been discovered are shaded.
Lucy was shorter than modern females
and had relatively long arms and a relatively small brain. (Based on a photograph by David Brill.)

Temporal line
Nuchal line
Chimpanzee, *Pan troglodytes*
Subnasal prognathism
Diastema
Broad (heavily pneumatized) cranial base
Australopithecus afarensis

FIGURE 11.10 The cranium
of *A. afaren-
sis* possesses a number of primitive features, including a small brain, a shallow
jaw joint, a pneumatized cranial base,
and subnasal prognathism in the face.
(Figure courtesy of Richard Klein.)

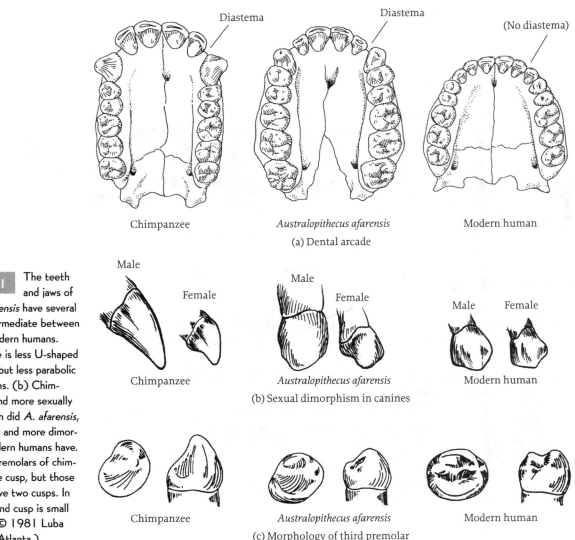

Diastema   Diastema   (No diastema)

Chimpanzee   *Australopithecus afarensis*   Modern human
                        (a) Dental arcade

Male   Male
        Female   Female   Male   Female

Chimpanzee   *Australopithecus afarensis*   Modern human
                    (b) Sexual dimorphism in canines

Chimpanzee   *Australopithecus afarensis*   Modern human
                    (c) Morphology of third premolar

FIGURE 11.11 The teeth and jaws of *Australopithecus afarensis* have several features that are intermediate between those of apes and modern humans. (a) The dental arcade is less U-shaped than in chimpanzees, but less parabolic than in modern humans. (b) Chimpanzees have larger and more sexually dimorphic canines than did *A. afarensis*, who in turn had larger and more dimorphic canines than modern humans have. (c) The lower third premolars of chimpanzees have only one cusp, but those of modern humans have two cusps. In *A. afarensis*, the second cusp is small but clearly present. (© 1981 Luba Dmytryk Gudz/Brill Atlanta.)

Thus, by studying the shape of fossils, we can make inferences about the animal's mode of locomotion. Changes in the pelvis provide a good example. In terms of shape and orientation, the human pelvis is very different from that of forest-dwelling apes like the chimpanzee (Figure 11.12). The pelvis of *A. afarensis* is much more like a human pelvis, so we infer that *A. afarensis* is likely to have been bipedal.

Other changes are more subtle but also diagnostic. When modern humans walk, a relatively large proportion of the time is spent balanced on one foot. Each time you take a step, your body swings over the foot that is on the ground, and all of your weight is balanced over that foot. At that moment, the weight of your body pulls down on the center of the pelvis, well inward from the hip joint (Figure 11.13). This weight creates a twisting force, or **torque**, that acts to rotate your torso down and away from the weighted leg. But your torso does not tip, because the torque is opposed by **abductors**, muscles that run from the outer side of the pelvis to the femur. At the appropriate moment during each stride, these muscles tighten and keep you upright. (You can demonstrate this by walking around with your open hand on the side of your hip.

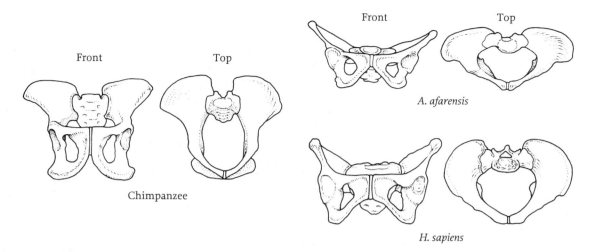

FIGURE 11.12 The pelvis of *A. afarensis* resembles the modern human pelvis more than the chimpanzee pelvis. Notice that the australopithecine pelvis is flattened and flared like the modern human pelvis. These features increase the efficiency of bipedal walking. The australopithecine pelvis is also much wider side to side and narrower front to back than that of modern humans. Some anthropologists believe these differences indicate that australopithecines did not walk the same way that modern humans do.

You'll feel your abductors tighten as you walk, and your torso tip if you relax these muscles. You might want to do this in private.) The abductors are attached to the **ilium** (plural *ilia*; a flaring blade of bone on the upper end of the pelvis). The widening and thickening of the ilium and the lengthening of the neck of the **femur** (the thigh bone) add to the leverage that the abductors can exert, and make bipedal walking more efficient. The existence of these morphological features in *A. afarensis* implies that it was bipedal.

The designs of the knee and foot of *A. afarensis* are also consistent with the idea that *A. afarensis* was bipedal. The modern human knee joint is quite different from

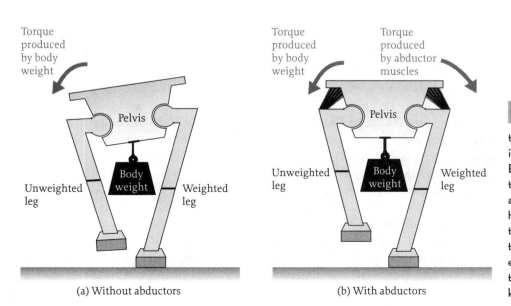

FIGURE 11.13 A schematic diagram of the lower body at the point of the stride in which all of the weight is on one leg. Body weight acts to pull down through the centerline of the pelvis. This creates a torque, or twisting force, around the hip joint of the weighted leg. (a) If this torque were unopposed, the torso would twist down and to the left. (b) During each stride the abductor muscles tighten to create a second torque that keeps the body erect.

FIGURE 11.14 The knees of *A. afarensis* are more like the knees of modern humans than like the knees of chimpanzees. Consider the lower end of the femur, where it forms one side of the knee joint. In chimpanzees, this joint forms a right angle with the long axis of the femur. In humans and australopithecines, the knee joint forms an oblique angle, causing the femur to slant inward toward the centerline of the body. This slant causes the knee to be carried closer to the body's centerline, which increases the efficiency of bipedal walking. (© 1981 Luba Dmytryk Gudz/Brill Atlanta.)

Human   *A. afarensis*   Ape

the chimpanzee knee joint (Figure 11.14). Efficient bipedal locomotion requires that the knees lie close to the centerline of the body. As a result, the human femur slants down and inward, and its lower end is angled at the knee joint to make proper contact with the bones of the lower leg. In contrast, the chimpanzee femur descends vertically from the pelvis, and the end of the femur at the knee joint is not slanted. The femur of *A. afarensis* has the same angled shape as that of modern humans. The feet also show a number of derived features associated with bipedal locomotion, including a longitudinal arch and a humanlike ankle.

Australopithecus afarensis may not have walked with the same efficient, striding gait that modern humans have.

Although there is no doubt that *A. afarensis* was bipedal, it is not entirely clear whether this hominin had the same striding gait as modern humans have. Many features of the pelvis and legs of *A. afarensis* are different from the pelvis and legs in modern humans, and these differences make some researchers believe that Lucy and her colleagues walked with an inefficient, bent-legged gait. For example, the ilium is oriented more toward the back than in modern humans, and biomechanical calculations suggest that the abductors would be less efficient in this orientation. The legs of *A. afarensis* were also much shorter in relationship to body size than are the legs of modern humans, and this would reduce the efficiency and speed of their walking. However, other researchers have argued that *A. afarensis* was an efficient biped even though it did not walk in exactly the same way modern humans do. These researchers note, for example, that the pelvis of *A. afarensis* is much wider in relationship to its body size, compared with the modern human pelvis (see Figure 11.12). This extra width may have minimized vertical motion of the body during walking. The longer legs of modern humans produce the same effect.

A trail of fossil footprints proves that a striding biped lived in East Africa at the same time as A. afarensis.

The conclusion that *A. afarensis* had an efficient striding gait was dramatically strengthened by a remarkable discovery by Mary Leakey and her coworkers at Laetoli in Tanzania. They uncovered a trail of footprints 30 m (about 100 ft) long that had been made by three bipedal individuals who had crossed a thick bed of wet volcanic ash about 3.5 mya (Figure 11.15). Paleontologists estimate that the tallest of the individuals who made these prints was 1.45 m (4 ft 9 in.) and the shortest was 1.24 m (4 ft 1 in.) tall. The path of these three individuals was preserved because the wet ash solidified as it dried, leaving us a tantalizing glimpse of the past. University of Chicago anthropologist Russell Tuttle has compared the Laetoli footprints with the footprints made by members of a group of people called the Machigenga, who live in the tropical forests of Peru. Tuttle chose the Machigenga because their average height is close to that of the makers of the Laetoli footprints, and they do not wear shoes. Tuttle found that the Laetoli footprints are functionally indistinguishable from those made by the Machigenga, and he concluded that the creatures who made the footprints walked with a fully modern striding gait.

Who made these footprints? The suspects are *A. afarensis* and *Kenyanthropus platyops* (a hominin you will meet later in this chapter) because they are the only hominins known to have lived in East Africa at the time the tracks were made. *Australopithecus afarensis* is the most likely culprit because it is the only hominin whose remains have been found at Laetoli. If *A. afarensis* did make the footprints, then the researchers who doubt that they were striding bipeds are wrong. However, some anthropologists are convinced by the anatomical evidence that *A. afarensis* was not a modern biped. If they are correct, then *K. platyops* made the footprints, or there was another, as yet undiscovered, hominin species living in East Africa 3.5 mya.

FIGURE 11.15 Several bipedal creatures walked across a thick bed of wet volcanic ash about 3.5 mya. Their footprints were preserved when the ash solidified as it dried.

Australopithecus afarensis probably spent a good deal of time in trees.

All nonhuman primates, except some gorillas, spend the night perched in trees or huddled on cliffs to protect themselves from nocturnal predators like leopards. Even chimpanzees, who are about the size of Lucy, make leafy nests and sleep in trees each night (Figure 11.16). Thus it seems likely that *A. afarensis* slept in trees too, and that their skeletons might show features related to arboreality. Anatomists such as Randall Susman of Stony Brook University have argued that traits of the feet, hands, wrists, and shoulder joints suggest that Lucy and her friends were partly arboreal. For example, the bones of their fingers and toes are slender and curved like those of modern apes, and unlike modern human fingers and toes. Such hands would have been well suited to grasping branches as *A. afarensis* hung below them. Certain distinctive features of their shoulder blades are also well suited to supporting the body in a hanging position.

FIGURE 11.16 Each night, chimpanzees sleep in nests that they make by bending down branches. Sometimes chimpanzees also rest in nests during the day, as this chimpanzee is doing.

Australopithecus afarensis *was sexually dimorphic in body size.*

Anatomical evidence suggests that there was considerable variation in the body size of *A. afarensis* adults in the Hadar population. The bigger individuals were 1.51 m (5 ft) tall and weighed about 45 kg (100 lb). The smaller ones were about 1.05 m (3½ ft) and weighed about 30 kg (65 lb). Thus, the big ones were about 1.5 times larger than the small ones. There are two possible explanations for variation in the Hadar population. The variation could represent sexual dimorphism, with the larger adults being male and the smaller ones female. The difference between the Hadar males and females approaches the magnitude of sexual dimorphism in modern orang-utans and gorillas and is considerably greater than that in modern humans, bonobos, and chimpanzees.

On the other hand, it is possible that large and small individuals represent two different species. This interpretation was initially supported by the fact that larger individuals were much more common at Laetoli, which was then a savanna, while the smaller ones were found mainly in what were then forested environments. Some researchers also believe that the smaller individuals were less suited to bipedal locomotion than the bigger ones were. This suggests that one species was big, fully bipedal, and adapted for savanna life. The morphology of the smaller species represented a compromise between tree climbing and walking—an adaptation for life in the forest.

The fossils recently discovered in Ethiopia by Tim White and Donald Johanson suggest that the two-species theory is wrong. The new fossils encompass the full range of variation in size at a single site and over a fairly narrow range of dates. Moreover, a large femur shows many of the same features seen in Lucy's more petite femur. The new data also suggest that both large and small forms were found in the full range of environments from forest to savanna. All of these facts suggest that this assemblage of fossils represents a single, sexually dimorphic species.

A. AFRICANUS

Australopithecus africanus *is known from several sites in South Africa that date from 3 to 2.2 mya.*

Australopithecus africanus was first identified in 1924 by Raymond Dart, an Australian anatomist living in South Africa. Miners brought him a piece of rock from which he painstakingly extracted the skull of an immature, small-brained creature (Figure 11.17). Dart formally named this fossil *Australopithecus africanus*, which means "the southern ape of Africa," but there is now evidence that members of the same species may have been distributed throughout southern and eastern Africa. Dart's fossil is popularly known as "the Taung child." Dart believed that the Taung child was bipedal because the position of the foramen magnum was more like that of modern humans than that of apes. At the same time, he observed many similarities between the Taung child and modern apes, including a relatively small brain. Thus, he argued that this newly discovered species was intermediate between apes and humans. His conclusions were roundly rejected by members of the scientific community because in those days most physical anthropologists believed that large brains had evolved in the human lineage before bipedal locomotion. Controversy about the taxonomic status of *A. africanus* continued for the next 30 years.

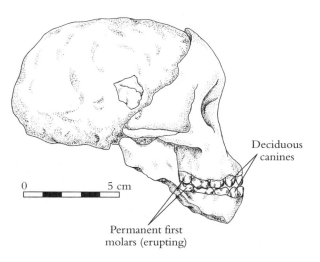

Deciduous canines

0   5 cm

Permanent first molars (erupting)

FIGURE 11.17

FIGURE 11.17 The first australopithecine specimen was identified in South Africa by Raymond Dart in 1924. Dart named it *Australopithecus africanus*, which means "the southern ape of Africa," but the specimen is often called the Taung child. Dart concluded that the Taung child was bipedal. Even though it had a very small brain, he believed it to be intermediate between humans and apes. His conclusions were not generally accepted for nearly 30 years. (Figure courtesy of Richard Klein.)

The creature who caused all the controversy was a small biped with relatively modern dentition and postcranial skeleton. As with *A. afarensis*, there is pronounced sexual dimorphism, in both canine and body size. Males stood 1.38 m (4 ft 6 in.) tall and weighed 41 kg (90 lb), and females were 1.15 m (3 ft 9 in.) tall and tipped the scales at about 30 kg (66 lb). The teeth are more modern than those of *A. afarensis* in several ways. The brain averaged 442 cc, somewhat larger than the average for *A. afarensis*. However, the difference in cranial capacity between *A. afarensis* and *A. africanus* is small compared with that among individuals and is likely due to sampling variation. Members of this species lived from 3.0 to 2.2 mya. The postcranial skeleton is virtually identical to that of *A. afarensis*. Dart's notion that the Taung child was bipedal was controversial because it relied primarily on the location of the foramen magnum, and he had no postcranial bones to corroborate his conclusions. This is partly because Dart's original find came from the rubble of mining operations where dynamite was used to excavate, and the fossils were not discovered in their original location. Subsequently, many adult skulls and postcranial bones were found at two other sites in South Africa: Makapansgat and Sterkfontein. The hip bone, pelvis, ribs, and vertebrae of *A. africanus* are much like those of Lucy and the First Family. The Taung child thus was proven to be fully bipedal, just as Dart had originally claimed.

The skull of A. africanus *has a number of derived features. Only some of these are shared with modern humans.*

Australopithecus africanus is less primitive than *A. afarensis* in a number of important details. For example, the base of the skull has fewer air pockets, the face is shorter and less protruding below the nose, the canines are less dimorphic, and the base of the cranium is bent further upward, or flexed. In all these traits *A. africanus* is more like modern humans and less like earlier primates. However, *A. africanus* exhibits a number of derived characters that it does not share with modern humans. Most of these characters seem to have to do with heavy chewing using the molars. The molars are quite big, and the lower jaw is larger and sturdier than in modern humans.

Australopithecus africanus matured rapidly like chimpanzees, not slowly like humans.

For many years it was thought that the Taung child was about six years old when it died. This estimate was based on the assumption that the australopithecines matured at the same rate that modern humans do. Recently, we have learned that this assumption is wrong; australopithecines grew up quickly. Among living primates, the age at which teeth, particularly molars, erupt is a very good predictor of the age of sexual maturity, age at first reproduction, and overall life span. Thus, if we know the rate at which teeth developed in extinct hominins, we can estimate how rapidly they developed overall. Christopher Dean and his colleagues at the University of London have found a way to tell how fast hominin teeth developed. Their method relies on the fact that enamel is secreted as teeth grow. Over the course of the day the rate of secretion varies, and this variation creates minute parallel lines that correspond to a day's growth. Dean and his colleagues used electron and polarizing light microscopes to make highly magnified images of the teeth of six australopithecines, and they carefully counted the daily layers of enamel. Then they calculated how long it took to grow to a particular stage of development. Their results indicate that australopithecines developed rapidly, somewhat faster than chimpanzees, not slowly like modern humans (Figure 11.18). So the Taung child was not six years old when it died; it was probably only about three.

These results are important because they suggest that australopithecine infants did not have as long a period of dependency as human children do. Many anthropologists believe that a number of the fundamental features of human foraging societies, such as the establishment of home bases, sexual division of labor, and extensive food sharing, were necessitated by a long period of infant dependency. If australopithecine infants matured faster than modern chimpanzees, then it seems likely that these features were not yet part of the hominin adaptation.

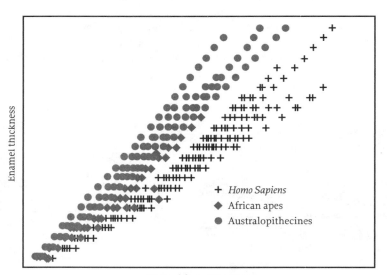

Enamel thickness (y-axis)

+ *Homo Sapiens*
◆ African apes
● Australopithecines

Enamel formation time (x-axis)

FIGURE 11.18 The rate of growth of enamel in the teeth of six australopithecines was comparable to that of African apes. The enamel growth rate of modern humans is slower.

A. GARHI

Australopithecus garhi lived about 2.5 mya in East Africa.

In 1999, a research team led by Berhane Asfaw and Tim White announced the discovery of a new species of australopithecine from the Awash valley of Ethiopia, named *Australopithecus garhi*. *Garhi* means "surprise" in the Afar language. In 1996, Asfaw, White, and their colleagues had recovered hominin remains from a site called Bouri, the ancient site of a shallow freshwater lake, not far from where A. *afarensis* was found. The findings included a number of postcranial bones and the partial skeleton of one individual. These specimens are well preserved and securely dated to 2.5

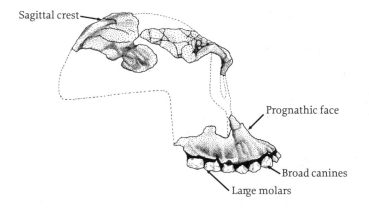

Sagittal crest

Prognathic face

Broad canines

Large molars

FIGURE 11.19 In 1999, the first descriptions of a 2.5-million-year-old hominin species from Ethiopia were published. This new species, named *A. garhi*, had a small brain and a prognathic face. It also had a sagittal crest, a fin of bone that runs along the top of the skull. Compared to *A. afarensis* and *A. africanus*, *A. garhi* had broader canines and larger molars. (Based on a photograph by David Brill.)

mya, but they don't contain diagnostic features that can be used to assign them to a specific species. In 1997, however, the research team had discovered a number of cranial remains about 300 m (1000 ft) away from the original site. These pieces of the skull, maxilla (upper jaw), and teeth come from the same stratigraphic level as the postcranial remains, and they reveal more about the taxonomic identity of the Bouri hominins.

These creatures had small brains (approximately 450 cc), like *A. afarensis* and *A. africanus*, perched above a very prognathic face (Figure 11.19). The canines, premolars, and molars of *A. garhi* were generally larger than those of *A. afarensis* and *A. africanus*. Certain detailed features of the dentition differed from *A. afarensis* as well. This creature also had a **sagittal crest**, a fin of bone that runs along the centerline of the skull, making it look a bit like a punk rocker's Mohawk haircut. The Bouri specimens were assigned to a new species of the genus *Australopithecus* because they differ from any of the known australopithecines but lack the derived characters associated with other hominins.

So far, the postcranial remains found near the type specimen of *A. garhi* cannot be assigned to a particular species, but they do reveal some interesting developments in the hominin lineage. In chimpanzees, the humerus, the radius and ulna (the lower bones of the arm), and the femur are about the same length; in modern humans, the bones of the forearm have become shorter and the femur has become longer than the humerus. *Australopithecus afarensis* resembles chimpanzees in the proportions of these bones. However, reconstructions of the humerus, radius, ulna, and femur of the hominins at Bouri suggest that these creatures' femurs had become somewhat elongated, while the relative proportions of the humerus and forearm bones had not changed. The postcranial remains suggest that there was considerable variation in the size and robustness of the Bouri hominins. This variation may reflect the fact that males were larger than females, but there is not yet enough evidence to be certain that this was the case.

A. HABILIS/RUDOLFENSIS

Fossils with a larger brain and more humanlike teeth have been discovered at many sites in East Africa.

In 1960, while working at Olduvai Gorge with his parents, renowned paleoanthropologists Louis and Mary Leakey, Jonathan Leakey found pieces of a hominin jaw,

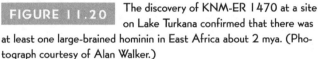

FIGURE 11.20   The discovery of KNM-ER 1470 at a site on Lake Turkana confirmed that there was at least one large-brained hominin in East Africa about 2 mya. (Photograph courtesy of Alan Walker.)

FIGURE 11.21   KNM-ER 1813 (shown here) had more modern teeth but a smaller brain than KNM-ER 1470. This variation led many investigators to argue that fossils assigned to the species *habilis* actually belonged to more than one species of hominin. (Photograph courtesy of Michael Day.)

cranium, and hand. The Leakeys assigned this specimen, labeled Olduvai Hominin 7 (OH 7), to the genus *Homo* because they believed the cranial bones indicated that it had a much larger brain than *Australopithecus* had, and small, more humanlike teeth. Louis Leakey named the species *Homo habilis*, or "handy man," because he believed he had found the hominin responsible for the simple, flaked-stone tools discovered nearby. Later the Leakeys found several more fossils that they assigned to *H. habilis*, including pieces of a second cranium, part of a foot, and more teeth. These fossils range in age from 1.6 to 1.9 million years old.

Many paleoanthropologists doubted that the Leakeys had found the oldest member of our genus. After all, the Leakeys' estimate of OH 7's brain size was based on only part of the cranium, and even then the complete cranium was estimated to be at most 50% larger than the brains of australopithecines. There was plenty of room for skepticism. Another member of the famous Leakey family helped prove that large brains were indeed present in a hominin living 1.9 mya. Mary and Louis Leakey's son Richard set up his own research team and began work at a site called Koobi Fora on the eastern shore of Lake Turkana. In 1972, a member of Richard Leakey's team, Bernard Ngeneo, found a nearly complete skull of a hominin. This find is usually referred to by its official collection number, KNM-ER 1470 (Figure 11.20). (This identification system is not as obscure as it may seem. *KNM* stands for Kenya National Museum, and *ER* stands for East Rudolf—Lake Turkana was known as Lake Rudolf when Leakey began his work there.) The most striking thing about KNM-ER 1470 is that it had a much larger brain than any known australopithecine had. Its endocranial volume is 775 cc, 75% bigger than the brains of specimens of *A. africanus*. Compared to OH 7, however, it had a relatively large, australopithecine-like face. Since the discovery of KNM-ER 1470, similar fossils have been found at several other sites, including Olduvai Gorge, the Omo basin, Sterkfontein, and a site near Lake Malawi. The oldest of these fossils dates to 2.4 mya.

Since the discovery of KNM-ER 1470, many other fossils have been assigned to the same species as OH 7 and KNM-ER 1470. The skulls and teeth of these fossils are quite variable. Some of them, like KNM-ER 1813 (Figures 11.21 and 11.22), have more humanlike teeth and less robust skulls with smaller faces and teeth than KNM-ER 1470, but they also have smaller brains than KNM-ER 1470, often about 500 cc. Some believe that the differences among these specimens represent variation within a single species. Others have argued that there were two species of relatively large-brained hominins present in East Africa 2 mya, and that the smaller-brained, less robust individuals should be classified as *habilis*, while the more robust ones with larger brains are a second species that should be named *rudolfensis*. Until very recently, both species would have been placed in the genus

0   5 cm

(a) KNM-ER 1470   (b) KNM-ER 1813

FIGURE 11.22 Fossils assigned to the species *habilis* show a mixture of derived and ancestral traits. (a) Some, like KNM-ER 1470, have larger brains but retain robust skulls and teeth. (b) Others, like KNM-ER 1813, have more humanlike skulls and teeth but retain the small brains of other australopithecines. Anthropologists are divided about whether these fossils are members of the same species. (Figure courtesy of Richard Klein.)

Homo, as the Leakeys originally proposed; but, as you will see shortly, many now advocate their placement in the genus *Australopithecus*.

The postcrania and developmental patterns of these creatures are similar to those of australopithecines. The first fragmentary postcranial material found at Olduvai Gorge suggested that OH 7 was very similar to the australopithecines from the neck down. A new discovery from Olduvai Gorge adds credence to this picture. During an expedition led by Don Johanson, Tim White discovered a specimen including an incomplete cranium and numerous postcranial bones. This specimen, labeled OH 62, had a very short stature and surprisingly long arms, suggesting that the postcranial skeletons of the Olduvai *habilis* specimens were similar to those of Lucy 1.4 million years earlier. Analysis of the layering of dental enamel indicates that specimens assigned to the species *habilis* and *rudolfensis* had rapid apelike developmental patterns, like other australopithecines.

It has recently been proposed that these fossils should be assigned to the genus Australopithecus because they are fundamentally more similar to other australopithecines than to other species assigned to Homo.

The fossils assigned to *habilis* and *rudolfensis* previously were classified as members of the genus *Homo* because they are similar to us in the following two ways:

1. The brain of these fossils is bigger than that of any of the australopithecines.
2. The teeth are smaller and have thinner enamel, and the dental arcade is more parabolic, than in the australopithecines. The skulls are more rounded, there are fewer air pockets in the bottom of the skull, the face is smaller and protrudes less, and the jaw muscles are reduced in size compared with the australopithecines.

In addition, it was initially assumed that these creatures were responsible for manufacturing the flaked-stone tools that appear in the archaeological record for the first time about 2.5 mya. As we will see in the next chapter, however, we do not know which hominin is responsible for these tools; it could have been *habilis* or *rudolfensis*, but it also could have been one of the other early hominins discussed here or *Homo ergaster*, a species we will introduce in Chapter 13.

Wood and Collard, whose taxonomic scheme we have adopted here, argue that these fossils do not belong in *Homo* but should be included in the genus *Australopithecus* instead. Remember from Chapter 4 that the rules of cladistic taxonomy specify that all the species comprising a genus must be descended from a common ancestor. However, this guideline does not tell us how to group species into genera; they could all be placed in one genus or divided into several (Figure 11.23). Wood and Collard argue that species grouped in a genus should share a common **adaptive grade**, meaning that they live in basically the same way. As we will see in Chapter 13, the other members of the genus *Homo* are larger than these creatures, they are fully committed to terrestrial life, and they have reduced sexual dimorphism. These features are correlated with important behaviors, such as hunting, complex extractive foraging, food sharing, and extensive paternal investment in offspring. Thus, Wood and Collard argue that *habilis* and *rudolfensis* should be grouped with the bipedal but otherwise apelike creatures in the genus *Australopithecus*, and we follow their suggestion here.

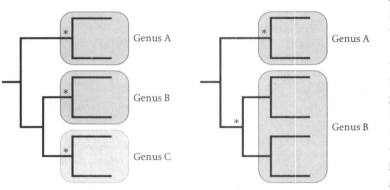

FIGURE 11.23 The same phylogeny with six species can be subdivided into different numbers of genera. In the first panel are three genera, each with two species; in the second panel are two genera, one with two species and the other with four. In each case, each genus includes all of the species that descend from the common ancestor, which is labeled with an asterisk. According to Wood and Collard, the second arrangement is better if the species in genus B share a common adaptive grade.

Paranthropus

Paranthropus aethiopicus is a hominin who has teeth and skull structures specialized for heavy chewing.

Alan Walker of Pennsylvania State University discovered the skull of a very robust australopithecine at a site on the west side of Lake Turkana in northern Kenya. Walker called it the "Black Skull" because of its distinctive black color, but its official name is KNM-WT 17000 (Figure 11.24) (*WT* stands for West Turkana, the site at which the fossil was found). This creature lived about 2.5 mya, and in some ways it is similar to *A. afarensis*. For example, the hinge of the jaw in KNM-WT 17000 has the same primitive structure as the jaw in *A. afarensis* has, which is very similar to the jaw joints of chimpanzees and gorillas. The later australopithecines and members of the genus *Homo* have a modified jaw hinge. In addition, both KNM-WT 17000 and *A. afarensis* were quite sexually dimorphic, they had a similar postcranial anatomy, and they were equipped with relatively small brains in relation to body size.

However, as shown in Figure 11.25, KNM-WT 17000 is very different from the skull of other australopithecines. The molars are enormous, the lower jaw is very large, and the entire skull has been reorganized to support the massive chewing apparatus. For example, it has a pronounced sagittal crest, which enlarges the surface area of bone available

The Black Skull (KNM-WT 17000), which was discovered on the west side of Lake Turkana in Kenya.

for attaching the **temporalis muscle**, one of the muscles that works the jaw. You can easily demonstrate for yourself the function of the sagittal crest. Put your fingertips on your temple and clench your teeth; you will feel the temporalis muscle bunch up. As you continue clenching your teeth, slowly move your fingertips upward until you can't feel the muscle any more. This is the top point of attachment for your temporalis muscle, about one inch above your temple. Australopithecines had bigger teeth than we do and so needed larger temporalis muscles, and these muscles required more space

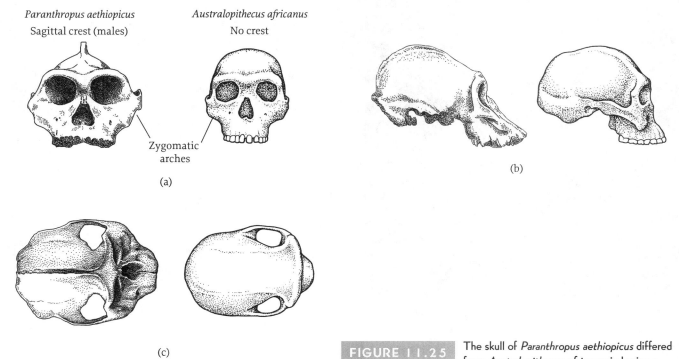

Paranthropus aethiopicus
Sagittal crest (males)

Australopithecus africanus
No crest

Zygomatic arches

(a)

(b)

(c)

5 cm

The skull of *Paranthropus aethiopicus* differed from *Australopithecus africanus* in having a sagittal crest (a), a flatter face and forehead (b), and a shorter snout (c).

(a) *P. aethiopicus*   (b) *Homo sapiens*

FIGURE 11.26 In these two skulls—of *P. aethiopicus* (a) and a modern human (b)—the area of attachment of the temporalis muscle is shown in red.

for attachment to the skull. In *A. africanus* the muscles expanded so that they almost met at the top of the skull. The even larger teeth of *P. aethiopicus* required even more space for muscle attachment, and the sagittal crest served this function (Figure 11.26). Other distinctive features of *P. aethiopicus* are also accommodations to the enlarged teeth and jaw musculature. For example, the cheekbones (zygomatic arches) are flared outward to make room for the enlarged temporalis muscle. The flared cheekbones caused the face to be flat, or even pushed in.

Paranthropus robustus *is a more recent species found in southern Africa.*

At Kromdraai, a site in South Africa, retired Scottish physician and avid paleontologist Robert Broom discovered fossils that seemed very different from the *A. africanus* specimens previously found at Sterkfontein (Figure 11.27). These creatures were much more robust (with more massive skulls and larger teeth) than their neighbors, so Broom called his find *Paranthropus robustus*. Many of his colleagues questioned this choice. They thought he had discovered another species of *Australopithecus*, and so for a time most paleontologists classified Broom's fossils as *Australopithecus robustus*. Recently, however, the consensus has been that the robust early hominins are so different from the gracile (more lightly built) australopithecines that they should be placed in a separate genus, and Broom's original classification has been restored.

There is a large sample of *P. robustus* fossils from Kromdraai and also from a second site nearby, named Swartkrans. These creatures appeared about 1.8 mya and disappeared about 1 mya. Their brains averaged about 530 cc. *Paranthropus robustus* males stood about 1.3 m (4½ ft) tall and weighed about 40 kg (88 lb); females were about 1.1 m (3½ ft) tall and weighed 32 kg (70 lb). Their postcranial anatomy shows that they were undoubtedly bipedal. They share many of the same derived features with humans that *A. africanus* does. In addition, they share with *A. africanus* several specialized features for heavy chewing, but these feature are much more pronounced in *P. robustus*.

It is unclear what the paranthropines were doing with this massive chewing apparatus. Until recently, most anthropologists believed that the paranthropines relied more on plant materials that required heavy chewing than *A. africanus* did. In other animals, large grinding teeth are often associated with a diet of tough plant materials, and omnivorous animals typically have relatively large canines and incisors. Moreover, the wear patterns on *P. robustus* teeth suggest that they ate very hard foods like seeds or nuts. However, recent research on the chemistry of *P. robustus* teeth suggests that they probably also ate substantial amounts of meat (Box 11.1).

FIGURE 11.27 A nearly complete skull of *Paranthropus robustus* was found at Sterkfontein in South Africa in 1999. This species has very large jaws and molars and relatively small incisors and canines.

BOX 11.1

Chemical Clues about the Diet of Paranthropines

Two kinds of chemical analyses of the fossilized teeth of paranthropines suggest that they may have eaten substantial amounts of animal matter. The first kind of evidence comes from the obscure but useful fact that the ratio of strontium (Sr) to calcium (Ca) in the bones of living animals declines as these elements are passed up the food chain: plants have higher Sr:Ca ratios than do the grazing herbivores that eat them, and grazing herbivores that feed mainly on grasses have higher Sr:Ca ratios than do the carnivores that prey on them. Browsing herbivores constitute the major exception to this rule. Browsers, such as deer and kudu, eat mainly the leaves and shoots of woody plants, but they have low Sr:Ca ratios like carnivores.

To find out what *P. robustus* was eating, Andrew Sillen of the University of Cape Town measured the Sr:Ca ratios in the fossilized bones of *P. robustus* and in the fossilized bones of a number of animal species found at Swartkrans. He needed to survey multiple species to be sure that fossil specimens showed the same relative Sr:Ca ratios that living members of the same species show (Figure 11.28). He found that they do, so we can be confident that the Sr:Ca ratios were not changed by geochemical processes after the animals died. Sillen's measurements of the Sr:Ca ratio for *P. robustus* suggest that these creatures were either browsers or carnivores but not grazing herbivores.

To determine whether *P. robustus* was a browser or a carnivore, we turn to another line of evidence. It turns out there are two chemically distinct kinds of photosynthesis. Trees, shrubs, and other woody plants utilize one type, called "C_3 photosynthesis"; and grasses use a second type, called "C_4 photosynthesis." C_4 plants and the animals that eat them have higher concentrations of the heavy isotope of carbon, carbon-13, than do C_3 plants and the animals that eat C_3 plants. Julia Lee-Thorp of the University of Cape Town and her colleagues measured the amount of carbon-12 and carbon-13 in the fossilized teeth of a number of species at Swartkrans, including *P. robustus*. The levels of carbon-13 found in the teeth of *P. robustus* are

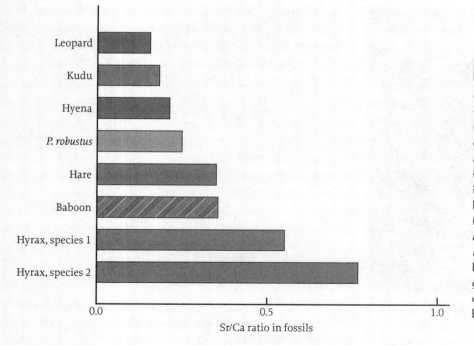

FIGURE 11.28 Measuring the ratio of strontium (Sr) to calcium (Ca) in the bones of both living and fossil species can help paleontologists deduce the kinds of diets that extinct creatures had. In general, the Sr:Ca ratio in the bones of living animals declines as you move up the food chain from pure herbivory to carnivory. An exception is browsing herbivores (like kudu), which have low Sr:Ca ratios. Here, the Sr:Ca ratios for typical herbivores (green) and carnivores (red) are plotted along with the Sr:Ca ratio for *P. robustus* (blue). Baboons, who combine herbivory and carnivory, are plotted in red and green. The low Sr:Ca ratio in *P. robustus* is consistent with carnivory or browsing herbivory, but not with general herbivory.

higher than the levels found in browsing species like kudu. This evidence indicates that *P. robustus* either ate grass and grass seeds or ate animals that ate grasses. Because the Sr:Ca ratios suggest that *P. robustus* did not eat grasses, these data indicate that *P. robustus* was at least partially carnivorous.

Taken together, these data suggest that *P. robustus* consumed some animal protein. Nonetheless, their massive teeth may have evolved for chewing tough plant material. For example, they might have specialized on tough plant material during the dry season but had a more diverse diet during the rest of the year.

Olduvai Gorge in Tanzania has been the site of many important paleontological and archaeological finds. Louis and Mary Leakey worked in Olduvai for more than 30 years.

Paranthropus boisei *was a robust* robustus.

Another paranthropine with large molars was discovered by Mary Leakey at Olduvai Gorge, Tanzania, in 1959 (Figure 11.29). This specimen, officially labeled Olduvai Hominin 5 (OH 5), was first classified as *Zinjanthropus boisei*. Zinj derives from an Arabic word for "East Africa," and *boisei* comes from Charles Boise, who was funding Leakey's research at the time. Leakey's find was later reclassified *Paranthropus boisei* because of its affinities to the South African forms of *P. robustus*. (Those who advocate classifying *P. robustus* as *Australopithecus robustus* would assign Leakey's find to the same genus, and call it *A. boisei*.) The discovery of OH 5 was important, partly because it ended nearly 30 frustrating years of work in Olduvai Gorge in which there had been no dramatic hominin finds. It was only the first of a very remarkable set of fossil discoveries at Olduvai.

Essentially, *P. boisei* is an even more robust *P. robustus*—that is, a hyperrobust paranthropine. Its body is somewhat larger than the body of *P. robustus*, and its molars are larger than those of *P. robustus*, even when the difference in body size is taken into account. The skulls are even more specialized for heavy chewing.

Paranthropus boisei appears in the fossil record at about 2.2 mya in eastern Africa. It became extinct about 1.3 mya, although the exact date of its disappearance is difficult to establish.

Kenyanthropus

Kenyanthropus platyops is a recently discovered species that lived in East Africa between 3.5 and 3.2 mya.

In 1999, Justus Erus, a member of a research team led by Meave Leakey, found a nearly complete hominin cranium, labeled KNM-WT 40000, on the western side of Lake Turkana in Kenya (Figure 11.30). KNM-WT 40000 has

The fossil cranium of *Kenyanthropus platyops* was found near Lake Turkana in northern Kenya. It dates to about 3.5 mya and has a unique combination of anatomical features.

what one commentator described as "a dizzying mosaic of features." As in chimpanzees, *A. anamensis*, and *A. ramidus*, the cranium has a small ear hole. Like most of the early hominins, the specimen has a chimpanzee-sized braincase and thick enamel on its molars. However, its molars are substantially smaller than those of any other early hominin except *A. ramidus*. Its face is broad and very flat, like those of *P. boisei* and *A. rudolfensis*. Because this specimen combines features not found in other hominins, Leakey and her coauthors placed it, and a fragmentary upper jaw found nearby some years earlier, in a new genus, *Kenyanthropus*, meaning "Kenyan man." The species name, *platyops*, is from the Greek for "flat face" and refers to the most notable anatomical feature of this specimen. Argon–argon dating methods have revealed that KNM-WT 40000 is 3.5 million years old. The fossils found in association with the cranium suggest that these creatures lived in a mix of woodland and savanna environments.

HOMININ PHYLOGENIES

It is difficult to infer the phylogenetic relationships among the Plio-Pleistocene hominins.

Remember, the goal of our enterprise is to reconstruct the evolutionary history of human beings. To do so, ideally we would like to understand the phylogenetic relationships among our ancestors. Unfortunately, as the hominin fossil record has become richer, this task has become harder. The problem is illustrated by the phylogeny shown in Figure 11.31, which accompanied the first published description of *Kenyanthropus platyops*, in the journal *Nature*. Clearly, a vast number of different phylogenies could be constructed, depending on which relationships are chosen and which are rejected.

The problem arises from the extensive convergence and parallelism in hominin evolution. This means that many alternative phylogenies are equally plausible, depending on what is assumed to be homologous and what is assumed to be convergent. Randall Skelton of the University of Wyoming and Henry McHenry of the University of California Davis performed a phylogenetic analysis of 77 traits of the skulls of a number of the early hominin species discussed here. They sorted the traits into groups according to their function and their location in the body. For example, one functional group of traits included features thought to be adaptations for heavy chewing, such as large teeth and a sagittal crest, and another group included all of the features of the bottom of the cranium. Then Skelton and McHenry determined the best trees to fit different combinations of traits. They found that the branching pattern of the best tree depends on

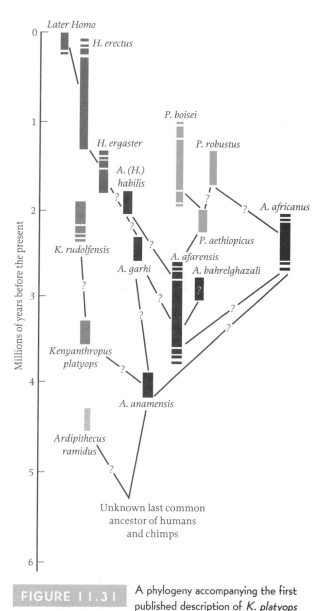

FIGURE 11.31 A phylogeny accompanying the first published description of *K. platyops* in the journal *Nature*. The question marks represent links that the article's author regards as tenuous or uncertain. Notice that nearly every link has a question mark. The author has chosen to classify *Australopithecus rudolfensis* as *Kenyanthropus rudolfensis*, and *A. bahrelghazali* is a specimen we consider to be *A. afarensis*.

which groups of traits are included. For example, the best fit based on traits in the heavy-chewing complex groups together all the paranthropines and shows *Homo* species as deriving from *A. afarensis* (Figure 11.32). In contrast, when the traits in the heavy-chewing complex are eliminated, the results are consistent with the radically different tree shown in Figure 11.33. In this case, *P. aethiopicus* is unrelated to *P. robustus* and *P. boisei*, and *Homo* species derive from *A. africanus*.

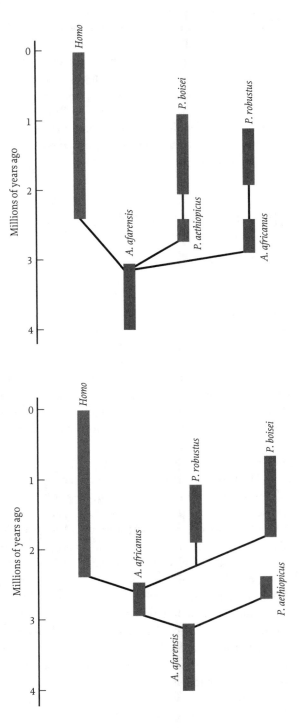

FIGURE 11.32 Before the discovery of *P. aethiopicus* (KNM-WT 17000), there was a general consensus about the hominin phylogeny: that *Homo* species derive from *A. afarensis*, and that *A. africanus* began a lineage of increasing robustness culminating in *P. boisei*.

FIGURE 11.33 If we assume that the similarities in traits other than those involved in heavy chewing are homologous, then we might obtain the phylogeny shown here, in which *A. afarensis* gives rise to *A. africanus*, who in turn gives rise to *Homo* species and the later paranthropines. According to this phylogeny the similarities between *P. aethiopicus* and the other paranthropines are due to parallel evolution.

THE EVOLUTION OF EARLY HOMININ MORPHOLOGY AND BEHAVIOR

The absence of a secure phylogeny for the early hominins does not prevent us from understanding human evolution.

It is easy to be discouraged by the uncertainties in the hominin fossil record and to doubt that we know anything concrete about our earliest ancestors. Although there are many gaps in the fossil record and much controversy about the relationship among the early hominin species, we do know several important things about them. In every plausible phylogeny, the human lineage is derived from a small biped who was adept in trees. Its teeth and jaws were suited for a generalized diet. The males were considerably larger than the females, their brains were the same size as those of modern apes, and their offspring developed rapidly like modern apes. This is the kind of creature that linked the apes of the Miocene to the earliest members of our own genus, *Homo*.

In the discussion that follows, we first consider why bipedal locomotion evolved, and we then review what we can infer about the behavior and life history of these hominins.

The Evolution of Bipedalism

There are several explanations for the evolution of bipedalism.

Ever since Darwin, evolutionists have speculated about why bipedal locomotion was favored by natural selection. Here we examine the most popular hypotheses.

Walking on two legs is an efficient form of locomotion on the ground. At first glance, this hypothesis seems to be an unlikely possibility. After all, there are far more quadrupedal species than bipedal species, and studies of the energetics of locomotion show that terrestrial quadrupeds like horses move about more efficiently than humans do. If bipedalism is a superior form of locomotion, we would expect it to be more common. However, Peter Rodman and Henry McHenry at the University of California Davis, who studied the locomotion of humans and of quadrupedal primates on the ground, found that bipedal and quadrupedal locomotion are more or less equivalent in efficiency.

If bipedal and quadrupedal locomotion are equally efficient means of traveling on the ground, why did humans become bipedal when they left the trees? Rodman and McHenry suggest that the answer has to do with the kind of quadrupedalism found in hominin ancestors. They conjecture that the ancestors of terrestrial monkeys were arboreal quadrupeds who fed on the tops of branches, but the ancestors of the hominins were suspensory feeders (hanging below branches to feed, as modern orangutans do). Selection might have favored quadrupedalism among animals descended from above-the-branch feeders and favored bipedalism among animals descended from suspensory feeders—in each case because that form of ground locomotion required fewer anatomical changes.

A recent study of the wrist morphology of *A. anamensis* and *A. afarensis* casts doubt on this explanation for bipedalism. Anthropologists Brian Richmond and David Strait of George Washington University have shown that the wrist bones of chimpanzees and gorillas have a suite of distinctive features that facilitate knuckle walking. They have also shown that the wrists of *A. anamensis* and *A. afarensis* share these knuckle-walking features. However, neither of these species exhibit other knuckle-walking adaptations that are seen in the hand bones of chimpanzees and gorillas. Richmond and Strait argue that these australopithecines had already become committed bipeds, but their wrists retained some features of their knuckle-walking ancestors. If this hypothesis is correct, then human bipedalism evolved in a creature already adapted to terrestrial locomotion, not a creature exclusively adapted for suspensory locomotion. This scenario leaves us with a puzzle: why did a knuckle-walking ape shift to bipedal locomotion?

Erect posture allowed hominins to keep cool. Heat stress is a more serious problem in the open, sun-baked savanna than in the shade of the forest. Although modern apes are restricted to forested areas, hominins apparently moved into more open areas. If an animal is active in the open during the middle of the day, it must have a way to prevent its body temperature, particularly the temperature of its brain, from rising too high. Many savanna creatures have adaptations that allow their body temperatures to rise during the day and to cool off at night. They also have adaptations (such as large nasal chambers) that keep the temperature of the blood in their brain well below the temperature of the blood in the rest of their bodies. However, this option does not seem to be available to hominins. Instead, humans have evolved a system of evaporative cooling: we sweat. Peter Wheeler of Liverpool John Moores University has pointed out that the erect posture associated with bipedal locomotion helps to reduce heat stress and lessens the amount of water necessary for evaporative cooling, in three different ways (Figure 11.34):

1. The sun strikes a much smaller fraction of the body of an erect hominin than of a quadrupedal animal of the same size. An erect hominin absorbs sunlight directly only on the top of its head and shoulders, while a quadruped absorbs the energy of the sun across its whole back and head. (Think about how much harder it is to get a tan standing up than lying down.) This difference is important because near the equator the sun is overhead during much of the middle of the day.
2. The air is warmer near the ground than it is higher up. The sun heats the soil, and the soil radiates and conducts heat back to the air, so air temperatures are highest close to the ground.
3. Wind velocities are higher 2 m (about 6 ft) off the ground than they are 1 m (about 3 ft) off the ground. Because moving air increases the efficiency of evaporative cooling, an erect hominin is better able to withstand the heat of the day.

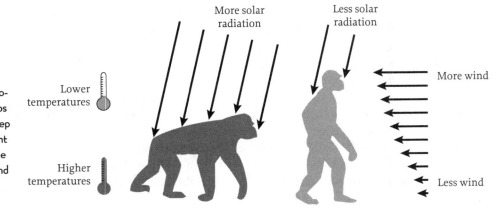

FIGURE 11.34 Bipedal locomotion helps an animal living in warm climates to keep cool by reducing the amount of sunlight that falls on the body, by increasing the animal's exposure to air movements, and by immersing the animal in lower-temperature air.

Using standard engineering methods, Wheeler calculated that these three factors would reduce heat stress and water consumption in bipedal hominins compared with quadrupeds. Interestingly, the same calculations show that loss of body hair provides a thermoregulatory advantage to a bipedal creature, but not to a quadruped of the same size.

Bipedal locomotion leaves the hands free to carry things. The ability to carry things is, in a word, handy. Quadrupeds can't carry things in their hands without interfering with their ability to walk and to climb. As a consequence, they must carry things in their mouths. Some Old World monkeys pack great quantities of food into their cheeks to be chewed and swallowed later. Other primates must eat their food where they find it—a necessity that can cause problems when food is located in a dangerous place, or when there is a lot of competition over food. Bipedal hominins can carry larger quantities of food in their hands and arms.

Bipedal posture allows efficient harvesting of fruit from small trees. Indiana University anthropologist Kevin Hunt has argued that the anatomy of A. *afarensis* is well suited to standing erect but not well designed for efficient bipedal walking. Hunt thinks that bipedal posture was favored because it allows efficient harvesting of fruit from the small trees that predominate in African woodlands. Two kinds of data support this hypothesis. First, Hunt found that chimpanzees rarely walk bipedally, but they spend a lot of time standing bipedally as they harvest fruit from small trees (Figure 11.35). Using their hands for balance, they pick the fruit and slowly shuffle from depleted patches to fresh ones. Standing upright allows the chimpanzees to use both hands to gather fruit, and the slow bipedal shuffling allows them to move from one fruit patch to another without lowering and raising their body weight. Second, Hunt argues that many anatomical features of A. *afarensis* are consistent with standing upright but not with walking bipedally. He points out that the very broad pelvis of A. *afarensis* would make a stable platform for standing on both feet. Hunt also argues that the features of the shoulders, hands, and feet that many anthropologists believe are adaptations for climbing trees are actually adaptations that enabled A. *afarensis* to hang by one hand while standing bipedally and feeding with the other hand.

Any or all of these hypotheses may be correct. Bipedalism might have been favored by selection because it was more efficient than knuckle walking, because it allowed early hominins to keep cool, because it enabled them to carry food or tools from place to place, and/or because it enabled them to feed more efficiently. And once bipedalism had evolved, it might have facilitated other forms of behavior, such as tool use.

FIGURE 11.35 Chimpanzees sometimes stand bipedally as they harvest fruit from small trees. They use one hand for balance and feed with the other, shuffling slowly from one food patch to another.

Early Hominin Subsistence

Increased seasonality in rainfall favors a greater dependence on foods available during the dry season: corms, tubers, and meat.

Herbivorous animals that live in seasonal environments are faced with quite a variable food supply. When the rain falls, grasses sprout, flowers blossom, fruit ripens, and there are many pools of freshwater (Figure 11.36a). Food is abundant and diverse. Because food is plentiful, there is little competition among species over access to food. During the dry season, grasses go to seed, flowers die, and all but a few permanent water holes dry up (Figure 11.36b). Both the abundance and diversity of food are greatly reduced (Figure 11.37). Because there is very little to eat for most herbivorous animals, intense competition erupts among certain species. Many species respond to

(a)   (b)

FIGURE 11.36 In seasonal habitats, the landscape changes dramatically over the course of the year. Here you see the same area in Amboseli just after the seasonal rains have ended (a) and at the end of the long dry season (b).

this problem by focusing their foraging efforts on a particular type of food during the dry season. In Amboseli National Park, for example, baboons spend much of their time during the dry season digging up grass corms (the bulbous storage organs in grass stems). Another way to cope with shortages of plant foods is to become more omnivorous (Figure 11.38). Baboons at many different sites increase their meat intake during the dry season (Figure 11.39).

(a)   (b)

FIGURE 11.37 In seasonal habitats, resource availability is strongly affected by rainfall. (a) After the rains, lush growth sprouts, and baboon foods are abundant and diverse. (b) By the end of the dry season, the ground is parched, new growth has withered, and less food is available to baboons.

Cambridge University anthropologist Rob Foley has suggested that the hominin lineage may have adapted to increased seasonality in two different ways. The robust hominins in the genus *Paranthropus*, with their huge jaws and chewing muscles, may have specialized in processing tough plant materials in much the same way that modern baboons specialize on corms. The less robust species, on the other hand, may have shifted to a more omnivorous diet and relied more heavily on meat.

Chimpanzees are effective hunters who capture monkeys, bushpigs, and small antelope, but they rarely scavenge.

In the past, many anthropologists thought it was unlikely that the early hominins ate very much meat. Hunting, they argued, requires careful planning, subtle coordination, and extensive reciprocity. These interactions would require cognitive and linguistic skills that the relatively small-brained australopithecines must have lacked. Studies of chimpanzee hunting by Christophe and Hedwige Boesch in the Taï Forest of the Ivory Coast, Craig Stanford at Gombe Stream National Park in Tanzania, and John Mitani and David Watts in Ngogo, Uganda, suggest that we must revise this view.

At Taï, Gombe, and Ngogo, chimpanzees participate in hunts approximately once every two or three days. Most predatory activity focuses on monkeys, particularly red

FIGURE 11.38 A male baboon consumes a newborn bushbuck in the Okavango Delta of Botswana.

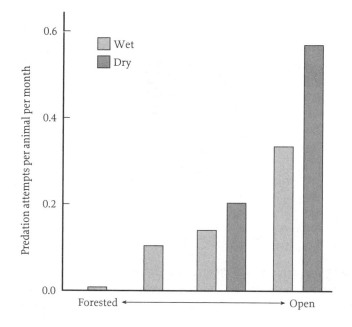

FIGURE 11.39   Observations at different sites in Africa show that baboons hunt meat more often in the dry season than in the wet season.

colobus (Figure 11.40). Gombe chimpanzees also prey on bushpigs and bushbucks (sheep-sized forest antelope) that they encounter on the forest floor (Figure 11.41). Unlike some other meat-eating species, chimpanzees never feed on the carcasses of dead animals that they encounter opportunistically, and they rarely take fresh kills from other predator species.

At Gombe, Ngogo, and Taï, many red colobus hunts begin when the chimpanzees encounter a group of monkeys in the forest or detect them at a distance. They often spend some time on the ground gazing up into the canopy before they begin to hunt. Then at least one chimpanzee climbs into the trees and gives chase. Others watch from the ground.

Although most hunts at Gombe and Ngogo seem to arise out of opportunistic encounters with groups of monkeys, about half of the hunts at Taï begin before there is any sign that monkeys are nearby. In these cases, the chimpanzees fall completely silent, stay very close to one another, frequently change direction, and stop often to search for monkeys in the canopy. The chimpanzees in the three study areas are effective hunters, making kills in approximately half of their hunts.

These observations invalidate the argument that a small-brained hominin must have lacked the necessary cognitive and linguistic skills for hunting. However, they do not tell us how likely it is that the early hominins actually hunted.

(a)   (b)

FIGURE 11.40   Chimpanzees hunt small mammals, particularly red colobus monkeys. (a) A red colobus monkey carrying an infant leaps from one tree to another at Gombe Stream National Park in Tanzania. (b) A male chimpanzee at Gombe consumes a red colobus monkey. (Photographs courtesy of Craig Stanford.)

Chimpanzee Prey at Gombe, 1974–1991

Other

Bushbuck

Bushpig

Colobus

FIGURE 11.41   Chimpanzees at Gombe most commonly hunt red colobus monkeys, although they sometimes prey on bushpigs, bushbucks, and other animals.

Early hominins may have used tools like contemporary chimpanzees do.

As we will see in the next chapter, the earliest identifiable tools first appear about 2.5 mya, and it is possible that one of the early hominins discussed here manufactured these tools. However, the absence of identifiable tools does not mean that early hominins were not tool users.

Chimpanzees make and use tools to perform a variety of different tasks. They use long, thin branches, vines, stems, sticks, and twigs to poke into ant nests, termite mounds, and bees' nests to extract insects and honey. They sometimes scrape marrow and other tissue from the bones and braincases of mammalian prey with wooden twigs. They pound stone hammers against heavy flat stones, exposed rocks, and roots to crack open hard-shelled nuts (Figure 11.42). They wad up leaves, dip them into pools of rainwater that have collected in hollow tree trunks, and then suck water from the leafy "sponges."

Moreover, chimpanzees modify natural objects for specific purposes. That is, they are toolmakers, as well as tool users. For example, chimpanzees at Mount Assirik in Senegal, studied by Caroline Tutin of Stirling University and William McGrew of the Miami University of Ohio, use twigs to extract termites from their mounds. The twigs are first detached from the bush or shrub; then leaves growing from the stem are stripped off, the bark is peeled back from the stem, and the twig is clipped to an appropriate length. Chimpanzees do not modify all of the materials that they use as tools. The stone hammers and anvils that chimpanzees use to crack open hard-shelled nuts are carefully selected, used repeatedly, and sometimes moved from one site in the forest to another, but they are not deliberately altered by the chimpanzees. However, none of these tools would leave a trace in the archaeological record.

Approximately half of the tasks for which chimpanzees manufacture and use tools are related to food processing and food acquisition. In some cases, these tools allow chimpanzees to exploit food resources that other animals cannot use. For example, many animals are attracted to termite mounds when the winged insects emerge in massive swarms to form new colonies, but only chimpanzees can obtain access to the termites inside the mounds at other times of the year. Some of the shells of nuts that chimpanzees eat in the Taï Forest are so hard that they can be opened only by repeated battering of the shell with a stone hammer.

Despite the examples of tool use by chimpanzees, humans are the only primates to use tools extensively. William McGrew argues that the reason chimpanzees don't make greater use of tools is that they can't transport them easily (Figure 11.43). If a chimpanzee can't carry a tool from place to place, then it must manufacture its tools at the site where they will be used. As a consequence, it doesn't pay off for chim-

FIGURE 11.42   In West Africa, chimpanzees use stones to crack open hard-shelled nuts.

panzees to put a lot of effort into making tools, so the tools they use are crude.

Early Hominin Social Organization

Chimpanzees share food, but only transfers from mothers to offspring account for a significant fraction of total consumption.

As we will see in the next chapter, food sharing plays a crucial role in the economies of modern foraging groups. We will learn that there are reasons to believe that hunting makes sharing necessary, and sharing makes hunting feasible. Thus, if meat eating played an important role in the lives of early hominins, then reciprocal exchanges of food must have been important as well. Again we look to chimpanzees for insights about the origins of this behavior.

Unlike most other primates, chimpanzees frequently share food. Mothers regularly share with their infants, and adults share food with each other under certain circumstances. Plant foods are what mothers generally share with their infants, but on the rare occasions when adults share food, it is usually meat. The patterns of food sharing between mothers and their infants have been the most carefully analyzed at Gombe. There, mothers are most likely to share foods that are difficult for the infants to obtain or to process independently (see Chapter 8). For example, infants have a hard time opening hard-shelled fruits and extracting seeds from sticky pods. A mother will often allow an infant to take bits of these items from her own hand, or sometimes she will spontaneously offer them to her infant. When chimpanzees capture vertebrate prey, they dismember, divide, and sometimes redistribute the meat among members of the foraging party. However, the amounts are a small fraction of all food calories consumed. In the Taï Forest, small prey are generally retained by the captor, and larger prey are typically divided among several individuals (Figure 11.44). The distribution of meat spans a continuum from outright coercion to apparently voluntary donations. High-ranking males sometimes take kills away from lower-ranking

FIGURE 11.43 It is awkward for chimpanzees to carry things. Sometimes they carry small objects in their mouths. They can carry large objects only if they walk bipedally. Here a male chimpanzee drags a log as he performs an aggressive display. (Photograph courtesy of William C. McGrew.)

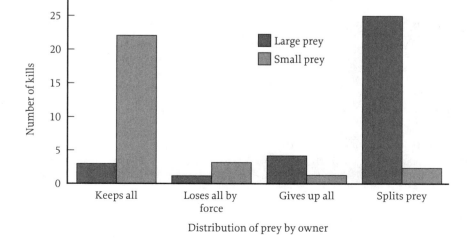

FIGURE 11.44 In the Taï Forest, chimpanzees sometimes share their kills. Infant and juvenile monkeys (small prey) are generally consumed by the captor, but adult monkey carcasses are generally divided by the captor and shared with other chimpanzees.

FIGURE 11.45 Male chimpanzees sometimes share their kills with other males, sexually receptive females, and immatures. (Photograph courtesy of Craig Stanford.)

males, and adult males sometimes take kills away from females. At Gombe, about one-third of all kills are appropriated by higher-ranking individuals. More often, however, kills are retained by the captor and shared with others who cluster closely around. Males, who are generally the ones who control the kills, share food with other males, adult females, juveniles, and infants (Figure 11.45).

It is plausible that early hominins lived in multimale, multifemale groups with little male investment in offspring.

The fossils themselves give us reason to believe that hominins lived in large groups. The australopithecines and early hominins showed pronounced dimorphism in body size: males were substantially larger than females. Sexual dimorphism in body size is consistent with the formation of multimale or one-male groups.

Comparative analyses indicate that terrestrial primates usually live in bigger groups, on average, than arboreal primates do. Baboons often live in groups of 60 individuals, but arboreal howler monkeys usually live in groups that number less than a dozen. Large group size may be a form of defense against terrestrial predators because animals living in large groups are less vulnerable to predators than animals living in smaller groups are.

Large groups tend to contain several adult males, as we saw in Chapter 7, because it is difficult for a single male to maintain exclusive access to a large number of females. In such groups there are no permanent bonds between males and females, and males invest little in offspring. In nonhuman primates, terrestrial life is generally associated with multimale, multifemale social organization.

FURTHER READING

Conroy, G. 1997. *Reconstructing Human Origins: A Modern Synthesis.* Norton, New York.

Foley, R. 1987. *Another Unique Species.* Longman Scientific and Technical, Harlow, England.

Klein, R. 1999. *The Human Career* (2nd ed.). University of Chicago Press, Chicago.

Wood, B., and M. Collard. 1999. The genus *Homo. Science* 284: 65–71.

STUDY QUESTIONS

1. What features distinguish modern humans from other great apes?
2. Many researchers refer to the early hominins as bipedal apes. Is this description accurate? In what ways do you think early hominins may have differed from other apes?

3. The map in Figure 11.4 indicates that early hominins were restricted to the eastern and southern parts of Africa. Why do you think this is the case?

4. What circumstances might have favored the divergence and subsequent diversification of hominin species in Africa 4 to 2 mya?

5. What do we mean when we label a trait as "primitive"?

6. Outline three reasons why natural selection may have favored bipedal locomotion in the hominin lineage. In each case, explain why hominins became bipedal but other terrestrial primates, such as baboons, did not.

7. What evidence suggests that australopithecines spent more time in trees than modern humans do?

8. What features do the *Australopithecus* species share? In what ways do they differ from *Paranthropus* and *Kenyanthropus*?

9. A number of different phylogenetic schemes have been proposed over the last few decades, including the two phylogenies illustrated in Figures 11.32 and 11.33. Note that these phylogenies do not include the newly discovered species of *Orrorin tugenensis*, *Kenyanthropus platyops*, and *Australopithecus garhi*. How do these new species alter these phylogenies?

10. Conventional wisdom has been that *A. habilis* was the first maker of stone tools and that this accomplishment merits its inclusion in the genus *Homo*. Does the conventional wisdom fit the current evidence? Is it likely that australopithecines were the first tool users?

11. From the comparative and morphological evidence on hand, what can we say about the behavior and social organization of the early hominins?

KEY TERMS

hominins	diastema
foramen magnum	torque
pneumatized	abductors
australopithecines	ilium
tibia	femur
humerus	sagittal crest
endocranial volume	adaptive grade
subnasal prognathism	temporalis muscle

CONTENT FROM *HUMAN EVOLUTION: A MULTI-MEDIA GUIDE TO THE FOSSIL RECORD*

Human Origins	The Australopithecine Adaptive Radiation
Overview	Overview
Ardipithecus ramidus	Robust Australopithecines
Australopithecus anamensis	Gracile Australopithecines
Australopithecus afarensis	Possible Relationships

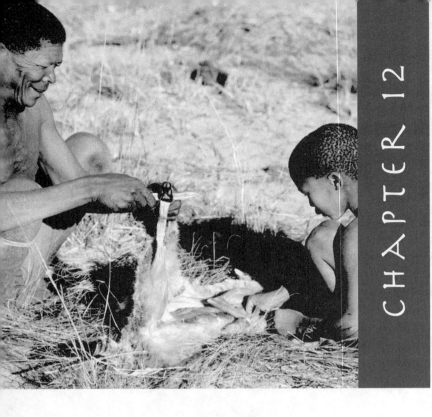

OLDOWAN TOOLMAKERS AND THE ORIGIN OF HUMAN LIFE HISTORY

THE OLDOWAN TOOLMAKERS

The earliest identifiable stone tools are from about 2.5 mya.

Hominins have been making stone tools for at least 2.5 million years. The first identifiable stone tools were found in the Awash region of Ethiopia and are dated to about 2.5 mya. Similar tools found at a number of other sites in East Africa are between 1.7 and 2.4 million years old. In South Africa the earliest stone tools date to about 2 mya. Tools made from bone appear in the fossil record between 2 and 1 mya at Olduvai Gorge and in South Africa.

The earliest toolmakers were already quite proficient at their craft. At a West Turkana site that dates to 2.3 mya, researchers have found an extensive array of stone artifacts, including **flakes** (small, sharp chips), **cores**, hammer stones, and debris from manufacturing. Preservation conditions were so good that workers were able to fit a number of flakes back onto the cores from which they had been struck. This reconstruction revealed that early hominins removed as many as 30 flakes from a single core, maintaining precise flaking angles during the entire toolmaking sequence.

These artifacts, collectively referred to as the **Oldowan tool industry**, are very simple. They consist of rounded stones, like the cobbles once used to pave city streets, that have been flaked (chipped) a few times to produce an edge (Figure 12.1). Toolmaking (**knapping**) leaves telltale traces on the cobble cores, so it's possible to distinguish natural breakage from deliberate modification. The Oldowan artifacts are quite variable in their shape and size, but this variation does not seem to be related to differences in how the tools were used, how they were made, or how toolmakers thought their tools should look. Instead, the tools vary because they were made out of different raw materials. There is now evidence that the flakes struck from these cobbles were at least as useful as the cores themselves (Box 12.1).

The Oldowan tool industry is an example of Mode I technology.

Tool industries like the Oldowan refer to collections of tools that are found in a particular region and time. It is also useful to have a name for a particular method of

Bifacial chopper

Hammer stone

Discoid

Flake scraper

Polyhedron

Flake

0   5 cm

Heavy-duty (core) scraper

FIGURE 12.1 Stone tools like these first appear in the archaeological record about 2.5 mya. Researchers are not sure how these tools were used. Some think that the large cores shown here were used for a variety of tasks; others think that the small flakes removed from these cores were the real tools.

BOX 12.1

Ancient Toolmaking and Tool Use

Recently, Kathy Schick and Nicholas Toth of Indiana University have done many experiments with simple stone tools. They have mastered the skills needed to manufacture the kinds of artifacts found at Oldowan sites and learned how to use them effectively. Their experiments have produced several interesting results. Schick and Toth believe the Oldowan artifacts that archaeologists have painstakingly collected and described are not really tools at all. They are cores left over after striking off small, sharp flakes, and the flakes are the real tools. Schick and Toth find that the flakes can be used for an impressive variety of tasks, even for butchering large animals like elephants. In contrast, although the cores can be used for some tasks, such as chopping down a tree to make a digging stick or a spear, or cracking bones to extract marrow, they are generally much less useful. Schick and Toth's conclusion is supported by microscopic analysis of the edges of a small number of Oldowan flakes, which indicates that they were used for both woodworking and butchery.

Schick and Toth have also been able to explain the func-

FIGURE 12.2 This diagram demonstrates why right-handed flint knappers make distinctive flakes. When a right-handed person makes a stone tool, she typically holds the hammer stone in her right hand and the core to be flaked in the left hand. When the hammer stone strikes the core, a flake spalls off, leaving a characteristic pattern of rays and ripple marks centered around the point of impact (here shown in red). The knapper then rotates the core and strikes it again. If she rotates the core clockwise as shown, the second flake has the percussion marks from the first flake on the upper left, and part of the original rough surface of the rock, or cortex (here shown in gray), on the right. If she rotates the core counterclockwise, the cortex will be on the left and the percussion marks on the upper right. Modern right-handed flint knappers make about 56% right-handed flakes and 44% left-handed flakes, and left-handed flint knappers do just the opposite. A sample of flakes from Koobi Fora dated to between 1.9 and 1.5 mya contains 57% right-handed flakes and 43% left-handed flakes, suggesting that early hominin toolmakers were right-handed.

Side view of flakes

tion of enigmatic objects that archaeologists call spheroids. These are smooth, approximately spherical pieces of quartz about the size of a baseball. Several suggestions for their function were put forth, including processing plants and bashing bones to extract marrow. Some researchers thought the spheroids were part of a bola, a hunting tool used on the grasslands of Argentina. In a bola, three stones are connected by leather thongs and thrown so that they tangle the prey's legs. Schick and Toth have shown there is a much more plausible explanation for these stones. If a piece of quartz is used as a hammer to produce flakes, bits of the hammer stone are inadvertently knocked off. The hammer surface is no longer flat, so the hammer stone is shifted in the toolmaker's hand. Thus the hammer gradually becomes more and more spherical. After a while, a quartz hammer becomes a spheroid.

Perhaps the most remarkable conclusion that Schick and Toth drew from their experiments is that early hominin toolmakers were right-handed. Schick and Toth found that right-handers usually hold the hammer stone in their right hand and hold the stone to be flaked in the left hand. After driving off the first flake, they rotate the stone clockwise and drive off the second flake. This sequence produces flakes in which the **cortex** (the rough, unknapped surface of the stone) is typically on the right side of the flakes (Figure 12.2). On flakes made by left-handers, the cortex is typically on the left side. With this result in hand, Schick and Toth studied flakes from sites at Koobi Fora, Kenya, dated to 1.9 to 1.5 mya. Their results suggest that most of the individuals that made these flakes were right-handed.

manufacturing tools so that we can compare industries from different times and places. J. Desmond Clark of the University of California Berkeley devised a scheme for classifying modes of production that we will use here. According to this scheme, crude flaked pebble tools like those associated with the Oldowan tool industry are classified as **Mode 1** technology. The distinction between industry and mode is not very meaningful for our discussion of early hominins, who used simple techniques to create a very limited set of tools, but it will become significant later when there are major regional and temporal variations in the composition of tool kits and modes of production.

We do not know which hominin species were responsible for making the tools.

As you learned in Chapter 11, a sizable number of hominin species were running around in East Africa between 2.5 and 1.7 mya, and it is not clear which of these species made the Oldowan tools. *Australopithecus garhi* is probably the best candidate for "first engineer." At Bouri, animal bones bearing the distinctive marks made by stone tools are found in the same strata as the fossils of *A. garhi*. Although no tools were found with the fossils at Bouri, many tools have been found at the nearby site of Gona, which is dated to 2.5 mya. Thus, *A. garhi* may have been the first stone toolmaker. But remember that *A. rudolfensis*, *Kenyanthropus platyops*, and *Paranthropus aethiopicus* were probably all present in East Africa at the same time; they could have made the tools found at Gona but impolitely failed to leave their own fossils behind.

It is also possible that the earliest stone tools were made by species that do not appear until later in the fossil record. Stone tools are more durable than bones, so the archaeological record is usually more complete than the fossil record. This means that the earliest tools typically appear in the fossil record before the first fossil of the creature that made them (see Box 10.3 for more discussion of this topic). Thus the first stone toolmaker may have been *Australopithecus habilis*, *Paranthropus boisei*, or even *Homo ergaster*, the oldest member of our own genus, who will be discussed in more detail in Chapter 13. Because of this ambiguity, in the rest of this chapter we will refer to the hominins who made the tools of this period as Oldowan hominins or Oldowan toolmakers.

Because it is likely that Oldowan toolmakers were human ancestors, we can learn a lot about the processes that shaped human evolution by studying Oldowan archaeological sites.

Homo ergaster appeared in Africa about 1.8 mya. Unlike the situation with *A. habilis* or *A. rudolfensis*, there is little doubt that these creatures belong in the same genus as *Homo sapiens*. As you will learn in the next chapter, *Homo ergaster* was a fully terrestrial creature with a large body—one quite similar to our own. These creatures developed more slowly than early hominins, and males and females were about as different in size as men and women are today. Thus, about 2 mya selection must have favored these more humanlike characteristics in one of the early hominin lineages. That we don't know which early hominin is ancestral to humans is annoying but not really fatal, because it seems very likely that whoever made the Oldowan tools is the culprit. By combining knowledge of contemporary foraging peoples with careful study of Oldowan tools, the sites where these tools were found, and the marks that they make on animal bones, we can learn a lot about the transition from a bipedal ape to a creature much more like modern humans.

In the discussion that follows, we will first see how a reliance on highly productive but very hard-to-learn foraging skills distinguishes humans from other primates, and how this novel foraging niche may have led to the evolution of other novel features of the human life cycle, such as slow maturation and reduced sexual dimorphism. We will then consider the archaeological evidence from Oldowan sites indicating that these hominins had begun to shift to a subsistence economy based on more challenging foraging techniques.

COMPLEX FORAGING SHAPES HUMAN LIFE HISTORY

Anthropologists divide the foods acquired by foragers into three types according to the amount of knowledge and skill required to obtain them. These are, in order of increasing difficulty of acquisition, collected foods, extracted foods, and hunted foods.

Hillard Kaplan, Kim Hill, Madgalena Hurtado, and Jane Lancaster of the University of New Mexico recently argued that the evolution of modern human life history was driven by a shift to valuable but hard-to-acquire food resources. They rank food resources into three categories according to the difficulty of acquisition:

1. **Collected foods** can be simply collected from the environment and eaten. Examples include ripe fruit and leaves.
2. **Extracted foods** come from things that don't move but are protected in some way. These things must be processed before the food can be eaten. Examples include fruits in hard shells, tubers or termites that are buried deep underground, honey hidden in hives high in trees, and plants containing toxins that must be extracted before the plants can be eaten.

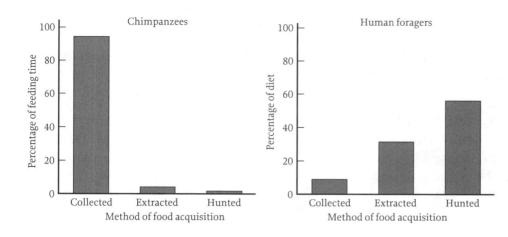

FIGURE 12.3 (a) Chimpanzees spend most of their time feeding on collected foods like fruit and leaves, which can be eaten without processing. (b) Human foragers get most of their calories from extracted foods like tubers, which must be processed before they can be eaten, and hunted foods like animal game, which must be caught or trapped.

3. **Hunted foods** come from things that run away, and thus must be caught or trapped. They may also need to be extracted and processed before consumption. Vertebrate prey are the prime example of hunted foods for both humans and chimpanzees.

Apes, especially chimpanzees, are the "brainiacs" of the primate world, at least when it comes to foraging. Gorillas and orangutans use elaborate routines to process some plant foods, but they don't hunt. Chimpanzees have a broader diet, including collected, hunted, and extracted foods, the latter two requiring considerable skill to acquire and process. Both orangutans and chimpanzees use tools to process some kinds of foods. Moreover, as we will see in Chapter 16, different ape populations use different techniques for the acquisition of extracted foods like hard-shelled nuts. However, even these clever apes do not come close to human expertise in foraging.

Humans depend on hard-to-learn skills to acquire food.

Kaplan and his colleagues note that contemporary foraging peoples depend on extracted and hunted foods to a much greater extent than chimpanzees do. Figure 12.3 compares the average dependence of chimpanzees and humans on each of the food types: collected, extracted, and hunted. The general pattern is clear: chimpanzees are overwhelmingly dependent on collected resources, but human foragers get almost all of their calories from extracted or hunted resources.

Unlike other predators, humans must learn a very diverse set of hunting skills. Most large mammalian predators capture a relatively small range of prey species using one of two methods: they wait in ambush, or they combine a stealthy approach with fast pursuit. Once the prey is captured, they process it with tooth and claw. In contrast, human hunters use a vast number of methods to capture and process a huge range of prey species. For example, the Aché, a group of foragers who live in Paraguay, have been observed to take 78 different species of mammals, 21 species of reptiles, 14 species of fish, and over 150 species of birds using a dizzying array of techniques that depend on the prey, the season, the weather, and many other factors (Figure 12.4). Some animals they track—a difficult skill that entails a great deal of ecological and environmental knowledge (see Chapter 15). Other animals they call by imitating the prey's mating or distress sounds. Still other animals they trap with snares or traps, or smoke out of burrows. They capture and kill animals using their hands,

FIGURE 12.4 Meat makes up about 70% of the diet of the Aché, a group of foragers from Paraguay. Here an Aché man takes aim at a monkey. (Photograph courtesy of Kim Hill.)

FIGURE 12.5 A !Kung San woman carries her young child on her back and digs for roots and tubers in the Kalahari Desert of Botswana. (Photograph courtesy of Nicholas Blurton Jones.)

arrows, clubs, or spears. And this is just the Aché; if we included the full range of human habitats, the list would be immeasurably longer.

It takes a long time to learn this range of skills. Among the Aché, men's hunting efficiency peaks at about age 35. Twenty-year-old men manage to capture only about a fourth of the maximum. Kaplan and Hill made strenuous efforts to become competent hunters when they were living with the Aché, but they could not come close to the production of 20-year-old Aché men.

Efficient extraction of resources also requires considerable skill. Nicholas Blurton Jones, a scientist at the University of California Los Angeles who has studied the Hadza, and the !Kung, two foraging groups, describes digging up deeply buried tubers from rocky soil as a complex mining operation involving much clever engineering of braces and levers (Figure 12.5). Among the Hiwi, a group of foragers who live in the tropical savanna of Venezuela, women do not achieve maximum efficiency in root acquisition until they are between 35 and 45 years old. Ten-year-old girls get only 10% as much as older, highly skilled women. Among the Aché, rates of starch extraction from palms and honey extraction also peak when people are in their 20s.

A reliance on hunting and extractive foraging favors food sharing and division of labor in contemporary foraging groups.

In all contemporary foraging groups, hunting and extractive foraging are associated with extensive food sharing and sexual division of labor. In nearly all foraging groups, men take primary responsibility for hunting large game, and women take primary responsibility for extractive foraging (Figure 12.6). This division of labor makes sense on two grounds: First, hard-to-learn techniques reward specialization. It takes a long time to learn how to be a good hunter, and it takes a long time to learn how to dig tubers. This means that everyone is better off if some individuals specialize in hunting and others specialize in extractive foraging. Second, because child care is more compatible with gathering than with hunting, and lactation commits women to child care for a substantial portion of their adult lives, it makes sense that men specialize in

FIGURE 12.6 Data on foraging behavior for three well-studied, modern foraging groups: the Aché, the Hadza, and the Hiwi. Men and women in these groups specialize in different foraging tasks. Men hunt, and women specialize in extractive foraging.

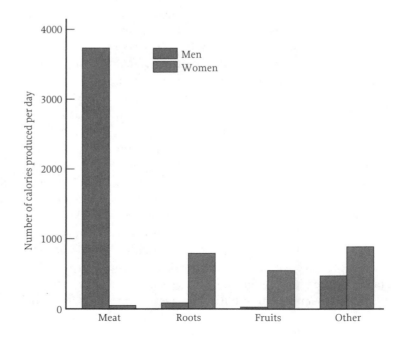

hunting and women specialize in extractive foraging. Of course, this all works only if members of the group regularly share food.

However, a reliance on meat eating favors the evolution of food sharing. Hunting is an uncertain endeavor. The best hunters can come home empty-handed, and even if hunters caught enough each day to feed themselves, a week or two of bad luck could lead to starvation. If several hunters share their catch, however, the chance of starvation is much lower (Box 12.2).

In foraging societies, food sharing and division of labor lead to extensive flows of food between people of different ages and sexes.

Remember from Chapter 11 that the total amount of food shared by chimpanzees is small: mothers share with their offspring, and males share small amounts of meat, mainly with other adult males. This means that, once they are weaned, chimpanzees obtain virtually all of their own food themselves. The story for other primates is very similar. Thus it seems likely that such self-sufficiency after weaning is the ancestral state in the hominin lineage.

The economy of human foragers is strikingly different: some people produce much more food than they consume, and others consume much more than they produce. Over the last 20 years, anthropologists have done careful quantitative studies of the subsistence economies of a number of different foraging groups. In these societies, anthropologists observed people's daily behavior, measuring how much food they produced and how much they consumed. For three of these groups—the Aché, the Hiwi, and the Hadza—researchers have meticulously computed average food production and consumption for men and women of different ages. Kaplan and his colleagues compiled these data to compare patterns of food production across societies. Their analysis reveals striking differences in the foraging economy of humans and chimpanzees, and important changes in productivity over the life course.

Figure 12.7 shows that human young continue to depend on others for food long after they are weaned. Men become self-sufficient around the age of 17, and women do not produce enough to feed themselves until they are in their late 40s. Older men

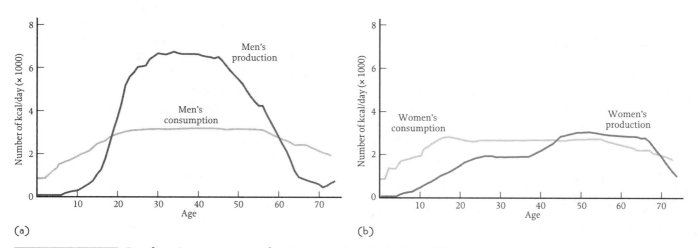

(a)   (b)

FIGURE 12.7 Data from three contemporary foraging groups show that both men (a) and women (b) do not become self-sufficient in terms of food production until they are adults. Adult men produce many more calories than they consume; adult women are approximately in balance.

BOX 12.2

Why Meat Eating Favors Food Sharing

Many anthropologists believe that a heavy dependence on meat makes food sharing necessary. Let's examine how food sharing provides insurance against the risks inherent in hunting. Hunting, especially for hunters who concentrate on large game, is a boom-or-bust activity. When a hunter makes a kill, a lot of very high quality food becomes available. Hunters are often unlucky, however, and each time one sets out to hunt there is a fairly high probability of returning empty-handed and hungry. Food sharing greatly reduces the risks associated with hunting by averaging returns over a number of hunters.

To see why this argument has such force, consider the following simple hypothetical example. Suppose there are five hunters in a group that subsists entirely on meat. Hunters are able to hunt every day, and each hunter has a 1-in-5 (0.2) chance of making a kill and a 4-in-5 (0.8) chance of bringing back nothing. Further, suppose that people starve after 10 days without food. We can calculate the probability of starvation for each hunter over any 10-day period by multiplying the probability of failing on the first day (0.8) by the probability of failing on the second day (0.8), and so on, to get

$$0.8 \times 0.8 \times 0.8 \times 0.8 \times 0.8 \times 0.8 \times$$
$$0.8 \times 0.8 \times 0.8 \times 0.8 \approx 0.1$$

Thus, there is about a 10% chance that a hunter will starve over any 10-day period. With these odds, it is impossible for people to sustain themselves by hunting alone.

A comparison with chimpanzee hunting provides good reason to think that these probabilities are realistic for early hominins. Craig Stanford of the University of Southern California and his colleagues have carefully analyzed records of hunting by chimpanzees at Gombe Stream National Park in Tanzania. In about half of the hunts, the chimpanzees succeeded in killing at least one monkey, and sometimes they made more than one kill. The average number of monkeys killed per hunt was 0.84. However, the hunting groups contained 7 males on average. Dividing 0.84 by 7 gives the average number of monkeys killed per male per hunt, which comes out to 0.12. Thus, on any given day, each male chimpanzee had only a 12% chance of making a kill, which is less than the 20% chance we posited for the five human hunters at the outset of our example.

Now let's consider how sharing food alters the probability of starvation for our human hunters. If each hunter has a 0.8 chance of coming back empty-handed, then the chance that all five hunters will come back on a given evening without food is

$$0.8 \times 0.8 \times 0.8 \times 0.8 \times 0.8 \approx 0.33$$

Thus, on each day there is a 1-in-3 chance that no one will make a kill. If the kill is large enough to feed all members of the group, then no one will go hungry as long as someone succeeds. The chance that all five hunters will face starvation during any 10-day period is

$$0.33 \times 0.33 \times 0.33 \times 0.33 \times 0.33 \times 0.33 \times$$
$$0.33 \times 0.33 \times 0.33 \times 0.33 \approx 0.000015$$

Sharing reduces the chance of starvation from one chance in 10 to roughly one chance in 60,000. Clearly, the risks associated with hunting could be reduced even further if there were alternative sources of food that unsuccessful hunters might share. For example, suppose one member of the group hunted while the others foraged, and they all contributed food to a communal pot.

The fact that food sharing is mutually beneficial is not enough to make it happen. As we pointed out in Chapter 8, food sharing is an altruistic act. Each individual will be better off if he or she gets meat but does not share it. For sharing to occur among unrelated individuals, as it often does in contemporary foraging societies, those who do not share must be punished in some way, such as by being excluded from future sharing or by being forced to leave the group.

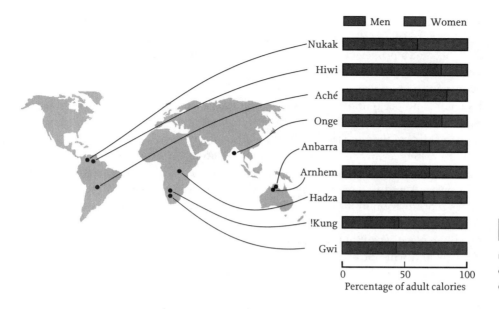

FIGURE 12.8 Males contribute significantly to subsistence in nine contemporary foraging groups from different parts of the world.

also depend on others for their daily needs. These deficits are made up by the production of young and middle-aged men and to a lesser extent, postmenopausal women. In contrast, chimpanzees obtain very little of their food from others after they are weaned.

Less detailed data from other foraging groups are consistent with this pattern. Figure 12.8 shows that men contribute more than half of the total calories consumed in seven of the nine foraging groups for which the necessary data are available. Notice that all of these groups live in tropical habitats. It seems likely from historical and ethnographic accounts that temperate and arctic foragers depended even more on meat than do tropical foragers, and thus in these societies men may make an even bigger caloric contribution.

Selection may have favored larger brains, a prolonged juvenile period, and a longer life span because these traits make it easier to learn complex foraging methods.

Complex, learned foraging techniques allow humans to acquire highly valuable or otherwise inaccessible food resources. Meat is a much better source of most nutrients that animals need than is the usual primate fare of leaves and ripe fruit. Meat is rich in energy, essential lipids, and protein. It is also dense enough to be economically transported from the kill site to home base. Some extracted resources like honey, insect larvae, and termites are also concentrated sources of important nutrients. Other kinds of extractive foraging unlock vast new food supplies. Tubers are a prime example. A number of tropical savanna plants store their reserve supplies of energy underground as various kinds of tubers, protected from the teeming herds of grazers and browsers by as much as a meter of rocky soil. By learning to recognize which plant species have tubers, how to use tools to dig them up, and when such work is likely to be profitable, humans were able to access a large supply of food for which there was relatively little competition from other organisms.

If learning is valuable, natural selection will favor adaptations that make a better learner. Thus a shift to hunting and extractive foraging would favor larger brains and greater intelligence. Reliance on complex learned foraging skills would also favor the evolution of a prolonged juvenile period. As we all know, learning takes time. You can't become a proficient skier, baker, or computer programmer in a day; practice and experience are needed. Similarly, learning the habits of animals and the lore of plants, acquiring the knowledge for tracking animals and the skills for shooting a bow or blowgun, and becoming adept at extracting starch from baobab pulp require years of practice. Thus it is plausible that selection favored a longer juvenile period to allow human children the time to acquire the skills they needed.

A prolonged juvenile period generates selection for a long life span. It is often said that time is money. In evolution, "time is fitness." To see why, suppose that two genotypes, A and B, have the same number of children on average, but type A completes reproduction in 30 years and type B in 60 years. If you do a bit of math, you will see that type A will have twice the population growth rate as type B, and it will quickly replace type B in the population. This means that a prolonged juvenile period is costly and will not be favored by natural selection unless it causes people to have sufficiently more children over their life span. Human childhood is like a costly investment; it costs time but the added time allows learning that produces more capable adults. Like any expensive investment, it will pay off more if it is amortized over a longer period. (The same logic explains why you are willing to spend more on something that you will use for a long time than on something you will use for a short time and then discard.) Selection favors a longer life because it allows people to get more benefit from the productive foraging techniques they learned during the necessary, but costly, extended juvenile period.

Food sharing and division of labor lead to reduced competition between males and reduced sexual dimorphism.

We saw in Chapter 7 that the intensity of competition between males depends on the amount of male investment in offspring. In most primate species, males do very little for their offspring, and selection consequently favors male traits that enhance their ability to compete with other males for matings. This increased competition leads to the pronounced sexual dimorphism seen in most primate species. When males do invest in offspring, there is less male–male competition and reduced sexual dimorphism.

The pattern of food sharing seen in contemporary foraging societies means that males are making substantial investments in offspring. This is clear from the data shown in Figure 12.7: males produce the bulk of the surplus calories that sustain children and teenagers. Thus we would expect selection to favor behavioral and morphological traits that make men good providers, and we would also expect selection favoring traits that enhance male–male competitive ability to be reduced. The reduction in male–male competition, in turn, should lead to reduced sexual dimorphism.

EVIDENCE FOR COMPLEX FORAGING BY OLDOWAN TOOLMAKERS

Let's stop and review for a second. So far, we have made two points. First, the Oldowan toolmakers (whoever they were) are plausible candidates for the species that links early apelike hominins to later hominins, who have more humanlike life history patterns. Second, contemporary foragers rely on complex, hard-to-learn foraging techniques to a much greater extent than other primates do, and this shift can explain the evolution of the main features of human life history. To link these points, we need to consider the evidence that Oldowan hominins had begun to rely on hunting and extractive foraging to make a living.

Contemporary experiments suggest that Oldowan tools could be used for a variety of tasks, including the butchery of large animals.

As described in Box 12.1, Kathy Schick and Nicholas Toth of Indiana University have mastered the skills needed to manufacture the kinds of artifacts found at Oldowan sites, and they have attempted to use them for different kinds of foraging activities. Schick and Toth found that stone flakes struck from cobble cores can be used for an impressive variety of tasks, even for butchering large animals like elephants. The cores can be used for a more limited number of jobs, such as chopping down a tree to make a digging stick or a spear. Microscopic analysis of the edges of a small number of Oldowan tools indicates that they were used for both woodworking and butchery.

Wear patterns on bone tools from South Africa suggest that they were used to excavate termite mounds.

Extractive foraging, which is commonly done with wooden digging sticks by modern peoples, is likely to leave few traces in the archaeological record. However, one interesting piece of evidence suggests that hominins from this period were extractive foragers. During their excavations at Swartkrans, Robert Brain and his coworkers identified a sizable number of broken bones that had wear patterns suggesting that they had been used as tools. Recently, Lucinda Backwell of the University of the Witwatersrand and Francesco d'Errico of the Institut de Préhistoire et de Géologie du Quaternaire in France carefully analyzed these bones to find out how they were used. First the researchers used freshly broken bones to do a number of foraging tasks, including digging in hard soil for tubers and digging in a termite mound. Each activity creates a distinctive wear pattern that can be detected under microscopic analysis. Then they compared these wear patterns with those on the fossil bones found at Swartkrans.

This analysis indicated that the fossil tools were used for digging in termite mounds. Figure 12.9 shows the wear patterns on the fossil tool and two experimental tools, one used for digging in soil and the other used for excavating a termite

Experimental tools used to dig

Swartkrans fossil　　　　　　　Tubers　　　　　　　Termites

(a)　　　　　　　　　　(b)　　　　　　　　　　(c)

FIGURE 12.9 Experiments indicate that bone tools found at Swartkrans were used to excavate termite mounds. The tool shown in (a) is a cast of the original tool found at Swartkrans. The experimental tools in (b) and (c) were used for subsistence tasks, digging for tubers and digging for termites. The wear pattern on the Swartkrans fossils was most similar to that on the experimental tool used to dig for termites.

mound. All of the tools have a smooth, rounded point. However, the tool experimentally used for digging in soil has deep marks of different depths going in all directions. In contrast, the tool used to dig in termite mounds has fine, parallel grooves. The fossil bone tools closely resemble the experimental tool used for digging in termite mounds, so it seems likely that this is what these tools were used for. If this is correct, then Oldowan hominins were using tools to do extractive foraging.

Archaeological Evidence for Meat Eating

At several archaeological sites in East Africa, Oldowan tools have been found along with dense concentrations of animal bones.

Archaeological sites with early stone tools occur at the Olduvai Gorge of Tanzania, Koobi Fora in Kenya, and a number of sites in Ethiopia. The sites in Bed I of the Olduvai Gorge excavated by Mary Leakey have been analyzed the most extensively. These sites, which are dated to 2 to 1.5 mya, measure only 10 to 20 m (33 to 66 ft) in diameter, but they are littered with fossilized animal bones (Figure 12.10). The densities of animal bones in the archeological sites are hundreds of times higher than those in the surrounding areas or in modern savannas. The bones belong to a wide range of animal species, including bovids (such as present-day antelope and wildebeest), pigs, equids (horses), elephants, hippopotamuses, rhinoceroses, and a variety of carnivores (Figure 12.11).

Along with these bones, Mary Leakey found several kinds of stone artifacts: cores, flakes, battered rocks that may have been used as hammers or anvils, and some stones that show no signs of human modification or use. The artifacts were manufactured

FIGURE 12.10 In this site map for one level of Bed I at Olduvai Gorge, most of the bones are from an elephant and tools are shown in black.

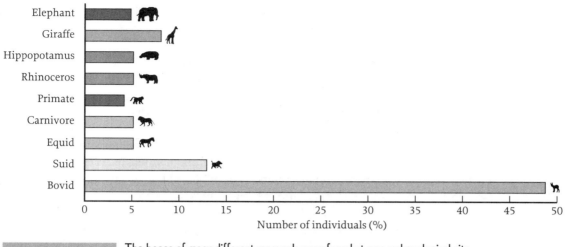

FIGURE 12.11 The bones of many different mammals were found at one archaeological site at Olduvai. Bovids (which include antelope, gazelles, sheep, goats, and cattle) clearly outnumber all other taxa.

from rocks that came from a number of different spots in the local area; some were made from rocks found several kilometers away (Figure 12.12).

The association of hominin tools and animal bones does not necessarily mean that early hominins were responsible for these bone accumulations.

It is easy to jump to the conclusion that the association of hominin tool and animal bones means that the Oldowan toolmakers hunted and processed the prey whose bones we find at these sites. If that is our assumption, these may have been sites where Oldowan hominins lived, like modern foragers' camps, or they may have been butchery sites where Oldowan hominins processed carcasses but did not live. However, there are also other possibilities. Bones may have accumulated at these sites without any help from early hominins. The bones may have been deposited there by moving water (which has now disappeared) or by other carnivores, such as hyenas. These sites also might be where many animals died of natural causes. Hominins might have visited the sites after the bones accumulated, perhaps hundreds of years later, and left their tools

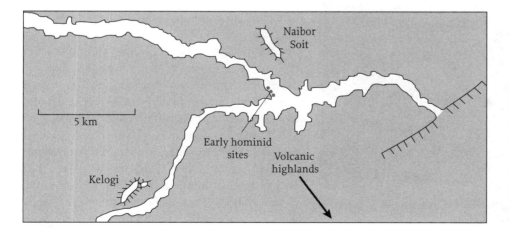

FIGURE 12.12 This map of Olduvai Gorge shows the major Bed I sites. Some of the tools were made of quartzite from Naibor Soit, others were made from gneiss from Kelogi, and some used lava cobbles that came from streams in the volcanic highlands to the south.

behind. Thus the association of stones and bones is not enough to prove that Oldowan hominins hunted or ate meat.

Archaeologists have resolved some of the uncertainty about these sites by studying how contemporary kill sites are formed.

The study of **taphonomy** provides one means to resolve questions about what happened at these sites. Taphonomy is the study of the processes that produce archaeological sites. Taphonomists examine the characteristics of contemporary kill sites—spots where animals have been killed, processed, and eaten by various predators, including contemporary human hunters. They monitor how each type of predator consumes its prey, noting whether limb bones are cracked open for marrow, which bones are carried away from the site, how human hunters use tools to process carcasses, and how bones are distributed by predators at the kill site. These data enable archaeologists to develop a profile of the characteristics of kill sites created by different types of predators. Taphonomists can also assess many of the same characteristics in archaeological sites. By comparing the features of archaeological and contemporary sites, they are sometimes able to determine what happened at an archaeological site in the past.

Taphonomic analyses at Olduvai Gorge suggest that the bones at most of these sites were not accumulated by natural processes.

Taphonomic studies of the Olduvai sites tell us, first of all, that the bones were not deposited by moving water. Animals sometimes drown as they try to cross a swollen river or when they are swept away in flash floods (Figure 12.13). The bodies are carried downstream and accumulate in a sinkhole or on a sandbar. As the bodies decompose, the bones are exposed to the surrounding elements. The study of modern sites shows that sediments deposited by rapidly moving water have a number of distinctive characteristics. For example, such sediments tend to be graded by size because particles of different size and weight sink at different spots. Sediments surrounding Olduvai sites do not show any of the features characteristic of sediments deposited by rapidly moving water.

Taphonomic analyses also tell us that the dense concentrations of bones were not due to the deaths of a large number of animals at one spot. Sometimes many animals die in the same place. In severe droughts, for example, large numbers of animals may die near water holes. Mass deaths usually involve members of a single species, and there is typically little mixing of bones from different carcasses. By contrast, the bones at the Olduvai sites come from a number of different species, and bones from different carcasses are jumbled together.

At some sites, however, bone accumulations do seem to be the product of natural processes, not hominin activity. There is one site where the pattern of bone accumulation is very similar to the pattern of bone accumulations near modern hyena dens. Hyenas often carry and drag carcasses from

FIGURE 12.13 Sometimes large numbers of wildebeest drown when trying to cross swollen rivers.

kill sites to their dens so that they can feed their young and avoid competition with other carnivores. At this site, there is no evidence of hominin activity, such as stone tools or tool marks on bones.

Taphonomic analyses suggest that hominins were active at a number of the Olduvai sites and used tools at these sites to process carcasses.

The bones at these sites provide direct evidence of hominin activity. When carnivores gnaw on meat, their teeth leave distinctive marks on the bones. Similarly, when humans use stone tools to butcher prey, their tools leave characteristic marks. Flaked-stone tools have microscopic serrations on the edges and make very fine parallel grooves when they are used to scrape meat away from bones (Figure 12.14). Many of the animal bones at Olduvai show signs of stone tool use.

(a)

(b)   (c)

FIGURE 12.14 The marks made on bone by teeth differ from the marks made by stone tools. (a) The smooth surfaces of teeth leave broad, smooth grooves on bones; the edges of stone tools, on the other hand, have many tiny, sharp points that leave fine parallel grooves. Cut marks made by carnivore teeth (b) and stone tools (c) can be distinguished when they are examined with a scanning electron microscope. These are scanning electron micrographs of 1.8-million-year-old fossil bones from Olduvai Gorge.

Hunters or Scavengers?

There has been controversy about whether the Oldowan hominins were hunters or scavengers.

The archaeological evidence indicates that Oldowan hominins processed the carcasses of large animals, and we assume that they ate the meat they cut from the bones. But eating meat does not necessarily imply hunting. Some carnivores acquire meat by hunting, but many carnivores rely at least partly on scavenging. Scavengers steal kills from other predators or rely on opportunistic discoveries of carcasses.

There has been considerable dispute about how early hominins acquired the meat they ate. Some have argued that Oldowan hominins killed the prey found at the archaeological sites; others have argued that Oldowan hominins could not have captured large mammals, because they were too small, too poorly armed, and too poorly encephalized. They contend that the Oldowan hominins were scavengers who occasionally appropriated kills from other predators or collected carcasses they found.

For most contemporary carnivores, scavenging is as difficult and dangerous as hunting.

To resolve the debate about whether early hominins were hunters or scavengers, we must first rethink popular conceptions of scavengers. Although scavengers have an unsavory reputation, scavenging is not an occupation for the cowardly or the lazy. Scavengers must be brave enough to snatch kills from the jaws of hungry competitors, shrewd enough to hang back in the shadows until the kill is momentarily left unguarded, or patient enough to follow herds and take advantage of natural mortality. Studies of contemporary carnivores show that the great majority of scavenged meat is acquired by taking a kill away from another predator. Most predators respond aggressively to competition from scavengers. For example, lions jealously guard their prey from persistent scavengers that try to steal bits of meat or to drag away parts of the carcass. These contests can be quite dangerous (Figure 12.15).

(a)

(b)

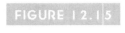 **FIGURE 12.15** Competition among predators at kill sites is frequently intense. Here lions have scavenged prey from a pack of hyenas (a), and the hyenas fight to get it back (b).

Most large mammalian carnivores practice both hunting and scavenging.

We also tend to think that some carnivores, like lions and leopards, only hunt, and that others, like hyenas and jackals, only scavenge. But the simple dichotomy between scavengers and hunters collapses when we review the data on the behavior of the five largest African mammalian carnivores: lion, hyena, cheetah, leopard, and wild dog. The fractions of meat obtained by scavenging vary from none for the cheetah, to 33% for hyenas, with the others ranging somewhere in between. Contrary to the usual stereotypes, the noble lion is not above taking prey from smaller competitors, including female members of his own pride, and hyenas are accomplished hunters (Figure 12.16). For most large carnivores in eastern Africa, hunting and scavenging are complementary activities.

No mammalian carnivores subsist entirely by scavenging. It would be difficult for any large mammal to do so. For one thing, many prey species create movable feasts, migrating in large herds over long distances. Although natural mortality in these herds might make scavenging feasible, their migratory habits eliminate this option. Mammalian carnivores cannot follow these migrating herds very far, because they have dependent young that cannot travel long distances (Figure 12.17). Only avian scavengers that can soar over great distances, like the griffon vulture, rely entirely on scavenging (Figure 12.18). When migratory herds are absent, mammalian carnivores rely on other prey, such as waterbuck

Male lions sometimes take kills from smaller carnivores and from female lions.

and impala. Natural mortality among resident species is not high enough to satisfy the caloric demands of carnivores, so they must hunt and kill much of their own prey, though they still scavenge when the opportunity arises.

Scavenging might be more practical if carnivores switched from big game to other forms of food when migratory herds were not present. This is a plausible option for early hominins. Most groups of contemporary foraging people rely heavily on gathered foods—including tubers, seeds, fruit, eggs, and various invertebrates—in addition to meat. A few, such as the Hadza, obtain meat from scavenging as well as from

FIGURE 12.17   As dusk falls, three cheetah cubs wait for their mother to return from hunting.

FIGURE 12.18   Vultures, which soar on thermals and have enormous ranges, are the only carnivores that rely entirely on scavenging.

hunting. It is possible that early hominins relied mainly on gathered foods and scavenged meat opportunistically.

Taphonomic evidence suggests that early hominins acquired meat both by scavenging and by hunting.

As we saw earlier, predators often face stiff competition for their kills. An animal that tries to defend its kill risks losing it to scavengers. For this reason, leopards drag their kills into trees and eat the meat in safety. Other predators, like hyenas, sometimes rip off the meaty parts of the carcass, such as the hindquarters, and drag their booty away to eat in peace. This means that limb bones usually disappear from a kill site first, and less meaty bones, such as the vertebrae and skull, disappear later or remain at the kill site (Figure 12.19). If hominins obtained most of their meat from scavenging, we would expect to find cut marks made by tools mainly on bones typically left at kill sites by predators, such as vertebrae. If hominins obtained most of their meat from their own kills, we would expect to find tool cut marks mainly on large bones, like limb bones. At Olduvai Gorge, cut marks appear on all kinds of bones—those usually left to scavengers and those normally monopolized by hunters (Figure 12.20). Moreover, some bones show cut marks on top of carnivore tooth marks, and other bones show tooth marks on top of cut marks. Thus, humans may sometimes have stolen kills from carnivores, and vice versa. Taken together, the evidence suggests that early hominins acquired meat by a combination of hunting and scavenging.

FIGURE 12.19 After other predators have left, vultures consume what remains at the kill site.

FIGURE 12.20 The numbers of cut marks on different kinds of bones vary at one site in the Olduvai Gorge. There are more than twice as many pieces of bones from large mammals (more than about 115 kg, or 250 lb) as there are from small mammals (less than 115 kg). The numbers in the figure are the percentages of all bones of a particular type that bear cut marks. For example, 14% of all rib bones of larger mammals showed cut marks. In general, cut marks are concentrated on bones that have the most meat.

Domestic Lives of Oldowan Toolmakers

We have reason to believe that Oldowan toolmakers used their tools for extractive foraging and to process prey carcasses. Oldowan hominins probably obtained these carcasses through a mix of hunting and scavenging. Thus they had probably come to rely on complex foraging skills that were difficult to master. In modern foraging societies, reliance on complex foraging skills is also linked to food sharing, sexual division of labor, and the establishment of home bases. Nearly all contemporary foraging peoples establish a temporary camp (**home base**), where food is shared, processed, cooked, and eaten. The camp is also the place where people weave nets, manufacture arrows, sharpen digging sticks, string bows, make plans, resolve disputes, tell stories, and sing songs (Figure 12.21). Because foragers often move from one location to another, their camps are simple, generally consisting of modest huts or shelters built around several hearths. If Oldowan hominins established home bases, we might be able to detect traces of their occupation in the archaeological record.

FIGURE 12.21   The Efe, a foraging people of central Africa, build temporary camps in the forest and shift camps frequently. (Photograph courtesy of Robert Bailey.)

Some archaeologists have interpreted the dense accumulations of stones and bones as home bases, much like those of modern foragers, but this view is not consistent with some of the evidence.

Some archaeologists, particularly the late Glyn Isaac, have suggested that the dense accumulations of animal bones and stone tools found at some sites mark the location of hominin home bases. They have speculated that early hominins acquired meat by hunting or scavenging and then brought pieces of the carcass home, where it could be shared. The dense collections of bones and artifacts were thought to be the result of prolonged occupation of the home base (and sloppy housekeeping). At one Olduvai Bed I site, there is even a circle of stones (Figure 12.22), dated to 1.9 mya, that is similar to the circles of stones anchoring the walls of simple huts constructed by some foraging peoples in dry environments today. Many Oldowan tools and bone fragments from a variety of prey species are found at the same site.

However, a number of other observations are inconsistent with the idea that these sites were home bases:

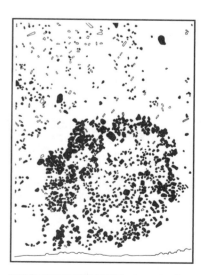

FIGURE 12.22   A circle of stones at one Olduvai Bed I site has been interpreted by some archaeologists as the remains of a simple shelter.

- Both hominins and nonhominin carnivores were active at many of the Olduvai sites. Many of the bones at the Olduvai sites were gnawed by nonhominin carnivores. Sometimes the same bones show both tooth marks and cut marks, but some show only the marks of nonhominin carnivores.
- Hominins and nonhominin carnivores apparently competed over kills. The bones of nonhominin carnivores occur more often than would be expected on the basis of their occurrence in other fossil assemblages or modern carnivore densities. Perhaps the carnivores were killed (and eaten) when attempting to scavenge hominin kills or when hominins attempted to scavenge their kills. Hominins may not have

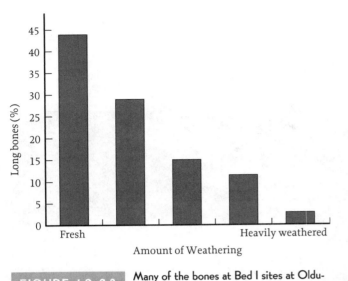

FIGURE 12.23 Many of the bones at Bed I sites at Olduvai are heavily weathered, suggesting that they were deposited and exposed to the elements over a fairly long period of time.

always won such contests; some fossilized hominin bones show the tooth marks of other carnivores.

- Modern kill sites are often the scene of violent conflict among carnivores. This conflict occurs among members of different species as well as the same species. It is especially common when a small predator, like a cheetah, makes a kill. The kill attracts many other animals, most of which are able to displace the cheetah.

- The bones accumulated at the Olduvai sites are weathered. When bones lie on the surface of the ground, they crack and peel in various ways. The longer they remain exposed on the surface, the greater the extent of weathering. Taphonomists can calibrate the weathering process and use these data to determine how long fossil bones were on the ground before being buried. Some of the bones at the Olduvai sites were exposed to the elements for at least four to six years (Figure 12.23).

- The Olduvai sites do not show evidence of intensive bone processing. The bones at these sites show cut marks and tooth marks, and many bones were apparently smashed with stone hammers to remove marrow. However, the bones were not processed intensively, as they are by modern foragers.

These observations are difficult to reconcile with the idea that the Olduvai sites were home bases—places where people eat, sleep, tell stories, and care for their children. First, foragers today do everything they can to prevent carnivores from entering their camps. They often pile up thorny branches to fence their camps and keep dogs that are meant to chase predators away. It is hard to imagine that early hominins could have occupied these sites if lions, hyenas, and saber-toothed cats were regular visitors. Second, bones at the Olduvai sites appear to have accumulated over a period of years. Contemporary foragers usually abandon their home bases permanently after a few months because the accumulating garbage attracts insects and other vermin. Even though they revisit the same areas regularly, they don't often reoccupy their old sites. Finally, the fossilized bones found at Olduvai were not processed as thoroughly as modern foragers process their kills.

Hominins may have brought carcasses to these sites and processed the carcasses with flakes made from previously cached stones.

Richard Potts, an anthropologist at the Smithsonian Institution, suggests that these sites were not home bases but butchery sites—places where hominins worked but did not live. He believes that hominins brought their kills to these sites and dismembered their carcasses there. Some of the carcasses were scavenged by hominins from other carnivores, and some of the hominins' kills were lost to scavengers. Hominins may have carried bones and meat away to other sites for more intensive processing. This would explain why bones accumulated over such a long time, why bones of nonhominin carnivores were present, and why bones were not completely processed.

At first glance, it might seem inconvenient for hominins to schlepp their kills to butchery sites. Why not process the carcass at the kill site? We have seen that hominins used tools to process the meat. However, they couldn't be sure of finding appropriate rocks for toolmaking at the sites of their kills. And they couldn't leave their kills unguarded while they went off to fetch their tools, lest a hungry scavenger steal their supper. So they must have had to carry the meat to where their tools were kept or to keep their tools with them all the time. Remember that these tools were fairly heavy, and early hominins had no pockets or backpacks. Potts suggests that the best strategy would have been to cache tools at certain places, and then to carry carcasses that they had acquired to the nearest cache.

BACK TO THE FUTURE: THE TRANSITION TO MODERN HUMAN LIFE HISTORIES

We have argued that complex foraging techniques favor food sharing, male parental investment, and sexual division of labor. These behavioral practices, in turn, create selective pressures for reduced sexual dimorphism and delayed maturation of offspring. The Oldowan toolmakers were extractive foragers, hunters, and scavengers of meat. As we will see in the next chapter, reduced sexual dimorphism and somewhat delayed maturation characterize hominins who appear in the fossil record about 2 mya. It seems likely that these morphological and developmental features, which also characterize modern humans, represent adaptations to this new way of life.

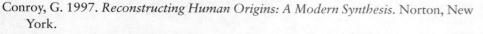

FURTHER READING

Conroy, G. 1997. *Reconstructing Human Origins: A Modern Synthesis.* Norton, New York.

Foley, R. 1987. *Another Unique Species.* Longman Scientific and Technical, Harlow, England.

Kaplan, H., K. Hill, J. Lancaster, and A. Hurtado. 2000. A theory of human life history evolution: Diet, intelligence, and longevity. *Evolutionary Anthropology* 9: 156–185.

McGrew, W. C. 1992. *Chimpanzee Material Culture.* Cambridge University Press, Cambridge, England.

Potts, R. 1984. Home bases and early hominins. *American Scientist* 72: 338–347.

Schick, K. D., and N. Toth. 1993. *Making Silent Stones Speak: Human Evolution and the Dawn of Technology.* Simon & Schuster, New York.

STUDY QUESTIONS

1. Who made the first stone tools? What kinds of evidence complicate this question?
2. What are the differences between collected, extracted, and hunted foods? How do comparative data help us understand the unique foraging adaptations of modern humans?

3. Why do complex foraging techniques favor slow development and long child-hoods? What kinds of data enable us to draw inferences about developmental patterns in early hominins?

4. Suppose we discovered that Oldowan foraging technology was very easy to master and required little skill. How would that change your ideas about the selective pressures acting on hominins? How would that change your ideas about who made Oldowan tools?

5. Why do we associate food sharing with meat eating, rather than with vegetarianism?

6. What were Oldowan tools like, and what were they used for?

7. Researchers argue about whether Oldowan toolmakers were hunters or scavengers. What are the main arguments on each side of this debate?

8. How would it change our views of human evolution if we found convincing evidence that the Oldowan hominins scavenged but did not hunt?

9. Some researchers have argued that Olduvai Bed I sites are the remains of hominin home bases; others think that they are workplaces where hominins processed carcasses. If you were an archaeologist, how would you go about testing this idea? Think about the kinds of data you would need to collect to examine the merits of each hypothesis.

10. We have discussed the Oldowan toolmakers at length, even though we don't really know who they were. Why is this a profitable exercise?

KEY TERMS

flakes

cores

Oldowan tool industry

knapping

Mode 1

collected foods

extracted foods

hunted foods

taphonomy

home base

CONTENT FROM *HUMAN EVOLUTION:*
A MULTI-MEDIA GUIDE TO THE FOSSIL RECORD

Early Homo
   Overview
   Large v. Small H. habilis
   Brain Reorganization
   Early Tools

CHAPTER 13

FROM HOMININ TO *HOMO*

About 1.8 mya, a new kind of hominin appeared in Africa. These creatures, which we will call *Homo ergaster*, were much more like modern humans than the apelike hominins who preceded them were. Like modern humans, they developed slowly, and their infants must have been largely helpless at birth. They had large, robust bodies with long legs and short arms. These adaptations tell us that they were fully committed to life on the ground, as we are. In contrast to the apelike hominins, the males were only slightly larger than the females. *Homo ergaster* invented a new kind of tool technology and probably learned to master fire and to hunt large game. Although we can see much of ourselves in these creatures, some important differences remain. They had smaller brains than we have, and their subsistence technology seems to have been much less flexible than ours.

We begin this chapter by describing what is known about *H. ergaster*. Then we trace the evolution of hominins as they migrated out of Africa and spread throughout temperate Asia and into Europe. We will see that hominins gradually evolved to have even larger brains and more sophisticated subsistence technology, and these incremental changes eventually led to the emergence of our own species, *Homo sapiens*, about 100 kya (thousand years ago). We will draw on evidence from the fossil and archaeological records to reconstruct the transformation of *H. ergaster* into *H. sapiens*.

· HOMININS OF THE LOWER PLEISTOCENE: *HOMO ERGASTER*

The Pleistocene epoch began 1.8 mya and saw a cooling of the world's climate.

Geologists subdivide the Pleistocene into three parts: the Lower, Middle, and Upper Pleistocene. The Lower Pleistocene began about 1.8 mya, a date that coincides with a sharp cooling of the world's climate. The beginning of the Middle Pleistocene is marked by sharply increased fluctuations in temperature and the first appearance of immense continental glaciers that covered northern Europe 900 kya, and its end is defined by the termination of the penultimate glacial period about 130 kya. The Upper Pleistocene ended about 12 kya when a warm, interglacial phase of the world climate began; this warm period has persisted into the present (Figure 13.1).

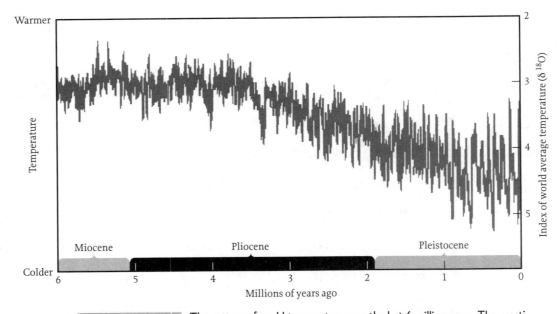

FIGURE 13.1   The pattern of world temperature over the last 6 million years. These estimates are based on the ratio of oxygen-16 to oxygen-18 in cores extracted from deep-sea sediments. During the Pliocene world temperatures declined, and in the Pleistocene climate fluctuations increased, especially during the Middle and Upper Pleistocene.

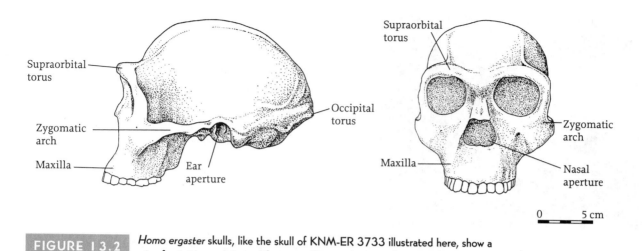

Homo ergaster skulls, like the skull of KNM-ER 3733 illustrated here, show a mix of primitive and derived features. (Figure courtesy of Richard Klein.)

Homo ergaster appears in the African fossil record about 1.8 mya and disappears about 0.6 mya.

Fossils of *H. ergaster* have been found at Konso-Gardula (Ethiopia), Daka (Ethiopia), Olduvai Gorge (Tanzania), Lake Turkana (Kenya), Olorgesailie (Kenya), Swartkrans (South Africa), and a number of other sites in Africa. Figure 13.2 shows a very well preserved skull (labeled KNM-ER 3733) from Lake Turkana that was found in 1976 by a team led by Richard Leakey. When *H. ergaster* fossils first appear on the scene, they are associated with Oldowan tools.

Until recently, most paleontologists assigned these East African fossils to the species *Homo erectus*, on the basis of their similarities to fossils that had been discovered in Indonesia many years before. However, a growing number of paleontologists have come to believe that the African specimens are distinctive enough to be assigned to a different species. According to the rules of zoological nomenclature, the Indonesian specimens retain the original name *H. erectus* because they were described first, and the African specimens must be given a new name. Advocates of the two-species view have given the African fossils the name *Homo ergaster*, or "work man." We will use *H. ergaster* to refer to African specimens of this group, and *H. erectus* for the Asian fossils. Keep in mind that it is not entirely clear whether the creatures leaving these fossils belonged to one or two species.

Homo ergaster appeared in Eurasia about the same time it was first known from Africa.

As you will recall from Chapters 11 and 12, the apelike hominins were restricted to Africa. *Homo ergaster* was the first hominin to make its way out of Africa. We know this because of a startling discovery in the Caucasus Mountains of the Republic of Georgia. In 1991, archaeologists working at a site called Dmanisi (see Figure 13.15) discovered a lower jaw and Oldowan tools in sediments dated to 1.1 or 1.8 mya. Many researchers were skeptical that hominins were present in Eurasia so early, but their doubts were soon put to rest. In 1999, a team of archaeologists from Georgia and the United States uncovered two nearly complete crania at Dmanisi that are very similar to African specimens of *H. ergaster* and are securely dated to about 1.7 mya (Figure 13.3). These crania are associated with more than a thousand Oldowan tools. Thus, *H. ergaster* migrated out of Africa and into Eurasia about 1.7 mya, taking their toolmaking skills along with them.

Morphology

Skulls of H. ergaster differ from those of both earlier hominins and modern humans.

FIGURE 13.3 One of the crania found at Dmanisi, a site in the foothills of the Caucasus Mountains in the Republic of Georgia. The Dmanisi fossils date to 1.7 mya and are very similar to *H. ergaster* fossils of the same age from Africa. The Dmanisi site is at latitude 41° north, well out of the tropics, indicating that *H. ergaster* was able to adapt to a wider range of habitats than previous hominins were.

Skulls of *H. ergaster* retain many of the characteristics of earlier hominins (Figure 13.4), including a marked narrowing behind the eyes, a receding forehead, and no chin. *Homo ergaster* also shows many derived features. Some of these are shared by modern humans, including a smaller, less prognathic face, a higher skull, and smaller jaws and teeth. However, *H. ergaster* also has some derived features that we don't see in earlier hominins or modern humans. For example, *H. ergaster* has a horizontal ridge at the back of the skull (**occipital torus**), which gives it a pointed appearance from the side. It also had quite large browridges.

Many of the derived features of the skull of *H. ergaster* are likely to be related to diet. These hominins were probably better adapted for tearing and biting with their canines and incisors, and less suited to heavy chewing with their molars. Thus, all their teeth are smaller than the teeth of the australopithecines and paranthropines, but their molars are reduced relatively more in comparison with their incisors. The large browridges and the point at the back of the skull are needed to buttress the skull against novel stresses created by an increased emphasis on tearing and biting.

Homo ergaster had a substantially larger brain than earlier hominins. The average brain volume for these creatures was about 800 cc (for reference, 1000 cc is 1 liter, just a little more than a quart)—larger than the brains of earlier apelike hominins (500 to 700 cc) but still considerably smaller than modern human brains, which average about 1400 cc. As we will see, however, *H. ergaster* had a much larger body than the earlier hominins. Brain size is proportional to body size in mammals, so it seems likely that in comparison with earlier hominin species, *H. ergaster* did not have a substantially larger brain in relation to body size.

The postcranial skeleton of H. ergaster is much more similar to the skeleton of modern humans than to that of earlier hominins, but it still differs from ours in interesting ways.

Kimoya Kimeu (Figure 13.5), the leader of the Koobi Fora paleontological team, found a fossilized skeleton of a young *H. ergaster* male in 1984. The find was made on the west side of Lake Turkana, the same region where fossils of *Australopithecus anamensis*, *Paranthropus aethiopicus*, and *Kenyanthropus platyops* were found. The skeleton, which is formally known as KNM-WT 15000, belonged to a boy who was about 12 years old when he died. The skeleton provides us with a remarkably com-

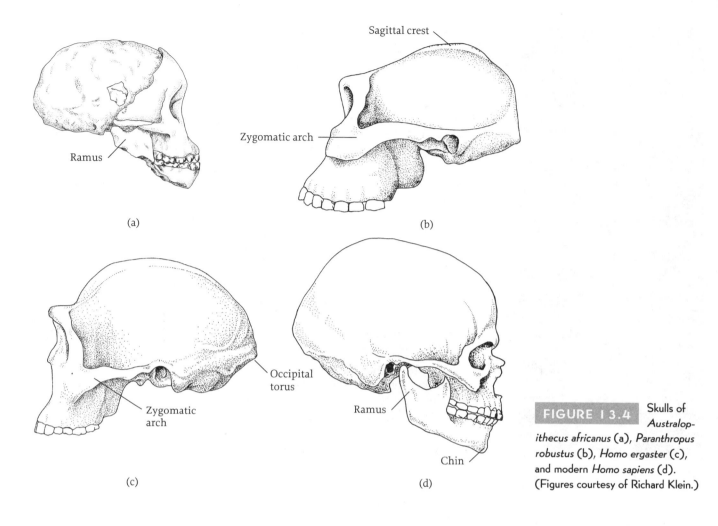

Ramus

(a)

Sagittal crest

Zygomatic arch

(b)

Zygomatic arch

Occipital torus

(c)

Ramus

Chin

(d)

plete picture of the *H. ergaster* body; even the delicate ribs and vertebrae are preserved (Figure 13.6). An extensive analysis of this skeleton, coordinated by Alan Walker, tells us a lot about this youngster's body and his way of life.

Remember that earlier hominins were bipeds but still had long arms, short legs, and other features suggesting that they spent a considerable amount of time in trees. In contrast, KNM-WT 15000 had the same body proportions as people who live in tropical savannas today: long legs, narrow hips, and narrow shoulders. KNM-WT 15000 also had short arms, compared with earlier hominins. Taken together, these features suggest that *H. ergaster* was fully committed to terrestrial life.

This skeleton, and less complete bits of the skeletons of other *H. ergaster* individuals, tells us several other interesting things about them:

• They were quite tall. KNM-WT 15000 stood about 1.625 m (5 ft 4 in.) in height. If *H. ergaster* growth patterns were comparable to those of modern humans, this boy would have been about 1.9 m (6 ft) tall when

FIGURE 13.5 Kimoya Kimeu is an accomplished field researcher. He has made many important finds, including KNM-WT 15000 (see Figure 13.6).

FIGURE 13.6 The fossil of the *H. ergaster* boy, KNM-WT 15000, found on the west side of Lake Turkana, is amazingly complete. (Photograph courtesy of Alan Walker.)

he was fully grown. However, he was also robust and heavily muscled. Think of him as a young shooting guard or a small forward.

- Their infants probably matured slowly and were dependent on their mothers for an extended period of time. Human infants are born well before brain growth is completed, because if they remained in the uterus long enough for the brain to finish developing, the head would be too large to pass through the birth canal. The same seems to have been true for *H. ergaster*, because the ratio of the size of the mother's birth canal to the size of the newborn's head was the same as it is in modern humans. Thus, *H. ergaster* infants were probably more like human infants in their growth and development. As we have already learned, prolonged dependence of infants may be functionally linked to the reduction of sexual dimorphism, paternal investment, and monogamous mating systems.

- Sexual dimorphism was reduced. *Homo ergaster* males were about 20% to 30% larger than females, making *H. ergaster* much less dimorphic than the apelike hominins and only slightly more dimorphic than modern humans.

- They may not have had spoken language. The vertebral canal in the thoracic (middle) region of the back is much larger in modern humans than it is in apes, and it contains a proportionally thicker spinal cord. Detailed studies of the neuroanatomy in the thoracic region suggest that all of the extra nerves that enlarge the spinal cord innervate the muscles of the rib cage and diaphragm. The thoracic vertebrae of KNM-WT 15000 are comparable to those of other primates, suggesting that this young male had less precise control over the muscles of his rib cage and diaphragm than modern humans do. Anatomist Ann McLarnon of Whitelands College in London argues that the enlargement of the thoracic vertebral canal is an adaptation for speech. When people talk, they subconsciously time their breathing to match the patterning of sentences. Sentences begin with a short, rapid intake of air, followed by a much slower outflow, and this breathing pattern allows production of the words of the sentence. Because sentences vary in length, the breathing pattern during speech is much more complex than normal rhythmic breathing is. McLarnon argues that the increased motor control of the diaphragm and thoracic muscles is an adaptation that allows people to manage this complex motor task.

- *H. ergaster* was the first hominin that could run for long distances. Compared to most other mammals, modern humans are not good sprinters. However, we are able to outrun all but a few species over distances of several kilometers. Biologist Dennis Bramble of the University of Utah and anthropologist Daniel Lieberman of Harvard University have recently argued that features of the *H. ergaster* boy like long legs and a long narrow waist are evidence that the capacity for long-distance running first appeared in this species. They believe that this talent may have been useful in long-distance scavenging and hunting in open country.

H. ergaster may have developed more rapidly than modern humans.

Remember from Chapter 11 that Christopher Dean and his colleagues used estimates of enamel growth rate to show that australopithecines developed relatively quickly, somewhat faster than chimpanzees. Using the same methods, these researchers estimate that *H. ergaster* developed more slowly than australopithecines but still faster than modern humans. If this estimate is correct, then *H. ergaster* did not have the same long childhood period that modern humans have, suggesting that learning did not play such an important role in the lives of these creatures (Figure 13.7). It is not clear

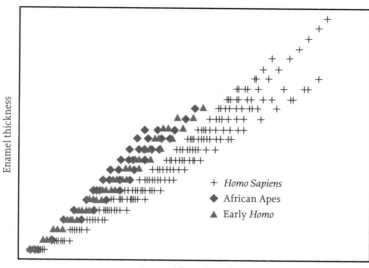

Enamel thickness

+ Homo Sapiens
◆ African Apes
▲ Early *Homo*

Enamel formation time

FIGURE 13.7 Rates of enamel growth estimated by counting daily growth marks for modern *Homo sapiens*, modern African apes, and early *Homo*. The latter category includes four individuals usually classified as *H. ergaster*, including KNM-WT 15000, one *Australopithecus habilis*, and one *A. rudolfensis*. Like australopithecines and modern apes, early *Homo* apparently grew rapidly.

whether this fact can be reconciled with the evidence that *H. ergaster* infants were highly dependent.

Tools and Subsistence

Homo ergaster made fancier tools than earlier hominins had made.

The earliest fossils of *H. ergaster* both in Africa and in Eurasia are associated with Oldowan tools, the same tools that we described in Chapter 12. However, sometime between 1.6 and 1.4 mya in Africa, *H. ergaster* added a new and more sophisticated tool to its kit. This totally new kind of stone tool is called a **biface**. To make a biface, the toolmaker strikes a large piece of rock from a boulder to make a core, and then flakes this core on all sides to create a flattened form with a sharp edge along its entire circumference. The most common type of biface, called a **hand ax**, is shaped like a teardrop and has a sharp point at the narrow end (Figure 13.8). A **cleaver** is a lozenge-shaped biface with a flat, sharp edge on one end; a **pick** is a thicker, more triangular biface. Bifaces are larger than Oldowan tools, averaging about 15 cm (6 in.) in length and sometimes reaching 30 cm (12 in.). Bifaces are categorized as **Mode 2** technology. Paleoanthropologists call the Mode 2 industries of Africa and western Eurasia (that is, Europe and the Middle East) the **Acheulean industry** after the French town of Saint-Acheul, where hand axes were first discovered. The oldest Acheulean tools found at West Turkana date to about 1.6 mya, just after *H. ergaster* first appeared in Africa. It is important to understand that Oldowan tools do not disappear when Acheulean tools make their debut. *Homo ergaster* continued making simple Mode 1 tools, perhaps when they needed a serviceable tool in a hurry—as foraging people do today.

The standardized form of hand axes and other Mode 2 tools in the Acheulean industry suggests that toolmakers had a specific design in mind when they made each tool. The Mode 1 tools of the Oldowan industry have a haphazard appearance; no two are alike. This lack of standardization suggests that makers of Oldowan tools simply picked up a core and struck off flakes; they didn't try to create a tool with a

0   5   10 cm
         4 in.

FIGURE 13.8 Acheulean hand axes, like the two shown here, were teardrop-shaped tools created by removing flakes from a core. The smallest ones would fit in the palm of your hand, and the largest ones are more than 0.6 m (2 ft) long.

particular shape that they had in mind beforehand. They may have done this because the flakes were the actual tools.

It is easy to see how a biface might have evolved from an Oldowan chopper by extending the flaking around the periphery of the tool. However, Acheulean tools are not just Oldowan tools with longer edges; they are designed according to a uniform plan. Hand axes have regular proportions: the ratio of height to width to thickness is remarkably constant from one ax to another. *Homo ergaster* must have started with an irregularly shaped piece of rock and whittled it down by striking flakes from both sides until it had the desired shape. Clearly, all the hand axes would not have come out the same if their makers hadn't shared an idea for the design.

Hand axes were probably used to butcher large animals.

If hand axes were designed, what were they designed for? The answer to this question is not obvious, because hand axes are not much like the tools made by later peoples. A number of ideas about what hand axes were used for have been proposed:

1. *Butchering large animals. Homo ergaster* acquired the carcasses of animals like zebra or buffalo either by hunting or by scavenging, and then used a hand ax as a modern butcher would use a cleaver, to dismember the carcass and cut it into useful pieces.
2. *Digging up tubers, burrowing animals, water.* Contemporary foragers in savanna environments spend a lot of their time digging up edible tubers. Although modern peoples generally use sharpened sticks for digging, some archaeologists have suggested that *H. ergaster* may have used hand axes for this purpose. Digging tools would also have been useful for capturing burrowing animals like warthogs and porcupines, and for making wells to acquire water.
3. *Stripping bark from trees to get at the nutritious cambium layer underneath.*
4. *Hurling at prey animals.*
5. *Dispensing flake tools.* Hand axes weren't tools at all. Instead they were "flake dispensers" from which *H. ergaster* struck flakes to be used for many everyday purposes.

Although we are not certain how hand axes were used, two kinds of evidence support the first hypothesis that they were heavy-duty butchery tools. Kathy Schick and Nicholas Toth, whose investigations into the function of Oldowan tools we discussed in Chapter 12, have also done experiments using Acheulean hand axes for each of the tasks just listed. From these experiments, Schick and Toth conclude that hand axes are best suited to butchery. The sharp end of the hand ax easily cuts through meat and separates joints; the rounded end provides a secure handle. The large size is useful because it provides a long cutting edge, as well as the cutting weight necessary to be effective for a tool without a long handle. Schick and Toth's results are supported by the work of University of Illinois–Chicago paleoanthropologist Lawrence Keely, who performed microscopic analysis of wear patterns on a small number of hand axes. He concluded that the pattern of wear is consistent with animal butchery.

Evidence from Olorgesailie, a site in Kenya at which enormous numbers of hand axes have been found, indicates that these axes may also have served as flake dispensers. A team led by Richard Potts discovered most of the fossilized skeleton of an elephant, along with numerous small stone flakes dated to about 1 mya. Chips on the edges of the flakes suggest that they were used to butcher the elephant, and the elephant bones show cut marks made by stone tools. Careful examination of the flakes reveals that they were struck from an already flaked core, such as a hand ax, not from an unflaked cobble. Moreover, when the flakes were removed from the hand axes, they did not leave a sharper hand-ax edge. Taken together, these data suggest that *H. ergaster* struck flakes from hand axes and used both hand axes and flakes as butchery tools.

The Acheulean industry remained remarkably unchanged for almost 1 million years.

There is relatively little change over space and time in the Acheulean tool kit from its first appearance about 1.6 mya until it was replaced around 300 kya. Amazingly enough, Acheulean tools that were made half a million years apart are just as similar as tools made at about the same time at sites located thousands of miles apart. Essentially the same tools were made for more than 1 million years. In fact, as we will see shortly, the Acheulean industry was longer-lived than *H. ergaster* itself, which disappeared from the fossil record in Africa about 1 mya. Most anthropologists assume that the knowledge necessary to make a proper hand ax was passed from one generation to the next by teaching and imitation. It is a remarkable notion that this form of knowledge might have been faithfully transmitted and preserved for so long in a small population of hominins spread from Africa to eastern Eurasia.

Homo ergaster *clearly ate meat, but there is controversy about whether they hunted or scavenged their kills.*

There is fierce controversy among paleoanthropologists about whether *H. ergaster* was a big-game hunter. The issues and the evidence are similar to the controversy surrounding hunting by Oldowan hominins. There is good evidence that *H. ergaster* ate meat, but less certainty about whether *H. ergaster* hunted or scavenged. One of the most compelling pieces of evidence that these hominins ate meat comes from the skeleton of an *H. ergaster* woman (KNM-ER 1808) that was discovered at Koobi Fora near Lake Turkana in northern Kenya by Alan Walker and his colleagues (Figure 13.9). This woman died about 1.6 mya. Her long bones are covered with a thick layer of abnormal bone tissue (Figure 13.10). This amorphous bone growth puzzled Walker, so he

FIGURE 13.9 Much of the skeleton of an *H. ergaster* female (KNM-ER 1808) was discovered at Koobi Fora. The bones marked in red are those that were recovered. (Diagram by Alan Walker.)

FIGURE 13.10 The long bones of KNM-ER 1808 are covered in a thick, amorphous layer of abnormal bone tissue. A fragment of the tibia of KNM-ER 1808 (bottom) is compared with the tibia of a normal *H. ergaster* (top). (Photograph courtesy of Alan Walker.)

FIGURE 13.11 A microscopic view of the bone structure of KNM-ER 1808. Note that the small band of normal bone at the top looks very different from the puffy, irregular, diseased bone in the rest of the picture. (Photograph courtesy of Alan Walker.)

consulted with some colleagues at a medical school. They told him that this kind of bone growth is symptomatic of vitamin A poisoning (Figure 13.11). This, of course, posed another puzzle: how could a hunter-gatherer get enough vitamin A to poison herself? The most likely way would be to eat the liver of a large predator, like a lion or a leopard. The same symptoms have been reported for Arctic explorers who ate the livers of polar bears and seals. If this woman's bones were deformed because she ate a large predator's liver, then we can assume that *H. ergaster* ate meat. Of course, we don't know how this woman obtained the liver that poisoned her. She might have scavenged the liver from a predator's carcass, or she might have killed the predator in a contest over a kill.

As we noted earlier, the bones of the elephant found at Olorgesailie show signs of cut marks from stone tools. It is not clear how hominins obtained the elephant carcass. The archaeological evidence indicates that the site was not repeatedly used by hominins or other animals. Perhaps the hominins killed the elephant and butchered it at the kill site. Perhaps they came upon the body of the elephant after it died, and butchered it there. It does not seem likely that they stole the kill from another predator, because there are no tooth marks on the bones.

Several lines of circumstantial evidence also suggest that *H. ergaster* relied on meat, at least during part of the year. First, hand axes seem to be well suited to the butchery of large animals. Second, the teeth of *H. ergaster* are well suited for biting and tearing and less suited for chewing tough plant foods. As we pointed out in Chapter 12, meat, seeds, and fibrous plant materials are the main alternative food sources for primates during the dry season. If *H. ergaster* was not eating tough plant foods during the dry season, then it might have relied on meat. Third, Dmanisi is at about the same latitude as Chicago, so *H. ergaster* was able to live outside of the tropics. Other primates rely heavily on fruit and other tender parts of plants for survival. To survive a temperate winter when such things are not available, *H. ergaster* might have relied on meat. Very few primates except humans live in places with severe winters, and these are only small, peripheral populations of species that are usually more tropical.

Homo ergaster *may have controlled fire.*

The earliest evidence that *H. ergaster* controlled fire comes from Koobi Fora, where archaeologists found baked earth beside stone tools at a site dated to about 1.6 mya. This association doesn't prove that *H. ergaster* controlled fire, because charred bones and ash could have been produced by natural fires that swept through sites where hominins had lived, perhaps many years after hominins occupied them. Taphonomic experiments conducted by Randy Bellomo of the University of South Florida help resolve this issue. Bellomo made campfires and set fire to grass and tree stumps in several African habitats and carefully examined the remains. He found that the soil under campfires reaches much higher temperatures than the soil under grass fires or the soil surrounding smoldering tree stumps. The higher temperatures of campfires produce two distinctive characteristics in the soil. First, a bowl-shaped layer of highly oxidized soil is formed directly under the fire. Second, the soil under the fire becomes highly magnetized compared with the surrounding soil, and this magnetization is quite stable. Soil beneath stump fires and grass fires does not have either of these features. Stump fires leave a distinctive hole filled with unconsolidated sediments.

With these experimental results in hand, Bellomo examined the fire sites at Koobi Fora. One of them contains a bowl of oxidized soil that has been magnetized to the same degree as his experimental samples. Moreover, the magnetization is in the same direction as the Earth's magnetic field would have been 1.6 mya, and not in the present direction. This is just what we would expect to find if these were campfire sites.

Excavations at Swartkrans Cave in South Africa provide more evidence that *H. ergaster* used fire. There, anthropologists found numerous fragmented fossil bones of antelope, zebra, warthog, baboon, and *Paranthropus robustus* that show evidence of having been burned. Such burnt fossils were found at 20 different levels dated from 1.5 to 1 mya. Oldowan tools and *H. ergaster* fossils were also found on some of these levels. To determine whether these bones had been burnt in campfires, C. K. Brain of the Transvaal Museum in Pretoria and Andrew Sillen of the University of Cape Town compared the fossils to modern antelope bones burned at a range of temperatures. They found that the very high temperatures characteristic of long-burning campfires produce clear changes in the microscopic structure of bone—changes that can also be seen in the burnt fossils at Swartkrans. Because Bellomo's experiments suggest that wildfires rarely produce high temperatures, the presence of bones burnt at high temperature provides good evidence that these bones were burned in campfires. (Unfortunately, marshmallows leave no trace in the archaeological record.)

Homo ergaster is classified in the genus Homo because it shares the same adaptive grade as later members of the genus.

Taken together, the archaeological and paleontological data suggest that *H. ergaster* represented a marked departure from its predecessors. This hominin shared important adaptive traits with modern humans: terrestrial life, complex foraging technology, slow development, reduced sexual dimorphism, and (probably) extensive paternal investment in offspring. Because we share these features, *H. ergaster* is classified in the same genus as we are. With its smaller brain and relatively static and inflexible technology, however, *H. ergaster* was still quite different from modern humans. In the next section we explain how *H. ergaster* was transformed into a larger-brained and highly flexible creature more like us.

HOMININS OF THE EARLY MIDDLE PLEISTOCENE (900 TO 300 KYA)

The world's climate became colder and much more variable during the Middle Pleistocene (900 to 130 kya).

During the Middle and Upper Pleistocene there were many long, cold glacial periods punctuated by short, warmer interglacial periods. Figure 13.12 shows estimates of global temperatures for this time period. Notice that the world climate has fluctuated wildly in the last 700,000 years. From geological evidence, we know that during the cold periods, glaciers covered North America and Europe and arctic conditions

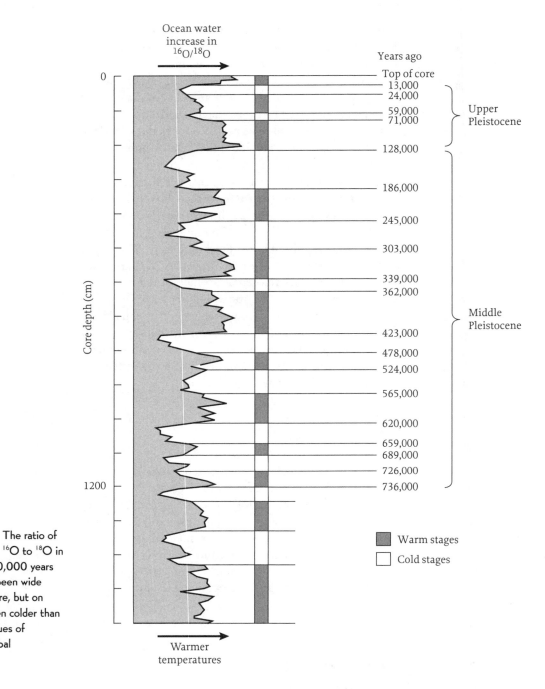

Ocean water increase in $^{16}O/^{18}O$ →

Years ago

0 — Top of core
— 13,000
— 24,000
— 59,000
— 71,000   } Upper Pleistocene

— 128,000

— 186,000

— 245,000

— 303,000

— 339,000
— 362,000

Core depth (cm)

— 423,000   Middle Pleistocene

— 478,000
— 524,000

— 565,000

— 620,000

— 659,000
— 689,000
— 726,000
1200 — 736,000

Warm stages
Cold stages

Warmer temperatures →

FIGURE 13.12 The ratio of ^{16}O to ^{18}O in seawater over the last 700,000 years indicates that there have been wide swings in world temperature, but on average, the world has been colder than it is now. Larger ocean values of ^{16}O:^{18}O signify higher global temperatures.

prevailed. These cold periods were intermittently interrupted by shorter warm periods during which the glaciers receded and the forests returned.

During glacial periods the world was dry, and Africa and Eurasia were isolated from each other by a massive desert. During interglacial periods the world was much wetter, and animals moved from Africa to Eurasia.

These temperature fluctuations had massive effects on the world's biological habitats, as Figure 13.13 shows. The map in Figure 13.13a shows the distribution of habitats about 7 kya during the warmest and wettest period of the current interglacial period. At this time, much of Eurasia and Africa was covered by forests, East and North Africa and Arabia were grasslands, and deserts were limited to small bits of Southwest Africa and central Asia. The map in Figure 13.13b shows what the world was like at the depth of the last glacial period, about 20 kya. The middle latitudes were dominated by vast expanses of extreme desert, as dry as the Sahara Desert today. North and south of this desert, grassland, scrub, and open woodland predominated, and forests were restricted to small regions of central Africa and Southeast Asia. Since the beginning of the Middle Pleistocene, the planet has oscillated between these two extremes, sometimes shifting from one extreme to the other in just a few hundred years.

These fluctuations had important effects on the dispersal of animal species, including hominins, in the Middle and Upper Pleistocene. During glacial periods,

(a) Interglacial conditions (~7000 years BP)

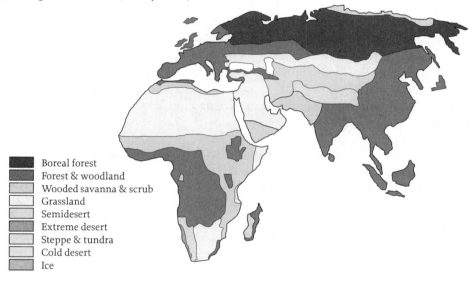

- Boreal forest
- Forest & woodland
- Wooded savanna & scrub
- Grassland
- Semidesert
- Extreme desert
- Steppe & tundra
- Cold desert
- Ice

(b) Glacial conditions (~20,000 years BP)

FIGURE 13.13 (a) A reconstruction of biological habitats about 7 kya during the warmest, wettest part of the present interglacial period. Much of Eurasia and Africa were covered with forest and were connected by a broad swath of grassland across northern Africa and southwestern Eurasia. (b) The habitats during the coldest, driest part of the last glacial period, about 20 kya. There was very little forest cover. Grassland and scrub predominated in central Africa and Southeast Asia. Northern Eurasia was covered with cold dry steppe and desert. Central and southern Africa were separated from Eurasia by a band of extreme desert across northern Africa, the Arabian Peninsula, and central Asia.

deserts spread across the northern part of Africa, making this region uninhabitable for most animal species. This corresponds to what we know from the fossil record: There was little movement of animal species between Africa and Asia during glacial periods. Instead, animal species moved mainly east and west across Eurasia. When the world was warmer, grasslands and savannas replaced most deserts, and animals were able to move between Africa and Eurasia much more easily. The fossil record indicates that animal species moved mainly from Africa to Eurasia, not vice versa. As we will see later, this fact has important implications for understanding human evolutionary history.

The evolutionary transition from H. ergaster *to modern humans occurred during the Middle Pleistocene.*

It was in this chaotic, rapidly changing world that natural selection reshaped the hominin lineage once again. *Homo ergaster* was transformed into a smarter and more versatile creature, which we call *Homo sapiens*. We will see that hominins were present in Africa and Eurasia for most of the Middle Pleistocene, and that hominins living in different parts of the world were morphologically distinct. A small-brained form, *H. erectus*, lived in eastern Asia until perhaps 30 kya; and a variety of larger-brained forms ranged through Africa and western Eurasia. About 300 kya, hominins in Africa and western Eurasia began to develop more sophisticated technology and behavior. This process of change continued, particularly in Africa, until the behavior and technology of hominins became indistinguishable from those of modern humans.

Although many of these events can be relatively well established in the fossil and archaeological record, there is considerable controversy about the phylogeny of the human lineage during this period. There are fierce debates about how many species of hominins there were during this period, and about how different species or forms were related. We will turn to these controversies at the end of the chapter. But first you need to learn something about the hominins of the Middle Pleistocene.

Eastern Asia: *Homo erectus*

Homo erectus, a hominin similar to H. ergaster, *lived in eastern Asia during most of the Middle Pleistocene.*

Fossils quite similar to what we now call *H. ergaster* were unearthed by Eugene Dubois near the Solo River in Java during the nineteenth century (Figures 13.14 and 13.15). Dubois named the species *Homo erectus*, or "erect man." Dubois's fossils were very poorly dated, and for many years they were believed to be about 500,000 years old. In the 1990s, however, Carl Swisher and Garness Curtis, both from the Berkeley Geochronology Center, used newly developed argon–argon dating techniques to determine the age of small crystals of rock from the sites at which Dubois's fossils had originally been found. Their analyses indicate that the two *H. erectus* sites in Java were actually 1.6 to 1.8 million years old, a million years older than previous estimates had suggested.

The main morphological differences between *H. erectus* and *H. ergaster* lie in the skull. In *H. erectus*, the skull is thicker, the browridges are more pronounced, the sides of the skull slope more steeply, the occipital torus is more pronounced, and there is a

FIGURE 13.14 Eugene Dubois was a Dutch anatomist who discovered the first *Homo erectus* fossil at a site called Trinil, in what is now Indonesia.

Lower and Middle Pleistocene Hominid Sites (1.8–.25 mya)

- *Homo ergaster*
- *Homo erectus*
- *Homo heidelbergensis*

FIGURE 13.15 The locations of fossil and archaeological sites mentioned in the text. *Homo ergaster* is found in Africa and Europe from 1.8 mya until about 1 mya. *Homo heidelbergensis* is found at sites in Africa and Europe that date to between 800 and 300 kya. Only *H. erectus* is found in East Asia during this period. The Bose Basin has yielded Mode 2 tools but no hominin fossils, so the identity of the toolmakers is unknown.

sagittal keel (a longitudinal V-shaped ridge along the top of the skull) (Figure 13.16). As you may recall from Chapter 11, the sagittal crest expands the area of attachment of the temporalis muscles in the paranthropines. The sagittal keel does not serve this function in *H. erectus*. In fact, we don't know what its function was.

Homo erectus is known from sites in Java and China and persisted until about 30 kya. Over this period, *H. erectus* changed very little. This species does not show the same increase in cranial capacity, technological sophistication, and behavioral flexibility that characterizes its contemporary hominin populations in Africa and western Eurasia. Even

Sagittal keel

Homo ergaster
(KNM-ER 3733)

Homo erectus
(Sangiran 17)

FIGURE 13.16 *Homo ergaster* and *Homo erectus* differed in a number of ways. Most notably, *H. erectus* had a sagittal keel and a more pronounced occipital torus, and the sides of the skull sloped more than in *H. ergaster*.

the most recent *H. erectus* fossils from eastern Asian are less like modern humans than are the African specimens of *H. ergaster*, which are 1 million years older.

Nonetheless, the presence of *H. erectus* fossils in eastern Asia suggests that this species mastered difficult environmental challenges. Somewhere between 500 and 250 kya, *H. erectus* occupied a cave at Zhoukoudian (or Choukoutien) near Beijing. Fossil pollen samples indicate that *H. erectus* occupied the cave only during the warmer interglacial periods. However, *warm* is a relative term; the climate of Zhoukoudian during the interglacial periods was probably something like that of Chicago today. Imagine living through a winter in Chicago without a roof over your head or clothes to keep you warm. To survive the rigors of cold temperate winters, *H. erectus* may have relied on fire and taken shelter in caves like the one at Zhoukoudian. Even this, however, might have been a challenge. The cave at Zhoukoudian is littered with the bones of large game, particularly two species of deer. It is clear that they were brought to the cave by a predator, perhaps *H. erectus*. However, there are also fossilized hyena bones and coprolites (fossilized feces) in these caves. Many of the animal bones show evidence of hyena tooth marks, and most of the faces of the hominins are absent. Thus, it is possible that *H. erectus* was sometimes the prey at Zhoukoudian rather than the predator.

Homo erectus *is associated with Mode 1 tools.*

Acheulean tools appear by 1.6 mya in Africa, but they are rarely found in eastern Asia. Instead, *H. erectus* is usually associated with the simpler Mode 1 tools, similar to those of the Oldowan industry. Some paleoanthropologists think that the differences in tool technology between eastern Asia and Africa provide evidence for cognitive differences between the two species; others think that environmental differences may be responsible for the tool differences. Remember that *H. ergaster* was present in eastern Asia by 1.7 mya. This means that *H. ergaster* left Africa before Mode 2 tools first appeared in Africa. It is possible that a cognitive change arose in the African *H. ergaster* population after the first members of the genus had migrated north into eastern Asia, and that this cognitive adaptation enabled later members of *H. ergaster* to manufacture bifaces. The absence of more symmetrical Mode 2 tools in eastern Asia may mean that they lacked this cognitive ability.

Other researchers argue that differences in tool technology between *H. erectus* and *H. ergaster* tell us more about their habitats than about their cognitive abilities. They point out that, during the Middle Pleistocene, *H. erectus* lived in regions that were covered with dense bamboo forests. Bamboo is unique among woods because it can be used to make sharp, hard tools suitable for butchering game. *Homo erectus* may not have made hand axes because they didn't need them. The recent discovery of a large number of hand axes in the Bose Basin in southern China may support this view (Figure 13.17). About 800 kya a large meteor struck this area and set off fires that destroyed a wide area of the forest. Grasslands replaced the forest. Although grasslands predominated, the residents of this area made Mode 2 tools like those seen in Africa around the same time. Before the forest was destroyed and after it regenerated, the inhabitants of this area made Oldowanlike Mode 1 tools. This evidence suggests that hand axes were an adaptation to open-country life.

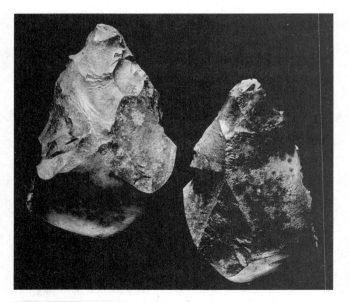

FIGURE 13.17 Hand axes found in the Bose Basin in southern China are the only Mode 2 tools discovered in East Asia. These tools date to about 800 kya. Mode 1 tools are found in the same area both before and after this date.

However, there are no hominin fossils associated with these tools, so we don't know whether *H. erectus* actually made them. It is possible that the Bose hand axes were made by members of more technologically advanced immigrant populations from farther west.

Africa and Western Eurasia: *Homo heidelbergensis*

Sometime during the first half of the Middle Pleistocene (900 to 130 kya), hominins with larger brains and more modern skulls appeared.

Hominins with substantially larger brains and more modern skulls appeared in Africa and western Eurasia during the first half of the Middle Pleistocene. Figure 13.18 shows two nearly complete crania from this period: the Petralona cranium found in Greece and the Kabwe (or Broken Hill) cranium from Zambia. These individuals had substantially

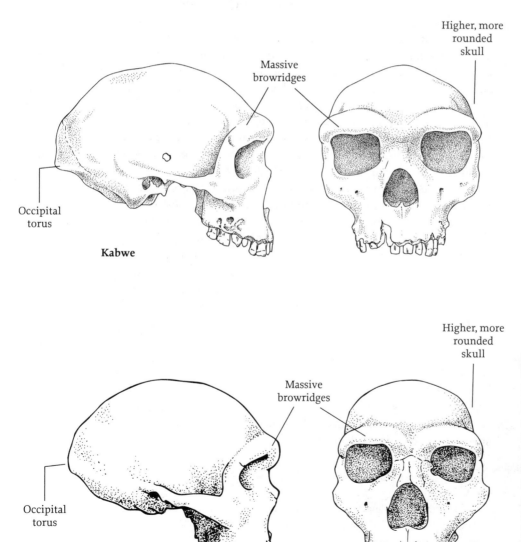

FIGURE 13.18 Sometime between 800 and 500 kya, hominins with higher, more rounded crania and larger brains first appear in the fossil record; and by 400 kya, *Homo heidelbergensis* was common in Africa and western Eurasia. Shown here are two *H. heidelbergensis* fossils: one from Kabwe (sometimes called Broken Hill) in Zambia, and the second from Petralona in Greece. Both are approximately 400,000 years old. (Figure courtesy of Richard Klein.)

larger brains—between 1200 and 1300 cc—in relation to their body size than *H. ergaster* had. The skulls also share a number of derived features with modern humans, including more vertical sides, higher foreheads, and a more rounded back than *H. ergaster* had. However, they also retained many primitive features, such as a long, low skull; very thick cranial bones; a large prognathic face; no chin; and very large browridges. Their bodies remained much more robust than modern human bodies are. Fossils with similar characteristics have been found at other sites in Africa (for example, Ndutu in Tanzania, Bodo in Ethiopia) and western Eurasia (for example, Mauer in Germany, Boxgrove in England) that date to the same period (see Figure 13.15). There has been no sign of these kinds of fossils in eastern Asia during this period, although they do appear later.

Traditionally, paleoanthropologists have referred to these larger-brained, more modern-looking hominins as **archaic *Homo sapiens*.** As we will explain shortly, however, nowadays only a minority of paleoanthropologists believe that these creatures should be classified as members of *H. sapiens*. There is considerable controversy about whether these hominins belonged to one species or several, and among the anthropologists who believe that there were several species, there is considerable disagreement over which specimens belong to which species. This dispute, which is far from resolved, creates a quandary about what we should call this group of hominins. Here we adopt what is perhaps the most common opinion and use the name ***Homo heidelbergensis*** to refer to all of the Middle Pleistocene hominins of Africa and western Eurasia. (The name *heidelbergensis* is taken from a specimen that was found near the German city of Heidelberg.) Keep in mind, though, that we are not at all sure that this category actually represents a single biological species.

Scientists are uncertain about when or where *H. heidelbergensis* first appeared. One candidate for the oldest *H. heidelbergensis* specimen is the cranium recently found at Buia in Eritrea. This skull has several derived features that are associated with *H. heilelbergensis*, but a small, *H. ergaster*–sized, braincase. A second possibility is the Kabwe fossil found in Zambia. Although it was originally dated to about 130 kya, more recent work has pushed the age of this fossil back to about 800 kya. A third candidate comes from Trinchera Dolina (also called Gran Dolina) in the Sierra de Atapuerca in northern Spain. This site has yielded a number of hominin fossils, including part of an adolescent's lower jaw and most of an adult's face. Although the Trinchera Dolina fossils are too fragmentary to provide an estimate of endocranial volume, they exhibit a number of facial features that are seen in more modern hominins. These fossils have been dated to about 800 kya by means of paleomagnetic methods, but rodent fossils found at the same site indicate a more recent date, perhaps 500 kya. Similar uncertainty afflicts our estimates of the ages of the other early *H. heidelbergensis* fossils, so the best that we can do is to bracket the first appearance of these creatures between 800 and 500 kya.

The tools used by early *H. heidelbergensis* are similar to those used by *H. ergaster*. Tool kits are dominated by Acheulean hand axes and other core tools at most sites, but in some cases the hand axes are more finely worked.

There is good evidence that H. heidelbergensis *hunted big game.*

The first solid evidence for hunting big game comes from this period. On the island of Jersey, off the coast of France, the remains of a large number of fossilized bones from mammoths and woolly rhinoceroses have been found at the base of a cliff. Some of the bones come from adults, which were too big to be vulnerable to most predators. The carcasses clearly have been butchered with stone tools. In some instances, the skull cavity has been opened, presumably to extract the brain tissue. At some places on this site, animal bones have been sorted by body parts (heads here, limbs there, and so on). All this suggests that *H. heidelbergensis* drove the animals over the headland, butchered the carcasses, and ate the meat.

More evidence for hunting comes from three wooden spears that were found in an open-pit coal mine in Schöningen, Germany. This site is dated to about 400 kya. Anthropologists are confident that these were throwing spears because they closely resemble modern javelins. They are about 2 m (6 ft) long and, like modern throwing spears, are thickest and heaviest near the pointed end, gradually tapering to the other end. Some modern people use similar spears for hunting, and it seems plausible that *H. heidelbergensis* used them in the same way. This hypothesis is strengthened by the fact that anthropologists found the bones of hundreds of horses along with the spears, and many of the bones show signs of having been processed with stone tools.

HOMININS OF THE LATER PLEISTOCENE (300 TO 50 KYA)

About 300 kya, and then slightly later in western Eurasia, hominins in Africa shifted to a new stone tool kit.

Beginning about 300 kya, hand axes became much less common and were replaced by tools that were manufactured by the production of sizable flakes, which were then further shaped or retouched. Unlike the small, irregular Oldowan flakes that had been struck from cobble cores, these tools were made from large, symmetrical, regular flakes via complicated techniques. One method, called the **Levallois technique** (after the Parisian suburb where such tools were first identified), involves three steps. First the knapper prepares a core with one precisely shaped convex surface. Then the knapper makes a striking platform at one end of the core. Finally, the knapper hits the striking platform, knocking off a flake, the shape of which is determined by the original shape of the core (Figure 13.19). A skilled knapper can produce a variety of different kinds of tools by modifying the shape of the original core. Such prepared core tools are classified as **Mode 3** technology.

Microscopic analyses of the wear patterns on Mode 3 tools made during this period suggest that some tools were **hafted** (attached to a handle). Hafting is an extremely important innovation because it greatly increases the efficiency with which humans can apply force to stone tools. (Try using a hammer without a handle.) *Homo heidelbergensis* probably hafted pointed flakes onto wooden handles to make stone-tipped spears, a major innovation for a big-game hunter.

Flake the margin of the core:

(a)   (b)

Prepare the surface of the core:

(c)   (d)

Remove Levallois flake:

Core   Flake

(e)   (f)

FIGURE 13.19 The process of making a Levallois tool. (a) The knapper chooses an appropriate stone to use as a core. The side and top views of the unflaked core are shown. (b) Flakes are removed from the periphery of the core. (c) Flakes are removed radially from the surface of the core, with the flake scars on the periphery being used as striking platforms. Each of the red arrows represents one blow of the hammer stone. (d) The knapper continues to remove radial flakes until the entire surface of the core has been flaked. (e) Finally, a blow is struck (large red arrow) to free one large flake (outlined in red). This flake will be used as a tool. (f) At the end, the knapper is left with the remains of the core (left) and the tool (right). (Figure courtesy of Richard Klein.)

Eastern Eurasia: *Homo erectus* and *Homo heidelbergensis*

During the second half of the Middle Pleistocene, H. heidelbergensis appeared in eastern Asia, where it may have coexisted with H. erectus.

Hominins with larger brains and more rounded skulls have been found at several sites in China that date to approximately 200 kya. The most complete and most securely dated fossil is from Yingkou (also called Jinniushan) in northern China (Figure 13.20). This specimen (Figure 13.21), which consists of a cranium and associated postcranial bones, is similar to early *H. heidelbergensis* fossils from Africa and Europe. Like the crania found at Kabwe and Petralona, it shares a larger braincase (about 1300 cc) and more rounded skull with modern humans, but it also has massive browridges and other primitive features. Other *H. heidelbergensis* fossils have been found in Dali in northern China and Maba in southern China, and they are probably somewhat younger than the Yingkou specimen. These fossils are associated with Oldowan-type tools. It is unclear whether these hominins were immigrants from the west or the result of convergent evolution in eastern Asia.

    H. heidelbergensis may have coexisted with *H. erectus* in East Asia during this period. Fossils of *H. erectus* that are between 200,000 and 300,000 years old have been found both at Zhoukoudian (Skull V) and at Hexian, also called He Xian (in southern China). The fossils of other animals found in association with *H. erectus* fossils at two sites in Java (Ngandong and Sambungmachan) are consistent with an age of 250,000 to 300,000 years. However, the teeth of bovids (buffalo and antelope) associated with the hominin fossils at these sites have been dated to about only 27 kya by means of electron-spin-resonance techniques.

Later Pleistocene Hominid Sites (250–50 kya)
- *Homo erectus*
- *Homo heidelbergensis*
- Neanderthals
- *Homo sapiens*

La Chapelle-aux-Saints,
La Ferrassie, Le Moustier,
Combe-Grenal, Mauran

Sima de los Huesos

Neander Valley

Yinkou

Zoukoudian

Shanidar

Dali

Dar es Soltan

Hexian

Maba

Omo-Kibish

Laetoli

Ngandong and
Sambungmachan

Florisbad

Border Cave

Klasies River Mouth

FIGURE 13.20 Locations of later-Pleistocene fossil and archaeological sites mentioned in the text. *Homo erectus* and *Homo heidelbergensis* are found in East Asia, Neanderthals in Europe, and both *H. heidelbergensis* and *H. sapiens* in Africa.

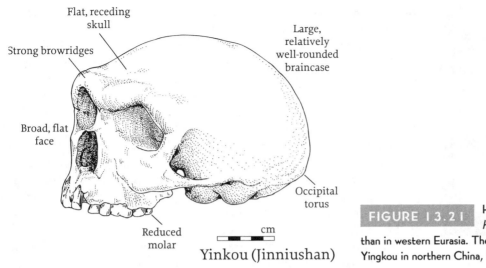

Flat, receding skull

Strong browridges

Large, relatively well-rounded braincase

Broad, flat face

Occipital torus

Reduced molar

cm

Yinkou (Jinniushan)

FIGURE 13.21 Hominins with the characteristics of *H. heidelbergensis* appeared in East Asia later than in western Eurasia. The specimen illustrated here, which is from Yingkou in northern China, is approximately 200,000 years old.

During the upper Pleistocene, H. erectus evolved into a tiny, small-brained hominin called Homo floresiensis on a small Indonesian island.

In the fall of 2004 a team of Indonesian and Australian researchers published what has been dubbed "the most surprising fossil hominin found in the last 50 years." Working at a cave site called Liang Bua on the Indonesian island of Flores (Figure 13.22), these researchers uncovered the remains of seven individuals. The fossil spec-

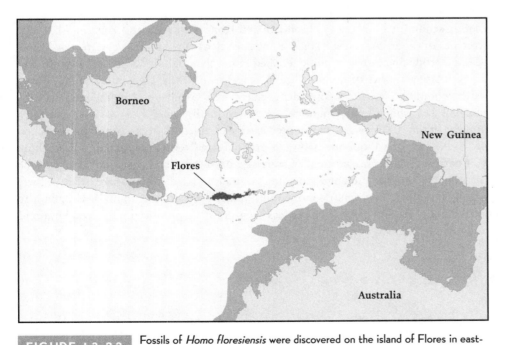

Borneo

New Guinea

Flores

Australia

FIGURE 13.22 Fossils of *Homo floresiensis* were discovered on the island of Flores in eastern Indonesia. The shaded areas give the approximate coastlines during glacial periods showing that Flores was isolated from both Asia and Australia even when sea levels were at their lowest levels. As a result, Flores was home to an odd mix of creatures, including a dwarf elephant, huge monitor lizards, and one-meter-tall hominins.

FIGURE 13.23 Three-quarter view of the skull of *Homo flore-siensis*. The skull is very small but shares a number of derived features with *H. erectus*. The brain of this creature was smaller than that of the smallest australopithecines.

imens included a complete skull (Figure 13.23), and bones from the arms, legs, and feet. The first surprise about these creatures, named *Homo flore-siensis*, was their size. They were slightly less than one meter tall (about 3 feet), much smaller than *H. erectus* elsewhere. Their brains were also very small (380 cc)—so small, in fact, that they may have been less encephalized than *H. erectus*. The second surprising thing about these creatures was their age. Using two different dating methods, the researchers estimated that *H. floresiensis* lived on Flores 35 to 14 kya.

Several lines of evidence indicate that these petite hominins are descended from *H. erectus*. First, the skulls share a number of derived characters with *H. erectus*. Second, a rich fossil record documents a long occupation of nearby Java by *H. erectus*. Third, it seems likely that *H. erectus* moved from Java to Flores because simple Mode 1 tools like those associated with *H. erectus* have been found on Flores and are dated to 800 kya.

Sophisticated flake tools were found at Liang Bua, together with the charred remains of many species of animals, including tortoises, lizards, rodents, bats, and numerous specimens of a species of dwarf elephant. Because these materials have dates that overlap with those of the hominin fossils, and there is no evidence of other hominins in the cave, the excavation team argues that *H. floresiensis* was able to hunt large game and make the kinds of sophisticated tools that are usually associated with *H. sapiens*. Other commentators have argued that these tools could not have been made by the tiny-brained *H. floresiensis*, because they are so much more sophisticated than those associated with *H. erectus*.

In addition to providing a remarkably unexpected addition to the human family tree, these fossils are important because they show us that the human lineage is subject to the same kinds of evolutionary forces as other creatures are. Flores and the islands around it have always been isolated from both Asia and Australia by wide stretches of ocean. As a result, only a few species of large animals ever reached these islands, producing a strange impoverished fauna that included Komodo dragons and an even larger species of monitor lizard, a species of dwarf elephant, and, of course, a dwarf hominin. It is not a coincidence that both the elephants and the humans were so small. Dwarfing of large mammal species on small, isolated islands has occurred a number of times. As we saw in Chapter 1, for example, red deer isolated on the island of Jersey shrank to about one-half their original size over 5000 years. Biologists think that natual selection favors smaller body size on small islands because typically such islands have less predation and more limited food supplies. If islands are isolated, there will be little gene flow from continental populations, and the animals will adapt to local conditions. On Flores this process seems to have produced pint-sized hominins and tiny elephants.

Western Eurasia: The Neanderthals

During the later Middle Pleistocene, the morphology of H. heidelbergensis in Europe diverged from the morphology of its contemporaries in Africa and Asia.

A large sample of fossils from a recently excavated site in Spain provides evidence that *H. heidelbergensis* in Europe had begun to diverge from other hominin populations during the Middle Pleistocene. This site, which is called Sima de los Huesos ("Pit of

FIGURE 13.24 The many hominin fossils found at Sima de los Huesos in Spain provide evidence that hominins in Europe began to evolve a distinctive cranial morphology at least 300 kya. The features—which include rounded browridges, a large pushed-out face, a skull with a rounded back, and a large brain—are important because they are shared with the Neanderthals, the hominins who dominate the European fossil record during the Upper Pleistocene.

the Bones") is located in the Sierra de Atapuerca only a few kilometers from Trinchera Dolina. There paleoanthropologists excavated a small cave 13 m (43 ft) below the surface and found 2000 bones from at least 24 different individuals. These bones, which date to about 300 kya, include several nearly complete crania, as well as many bones from other parts of the body. Figure 13.24 shows one of the crania, labeled SH 5. Like other fossils of *H. heidelbergensis*, these skulls mix derived features of modern humans and primitive features associated with *H. ergaster*. However, the crania from Sima de los Huesos also share a number of derived characters not seen in hominins living at the same time in Africa. Their faces bulge out in the middle and have double-arched browridges, and the backs of some of the skulls are rounded. The fossils from Sima de los Huesos also have relatively large cranial capacities, averaging about 1390 cc, close to the average value for modern humans. These characters are significant because they are shared by **Neanderthals**, the hominins who dominate the European fossil record from 127 to 30 kya.

Not all of the Sima de los Huesos crania express all the Neanderthal features to the same degree, and this variability has helped to settle an important question about hominin evolution in Europe. Before the Sima de los Huesos fossils were discovered, paleoanthropologists had been perplexed by the pattern of variation in Middle Pleistocene hominins in Europe. Fossils from some European sites resemble Neanderthals; fossils from other European sites that date to the same time period do not resemble Neanderthals. It was not clear whether these differences reflected variability within a single population of hominins or whether more than one type of hominin was present in Europe during the Middle Pleistocene. The large and variable sample of individuals at Sima de los Huesos has resolved this issue. These individuals, who likely belonged to a single population, vary in their expression of Neanderthal traits, and this variation mirrors the kind of variation seen at different sites in Europe. This evidence suggests that the features defining the Neanderthals had begun to evolve in European populations by 300 kya, but that these traits evolved independently, not as a single functional complex.

The Neanderthals appeared in western Eurasia about 130 kya.

The Neanderthals were an enigmatic group of hominins who lived in Europe and western Asia from about 127 to 30 kya. These creatures were among the first fossil hominins discovered, and they are still the best known. Their distinctive morphology (large browridges, short muscular bodies, and low foreheads) has become the archetypical image of "early man" for the general public. However, there is now good evidence that the Neanderthals became isolated from the lineage that led to modern humans and eventually became extinct. Molecular analyses of Neanderthal fossils and modern peoples provide convincing evidence that all modern peoples are descended from African populations living about the same time as the Neanderthals, and that Neanderthals did not contribute significantly to the modern human gene pool.

Although the Neanderthals are a dead-end branch of the human family tree, we know more about them than we do about any other extinct hominin species. The reason for this is simple: Neanderthals lived in Europe, and paleontologists have studied Europe much more thoroughly than they have studied Africa or Asia. Sally McBrearty of the University of Connecticut and Alison Brooks of George Washington University point out that there are more than 10 times as many Middle Pleistocene archaeological sites in France as there are on the entire continent of Africa. This difference is particularly striking when you consider that Africa is about 75 times the size of France. The upshot is that we know much more about the Neanderthals than we do about their contemporaries in other parts of the world.

The last warm interglacial period lasted from about 130 kya to about 75 kya. For most of the time since then, the global climate has been colder—sometimes much colder.

The data in Figure 13.25 give a detailed picture of global temperatures over the last 123,000 years. These data are based on the $^{18}O:^{16}O$ ratios of different layers of cores taken from deep inside the Greenland ice cap. Because snow accumulates at a higher rate than sediments on the ocean bottom do, ice cores provide more detailed information on past climates than do ocean cores like those used to construct the graph in Figure 13.1. You can see from Figure 13.25 that the end of the last warm interglacial period was marked by a relatively slow decline in temperature beginning about 120 kya. During this interglacial period, the world generally was substantially warmer than it is today. During this warm interglacial period, plants and animals were distributed quite differently than they are now. Plankton species currently living in subtropical waters (like those off the coast of Florida) extended their range as far as the North Sea during the last interglacial period. Animals now restricted to the tropics had much wider ranges. Thus, the remains of a hippopotamus have been found under Trafalgar Square, which lies in the center of London. In Africa, rain forests extended far beyond their present boundaries; and in temperate areas, broadleaf deciduous forests extended farther north than they do today.

As the last glacial period began, sometime between 100 and 75 kya, the world slowly cooled. In Europe, temperate forests shrank and grasslands expanded. The glaciers grew, and the world became colder and colder—not steadily, but with wide fluctuations from cold to warm. When the glaciation was at its greatest extent (about 20 kya), huge continental glaciers covered most of Canada and much of northern Europe. Sea levels dropped so low that the outlines of the continents were altered substantially: Asia and North America were connected by a land bridge that spanned the Bering Sea; the islands of Indonesia joined Southeast Asia in a landmass called Sundaland; and Tasmania, New Guinea, and Australia formed a single continent called Sahul. Eurasia south of the glaciers was a vast, frigid grassland, punctuated by dunes of loess (fine dust produced by glaciers) and teeming with

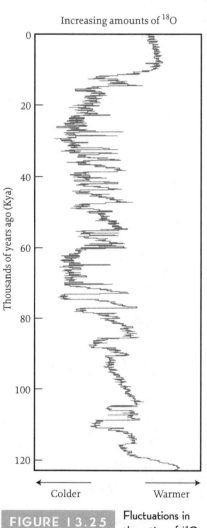

Increasing amounts of ^{18}O

Thousands of years ago (Kya)

Colder   Warmer

FIGURE 13.25 Fluctuations in the ratios of ^{18}O to ^{16}O over the last 123,000 years taken from an ice core drilled in northern Greenland. These data indicate that, between 120 and 80 kya, the world's climate got colder and less stable. In ice cores like this one, a higher ratio of ^{18}O to ^{16}O indicates higher temperatures. (In deep-sea cores, more ^{18}O relative to ^{16}O indicates lower temperatures.)

animals—woolly mammoths, woolly rhinoceroses, reindeer, aurochs (the giant wild oxen that are ancestral to modern cattle), musk oxen, and horses.

Sometime during the last interglacial period, Neanderthals came to dominate Europe and the Near East.

In 1856, workers at a quarry in the Neander Valley in western Germany found some unusual fossil bones. The bones found their way to a noted German anatomist, Hermann Schaafhausen, who declared them to be the remains of a race of humans who had lived in Europe before the Celts. Many experts examined these curious finds and drew different conclusions. Thomas Henry Huxley, one of Darwin's staunchest supporters, suggested that they belonged to a primitive, extinct kind of human. The Prussian pathologist Rudolf Virchow, on the other hand, proclaimed them to be the bones of a modern person suffering from a serious disease that had distorted the skeleton. Initially, Virchow's view held sway, but as more fossils were discovered with the same features, researchers became convinced that the remains belonged to a distinctive, extinct kind of human. The Germans called this extinct group of people *Neanderthaler*, meaning "people of the Neander Valley" (*Thal*, now spelled *Tal*, is German for "valley"). We call them the Neanderthals, and they were characterized by several distinctive, derived features:

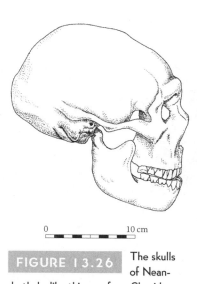

FIGURE 13.26 The skulls of Neanderthals, like this one from Shanidar Cave, Iraq, are large and long, with large browridges and a massive face. (Figure courtesy of Richard Klein.)

- *Large brains.* The Neanderthal braincase is much larger than that of *H. heidelbergensis*, ranging from 1245 to 1740 cc, with an average size of about 1520 cc. In fact, Neanderthals had larger brains than modern humans, whose brains average about 1400 cc. It is unclear why the brains of Neanderthals were so large. Some anthropologists point out that the Neanderthals' bodies were much more robust and heavily muscled than those of modern humans, and they suggest that the large brains of Neanderthals reflect the fact that larger animals usually have bigger brains than smaller animals.

- *More rounded crania than* H. erectus *or* H. heidelbergensis (Figure 13.26). The Neanderthal skull is long and low, much like the skulls of *H. heidelbergensis*, but relatively thin-walled. The back of the skull has a characteristic rounded bulge or bun and does not come to a point at the back like an *H. erectus* skull does. There are also detailed differences in the back of the cranium.

- *Big faces.* Like *H. erectus* and *H. heidelbergensis*, the skulls of Neanderthals have large browridges, but they are larger and rounder and they stick out less to the sides. Moreover, the browridges of *H. erectus* are mainly solid bone, while those of Neanderthals are lightened with many air spaces. The function of these massive browridges is not clear. The face, and particularly the nose, is enormous: every Neanderthal was a Cyrano, or perhaps a Jimmy Durante.

- *Small back teeth and large, heavily worn front teeth.* Neanderthal molars are smaller than those of *H. ergaster*. They had distinctive **taurodont roots** (Figure 13.27) in which the pulp cavity expanded so that the roots merged, partially or completely, to form a single broad root. Neanderthal incisors are relatively large and show very heavy wear. Careful study of these wear patterns indicates that Neanderthals may have pulled meat or hides through their clenched front teeth. There are also microscopic, unidirectional scratches on the front of the incisors, suggesting that these hominins held meat in their teeth while cutting it with a stone tool. Interestingly, the direction of the scratches suggests that most Neanderthals were right-handed, just as the Oldowan toolmakers were.

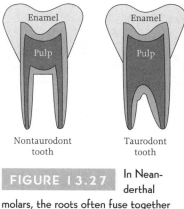

FIGURE 13.27 In Neanderthal molars, the roots often fuse together partially or completely to form a single massive taurodont root. The third root is not shown.

FIGURE 13.28   The Neanderthals were very robust people. Contrast the bones of a Neanderthal (a) with those of a modern human (b).

(a)   (b)

- *Robust, heavily muscled bodies.* Like *H. ergaster*, *H. erectus*, and *H. heidelbergensis*, Neanderthals were extremely robust, heavily muscled people (Figure 13.28). Their leg bones were much thicker than ours, the load-bearing joints (knees and hips) were larger, the **scapulae** (shoulder blades; singular *scapula*) had more extensive muscular attachments, and the rib cage was larger and more barrel-shaped. All these skeletal features indicate that Neanderthals were very sturdy and strong, weighing about 30% more than contemporary humans of the same height. A comparison with data on Olympic athletes suggests that Neanderthals most closely resembled the hammer, javelin, and discus throwers and shot-putters. They were a few inches shorter, on average, than modern Europeans and had larger torsos and shorter arms and legs.

This distinctive Neanderthal body shape may have been an adaptation to conserve heat in a very cold environment. In cold climates, animals tend to be larger and have shorter and thicker limbs than do members of the same species in warmer environments. This is because the rate of heat loss for any body is proportional to its surface area, so any change that reduces the amount of surface area for a given volume will conserve heat. The ratio of surface area to volume in animals can be reduced in two ways: by increasing overall body size or by reducing the size of the limbs. In contemporary human populations there is a consistent relationship between climate and body proportions. One way to compare body proportions is to calculate the **crural index**, which is the ratio of the length of the shin bone (tibia) to the length of the thigh bone (femur). As Figure 13.29 shows, people in warm climates tend to have relatively long

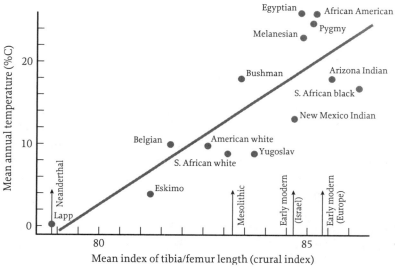

FIGURE 13.29 People have proportionally longer arms and legs in warm climates than in cold climates. Local temperature is plotted on the vertical axis; crural index is plotted on the horizontal axis. Smaller values of the crural index are associated with shorter limbs relative to body size. Populations in warm climates tend to have high crural-index values, and vice versa. Neanderthals had a crural index similar to those of present-day Lapps, who live above the Arctic Circle.

limbs in proportion to their height. Neanderthals resemble modern peoples living above the Arctic Circle.

Some authorities believe that Neanderthals lacked modern language.

The larynx (or voice box) of modern humans is much lower than in other primates—an arrangement that allows us to produce the full range of vowels used in modern human languages. On the basis of reconstructions of the Neanderthal vocal tract, anatomist Jeffrey Laitman of Mount Sinai School of Medicine argues that the Neanderthals had vocal tracts much like those of other primates, and could not have produced the full range of sounds necessary for modern speech. Laitman and his colleagues recorded the positions of several anatomical landmarks on the **basicrania** (singular *basicranium*; bottom of the skull) of humans and several other primates. In infant humans, this basicranial hump is gentle, like those of other primates; but as humans mature, the bottom of the cranium develops a pronounced upward indentation. Laitman believes that this relatively high hump helps make room for the elongated human vocal tract. Australopithecine adults have apelike basicrania, but the basicranium in *H. ergaster* is intermediate between those in apes and modern humans. Laitman argues that the initial shift in *H. ergaster* may have facilitated breathing through the mouth during heavy aerobic exercise. The basicrania in Neanderthals show a less humped profile than those of *H. ergaster*, suggesting that the Neanderthals' capacity for language was more restricted than the language capacities of even their own ancestors.

It is also possible that Laitman's reconstructions are correct, but that grammatically complex language still appeared long before modern humans evolved. It is possible for a creature with a high larynx to make all of the vowel sounds by using the nasal cavity. In modern humans, such nasalized vowels take longer to produce and are harder to understand. Thus the lowering of the larynx might have served merely to decrease the error rate of understanding a language that was otherwise very modern. Second, as Harvard University linguist Steven Pinker points out in his book *The Language Instinct*, "e lengeege weth e smell nember ef vewels cen remeen quete expresseve." So, even if Laitman is correct, early hominins could have had fancy languages.

(a)

(b)

FIGURE 13.30 Neanderthals and their contemporaries are believed to have hunted large and dangerous game, such as red deer (a) and bison (b).

There is a lot of evidence that Neanderthals made Mode 3 tools and hunted large game.

Although Neanderthals are popularly pictured as brutish dimwits, this is an unfair characterization. As we noted earlier, their brains were larger than ours. And the archaeological evidence suggests that they were skilled toolmakers and proficient big-game hunters. The Neanderthal's stone tool kit is dominated by Mode 3 tools, which are characterized by flakes struck from prepared cores. Their stone tool industry is called the **Mousterian industry** by archaeologists. Neanderthal sites are littered with stone tools and the bones of red deer (called "elk" in North America), fallow deer, bison, aurochs, wild sheep, wild goats, and horses (Figure 13.30). Archaeologists find few bones of very large animals, like hippopotamuses, rhinoceroses, and elephants, even though they were plentiful in Europe at that time.

Again, the conjunction of animal bones and stone tools does not necessarily mean that Neanderthals hunted large game, and there is a reprise of the same debate we have discussed several times before. Some archaeologists, such as Lewis Binford of Truman State University, believe that Neanderthals never hunted anything larger than small antelope, and even these prey were taken opportunistically. These researchers claim that the bones of larger animals found at these sites were acquired by scavenging. Binford believes that the hominins of this period did not have the cognitive skills necessary to plan and organize the cooperative hunts necessary to bring down large prey.

However, this position seems hard to sustain in the face of the archaeological evidence. Stanford archaeologist Richard Klein contends that Neanderthals were proficient hunters who regularly killed large animals. He points out that animal remains at sites from this period are often dominated by the bones of only one or two prey species. At Mauran, a site in the French Pyrenees, for example, over 90% of the assemblage is from bison and aurochs. The same pattern occurs at other sites scattered across Europe. It is hard to see how an opportunistic scavenger would acquire such a nonrandom sample of the local fauna. Moreover, the age distribution of prey animals does not fit the pattern for modern scavengers like hyenas, which prey mainly on the most vulnerable members of prey populations: sick or wounded animals, the old, and the very young (Figure 13.31). At these European sites, the bones of apparently healthy, prime-age adults are well represented. The distribution of animal bones is what we would expect to see at sites of catastrophic events in which whole herds of animals are killed. For example, several sites are located at the bottoms of cliffs. There are huge jumbles of bones and tools at these sites, suggesting that Neanderthals drove game over the cliffs and butchered the carcasses where they fell. At several sites, such as Combe Grenal in France, the bones from the meatiest parts of prey animals are overrepresented, and the cut marks on these bones suggest that Neanderthals stripped off the fresh flesh. (Remember that hunters often haul away the meatiest bones to eat in peace.) Taken together, these data suggest that Neanderthals were big-game hunters, not opportunistic scavengers.

There is little evidence for shelters or even organized camps at Neanderthal sites.

There are many Neanderthal sites, some very well preserved, where archaeologists have found concentrations of tools, abundant evidence of toolmaking, many animal remains, and concentrations of ash. Most of these sites are in caves or **rock shelters**, places protected by overhanging cliffs. This doesn't necessarily mean that Neanderthals preferred these kinds of sites. Cave sites are more likely to be found by researchers because they are protected from erosion, and they are relatively easy to locate because the openings to many caves from this period are still visible. Most archaeologists believe that cave sites represent home bases, semipermanent encampments from which Neanderthals sallied out to hunt and to forage.

The archaeological record suggests that Neanderthals did not build shelters. Most Neanderthal sites lack evidence of postholes and hearths, two features generally associated with simple shelters. The few exceptions to this rule occur near the end of the period. For example, hearths were built at Vilas Ruivas, a site in Portugal dated to about 60 kya.

FIGURE 13.31 Hyenas frequently scavenge kills, and they prey mainly on very young and very old individuals.

Neanderthals probably buried their dead.

The abundance of complete Neanderthal skeletons suggests that, unlike their hominin predecessors, Neanderthals frequently buried their dead. Burial protects the corpse from dismemberment by scavengers and preserves the skeleton intact. Detailed study of the geological context at sites like La Chapelle-aux-Saints, Le Moustier, and La Ferrassie in southern France also supports the conclusion that Neanderthal burials were common.

It is not clear whether these burials had a religious nature, or if Neanderthals buried their dead just to dispose of the decaying bodies. Anthropologists used to interpret some sites as ceremonial burials in which Neanderthals were interred along with symbolic materials. In recent years, however, skeptics have cast serious doubt on such interpretations. For example, anthropologists used to think that the presence of fossilized pollen in a Neanderthal grave in Shanidar Cave, Iraq, was evidence that the individual had been buried with a garland of flowers. More recent analyses, however, revealed that the grave had been disturbed by burrowing rodents, and it is quite possible that they brought the pollen into the grave.

Neanderthals seem to have lived short, difficult lives.

Careful study of Neanderthal skeletons indicates that Neanderthals didn't live very long. The human skeleton changes throughout the life cycle in characteristic ways, and these changes can be used to estimate the age at which fossil hominins died. For example, human skulls are made up of separate bones that fit together in a three-dimensional jigsaw puzzle. When children are first born, these bones are still separate, but later they fuse together, forming tight, wavy joints called **sutures**. As people age, these sutures are slowly obliterated by bone growth. By assessing the degree to which the sutures of fossil hominins have been obliterated, anthropologists can estimate how old the individual was at death. Several other skeletal features can be used in similar ways. All of these features tell the same story: Neanderthals died young. Few lived beyond the age of 40 to 45 years.

Many of the older Neanderthals suffered disabling disease or injury. For example, the skeleton of a Neanderthal man from La Chapelle-aux-Saints shows symptoms of severe arthritis that probably affected his jaw, back, and hip. By the time this fellow died, around the age of 45, he had also lost most of his teeth to gum disease. Another individual, Shanidar 1 (from the Shanidar site in Iraq), suffered a blow to his left

FIGURE 13.32 Many Neanderthal skeletons show signs of injury or illness. The orbit of the left eye of this individual was crushed, the right arm was withered, and the right ankle was arthritic.

temple that crushed the orbit (Figure 13.32). Anthropologists believe that his head injury probably caused partial paralysis of the right side of his body, and this in turn caused his right arm to wither and his right ankle to become arthritic. Other Neanderthal specimens display bone fractures, stab wounds, gum disease, withered limbs, lesions, and deformities.

In some cases, Neanderthals survived for extended periods after injury or sickness. For example, Shanidar 1 lived long enough for the bone surrounding his injury to heal. Some anthropologists have proposed that these Neanderthals would have been unable to survive their physical impairments—to provide themselves with food or to keep up with the group—had they not received care from others. Some researchers argue further that these fossils are evidence of the origins of caretaking and compassion in our lineage.

Katherine Dettwyler, an anthropologist at Texas A&M University, is skeptical of this claim. She points out that in some contemporary societies, disabled individuals are able to support themselves, and they do not necessarily receive compassionate treatment from others. In addition, nonhuman primates sometimes survive despite permanent disabilities. At Gombe Stream National Park, a male chimpanzee named Faben contracted polio, which left him completely paralyzed in one arm. Despite this impairment, he managed to feed himself, traverse the steep slopes of the community's home range, keep up with his companions, and even climb trees (Figure 13.33).

FIGURE 13.33 At Gombe, a male chimpanzee named Faben contracted polio, which left one arm completely paralyzed. After the paralysis, Faben received no day-to-day help from other group members, but he was able to survive for many years. Here, Faben climbs a tree one-handed.

Africa: The Road to *Homo sapiens*?

Hominins living in Africa during the later Middle Pleistocene were more similar to modern humans than were Neanderthals.

The fossil record in Africa indicates fairly clearly that African humans of this period were not like the Neanderthals, although it is not entirely clear what they were like, because the fossil record for this time in Africa is not nearly as good as it is in Europe. A number of fossils dated to later in the Middle Pleistocene (300 to 200 kya) have robust features similar to those of *H. heidelbergensis*. Examples include the Florisbad cranium found in South Africa (Figure 13.34) and the Ngaloba cranium (LH 18) from Laetoli, Tanzania. Like the Neanderthals, these African hominins show large cranial volumes, ranging from 1370 to 1510 cc. However, none of the African fossils show the complex of specialized features that are diagnostic of the European Neanderthals. Although these fossils are variable and some are quite robust, many researchers believe that they are more like modern humans than are the Neanderthals or earlier African hominins.

About 190 kya, hominins belonging to our own species began to appear in Africa, although some of the evidence is problematic. The oldest fossils classified as *Homo sapiens* were excavated in 1963 at a site in southern Ethiopia called Omo-Kibish, where paleoanthropologists found most of two fossil skulls and a number of other bone fragments. These skulls are quite robust, with prominent browridges and large faces. However, one of them has a number of modern features—most notably a high, rounded braincase (Figure 13.35). Initially these specimens could not be dated, but they were recently dated to about 190 kya by new radiometric methods. Several similar skulls were uncovered at Herto, another site in Ethiopia, and are dated to 160 kya. Other more fragmentary fossil materials from other sites in Africa also suggest that more modern hominins were present in Africa between 200 and 100 kya. The archaeological record indicates that Africans during this period developed more sophisticated technology and social behavior than did their contemporaries in Europe or Asia—a pattern that is consistent with the idea that this period saw the gradual accumulation of the cognitive and behavioral characteristics that make modern humans so different from other hominins. We turn to this evidence in the next chapter.

FIGURE 13.34 This cranium found at Florisbad in South Africa shows a mixture of features of *H. heidelbergensis* and modern *H. sapiens*. Although still quite robust, it has reduced browridges and a more rounded shape. It dates to between 300 and 200 kya.

THE SOURCES OF CHANGE

Europe may have been invaded repeatedly by hominins from Africa during the Middle Pleistocene.

The changes in hominin morphology and technology that we have described in this chapter may be the product of a number of different kinds of processes. It is possible that the changes we see reflect adaptive modifications in tool technology in particular regions of the world. Thus it is likely that Africa has been occupied continuously by members of the genus *Homo*, which first appeared 1.8 mya. This means that the makers of Mode 1 tools evolved slowly into the makers of Mode 2 tools, and the makers of Mode 2 tools evolved into the makers of Mode 3 tools.

However, it is also possible that some of the changes in the fossil record are the product of the replacement of one population of hominins by another. Cambridge University anthropologists Marta Lahr and Rob Foley recently suggested that Europe and western Eurasia were subjected to repeated invasions by hominins from Africa. They argue that the technological shifts seen in Eurasia were associated with the migration of hominins from Africa during interglacial periods. Remember that, during glacial periods, Africa and Eurasia were separated by a formidable desert barrier (see Figure 13.13b), and Eurasia was a cold, dry, and inhospitable habitat for primates. During these glacial periods, hominin populations in western Eurasia may have shrunk or disappeared altogether. When the glacial periods ended and the world became warmer, there was substantial movement of animal species from Africa into Eurasia. It is possible that

FIGURE 13.35 This fossil skull, called Omo-Kibish 1, was found in southern Ethiopia in 1963 and recently dated to 190 kya. It lacks the distinctive features of Neanderthals: the face does not protrude, and the braincase is higher and shorter than that of Neanderthals.

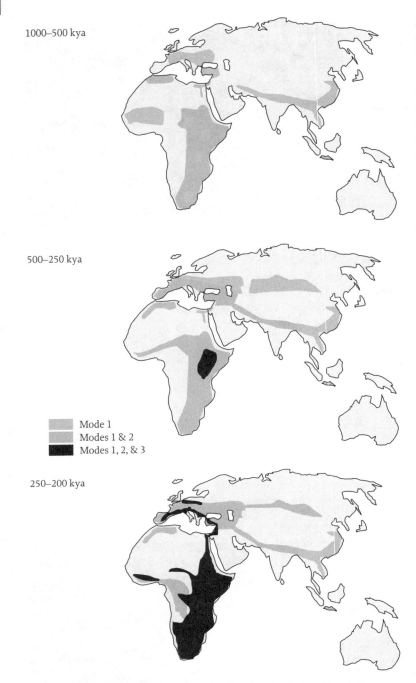

1000–500 kya

500–250 kya

Mode 1
Modes 1 & 2
Modes 1, 2, & 3

250–200 kya

FIGURE 13.36 The geography of tool technologies through time suggests that Eurasia was subjected to repeated invasions of hominins from Africa. Between 1 mya and 500 kya, Mode 2 technologies were confined to Africa, and hominins in Eurasia were restricted to Mode 1 tools. Beginning about 500 kya, Mode 2 technologies appeared in Eurasia. The introduction of Mode 2 coincided with a relatively warm, moist period, which could have facilitated the movement of hominins from Africa to Eurasia. About 300 kya, elements of Mode 3 technology appeared in East Africa, and by about 250 kya, Mode 3 technology had spread throughout Africa and southern Europe. Once again, this spread coincided with a period of warmer climate.

hominins staged repeated invasions of Eurasia during each of these warm interglacial periods, bringing new technologies along with them.

Lahr and Foley's argument is buttressed by archaeological evidence. Remember that the earliest evidence for hominins in Europe dates to about 800 kya. Up until about 500 kya, only Mode 1 tools are found in Europe. Then, Mode 2 technologies appear in Europe and persist until about 250 kya, when they are replaced by Mode 3 technologies. In each case the new technology appears first in Africa and then later in Europe and (sometimes) in Asia (Figure 13.36). The appearance of new tool technologies at 500 kya and 250 kya coincides neatly with the timing of interglacial periods, consistent with the repeated replacement of Eurasian populations by African populations.

THE MUDDLE IN THE MIDDLE

Anthropologists strongly disagree about how to classify Middle Pleistocene hominins.

You will notice that we avoided assigning a species name to the Neanderthals. This is partly because there is a lot of disagreement about how to classify Middle Pleistocene hominins. The disagreement stems from different ideas about the processes that shape human evolution during this period. One school of thought, most closely associated with University of Michigan anthropologist Milford Wolpoff, contends that hominins in Africa and Eurasia formed a single interbreeding population throughout the Pleistocene. The size of Africa and Eurasia limited gene flow and allowed regional differences to evolve, but there was always enough interbreeding to guarantee that all hominins belonged to single species during this entire period. Thus, Wolpoff and others prefer to include all hominins who lived during the Middle Pleistocene in a single species, *Homo sapiens*, as shown in Figure 13.37a. As we will show in the next chapter, this point of view has become hard to sustain in the face of information that has become available from molecular genetic studies in the last few years.

Other anthropologists believe that hominins split into several new species as they migrated out of Africa and into Eurasia although there are

(a)

(b)

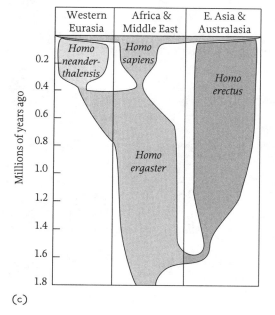

(c)

FIGURE 13.37 Numerous phylogenies have been proposed to account for the temporal and geographic patterns in hominin evolution during the Pleistocene. Illustrated here are three recent proposals: (a) Milford Wolpoff holds that, beginning about 1.8 mya, there was only one human species. Because there have been no speciation events since that time, all human fossils should be classified as *H. sapiens*. (b) G. Phillip Rightmire believes that both African and Asian specimens of *H. erectus* should be classified as a single species. Approximately 800 kya, a larger-brained species, *H. heidelbergensis*, evolved in Africa and eventually spread to Europe and perhaps East Asia. In Europe, *H. heidelbergensis* gave rise to the Neanderthals; in Africa, it gave rise to *H. sapiens*. (c) Richard Klein argues that *H. ergaster* evolved in Africa about 1.8 mya and soon spread to Asia, where it differentiated to become a second species, *H. erectus*. About 500 kya, *H. ergaster* spread to western Eurasia, where it evolved into *H. neanderthalensis*. In Africa, *H. ergaster* evolved into *H. sapiens* at about the same time.

disagreements about the details of phylogenetic history. Figure 13.37b and c illustrate two recent hypotheses. According to G. Phillip Rightmire of Binghamton University, the specimens that we have identified as *H. ergaster* and *H. erectus* are members of a single species (which would be called *H. erectus* because that was the name first used) (Figure 13.37b). However, he draws a distinction between early Middle Pleistocene hominins in Europe and Africa and those who came later. He groups all of the early Middle Pleistocene hominins in Europe and Africa into one species, which he labels *H. heidelbergensis*, and he lumps the hominins of the later Middle Pleistocene in Europe and the Neanderthals into one species, *H. neanderthalensis*. Although it may seem peculiar to include specimens without the distinctive Neanderthal features in the species *H. neanderthalensis*, this name is used because it has historical priority.

Richard Klein believes that hominin populations in Africa, western Eurasia, and eastern Eurasia were genetically isolated from each other during most of the Pleistocene and represent three distinct species (Figure 13.37c). In Africa, *H. ergaster* gradually evolved into *H. sapiens* about 500 kya. Isolated in Asia, *H. ergaster* evolved into *H. erectus* early in the Pleistocene. Klein considers the development of larger brains and more modern-looking skulls in the eastern Eurasia fossils, like those found at Yingkou, to be the result of convergent evolution and includes them in *H. erectus*. Once hominins reached Europe about 500 kya, they became isolated from African and East Asian populations, and diverged to become *H. neanderthalensis*.

This kind of disagreement is to be expected because the timescales of change become short as we come closer to the present. Instead of being interested in events that took place over millions of years, we are now interested in events that took place in just a hundred thousand years. But this may be roughly how long it took for two species to diverge during the process of allopatric speciation (see Chapter 4). Thus, as hominins spread out across the globe and encountered new habitats, regional populations may have become isolated and experienced selection—conditions that would eventually lead to speciation. The rapidly fluctuating climates of the Pleistocene, however, caused the ranges of hominins and other creatures to shift as well. As their ranges expanded and contracted, some populations may have become extinct, some may have become fully isolated and even more specialized, and others may have merged together. This complex set of possibilities is very difficult for paleontologists to unravel.

FURTHER READING

Conroy, G. 1997. *Reconstructing Human Origins: A Modern Synthesis*. Norton, New York.

Klein, R. 1999. *The Human Career* (2nd ed.). University of Chicago Press, Chicago.

McBrearty, S., and A. Brooks. 2000. The revolution that wasn't: A new interpretation of modern human behavior. *Journal of Human Evolution* 39: 453–563.

Rightmire, G. P. 1998. Human evolution in the Middle Pleistocene: The role of *Homo heidelbergensis*. *Evolutionary Anthropology* 6: 218–227.

Stringer, C., and C. Gamble. 1993. *In Search of the Neanderthals*. Thames and Hudson, New York.

Walker, A., and P. Shipman. 1996. *The Wisdom of the Bones: In Search of Human Origins*. Knopf, New York.

STUDY QUESTIONS

1. Which derived features are shared by modern humans and *Homo ergaster*? Which derived features are unique to *H. ergaster*?
2. What does the specimen KNM-WT 15000 tell us about *H. ergaster*?
3. What is a hand ax, and what did *H. ergaster* use hand axes for? How do we know?
4. What evidence suggests that *H. ergaster* controlled fire?

5. What evidence suggests that *H. ergaster* ate significant amounts of meat? Is the evidence for *H. ergaster* carnivory better than that for the Oldowan hominins? Explain.

6. What are the main differences between *H. ergaster* and *H. erectus*? How would you explain the evolution of these differences?

7. Using present-day examples, describe the variation in climate during the Middle Pleistocene. Why is this variation important for understanding human evolution?

8. How is *H. heidelbergensis* different from *H. erectus*?

9. What important technological transition occurred about 300 kya? Why was it important?

10. Explain why the fossils found at Sima de los Huesos are significant.

11. What is the crural index? What does it measure? How does the crural index of the Neanderthals differ from that of modern tropical peoples?

12. How did the Neanderthals differ from their contemporaries in Africa and eastern Asia?

13. What evidence suggests that western Eurasia was subjected to repeated invasions from Africa during the Middle Pleistocene?

KEY TERMS

occipital torus
biface
hand ax
cleaver
pick
Mode 2
acheulean industry
sagittal keel
archaic *Homo sapiens*
Homo heidelbergensis
Levallois technique

Mode 3
hafted
neanderthals
taurodont roots
scapulae
crural index
basicrania
Mousterian industry
rock shelters
sutures

CONTENT FROM *HUMAN EVOLUTION: A MULTI-MEDIA GUIDE TO THE FOSSIL RECORD*

Homo erectus
  Overview
  Distinguishing Features
  Homo ergaster
  Homo erectus Lifeways
Archaic Homo sapiens
  Overview
  Distinguishing Features

Origin Theories
Archaic H. sapiens Lifeways
The Neanderthals
  Overview
  Distinguishing Features
  Adaptive Significance
  Neanderthal Lifeways

HOMO SAPIENS AND THE EVOLUTION OF MODERN HUMAN BEHAVIOR

Between 40 and 30 kya the fossil and archaeological record in Europe undergoes a striking change: the Neanderthals disappeared and were replaced by essentially modern people. These people looked much like people in the world today, with high foreheads, sharp chins, and less robust physiques. The archaeological record suggests that they also behaved like modern people, using sophisticated tools, trading over long distances, and making jewelry and art. Anatomically and behaviorally similar people appeared in Australia around the same time. There is evidence that similar kinds of peoples also lived in Africa at this time, and most anthropologists think that modern people first appeared in Africa well before they appeared in Europe.

In this chapter we first describe the fossil and archaeological record for these early modern people in more detail. Then we consider how they evolved. You will see that evidence from the fossil record and from molecular genetic studies of DNA extracted from fossils gives us a fairly clear picture of where and when modern human morphology evolved. These data tell us that modern humans evolved in Africa between 200 and 100 kya and then migrated from Africa and spread throughout the world about 50 kya. We are less certain when and where modern human behavior evolved. According to one view, anatomically modern people inhabiting Africa 100 kya still lived much like the more robust hominins in Europe and Asia. Then about 50 kya an important cognitive innovation arose that allowed people to develop more complex technology and social lives, producing what anthropologists call the "human revolution." Adherents of a second view argue that the components of modern human behavior and technology gradually evolved in Africa along with modern human morphology over a period of about 200,000 years. There was not a human revolution in Europe or elsewhere in the world; what seems like a revolutionary change in Europe simply reflects the migration of modern people from Africa to Europe and the existence of an extremely rich archaeological record that is heavily biased in favor of European sites.

MODERN *HOMO SAPIENS*

Modern humans are characterized by several derived morphological traits, including a small face and teeth, a pointed chin, a high rounded cranium, and a less robust postcranium.

The first fossils of modern humans in Europe were found in 1868 by railroad workers in southwestern France at a site known as the Cro-Magnon rock shelter. This site eventually yielded bones from at least five different individuals who lived about 30 kya. Since 1868, many other sites in Europe have yielded fossils of modern humans or their artifacts. These creatures are classified by anthropologists as *Homo sapiens* because they shared a number of important derived features with contemporary humans that were not present in previous hominins (Figure 14.1):

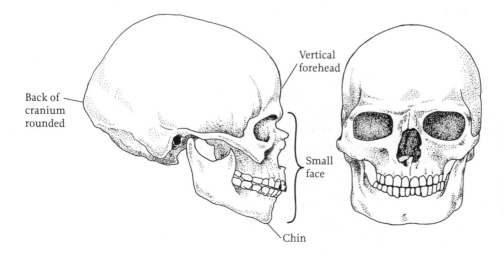

FIGURE 14.1 The skulls of modern humans have higher, rounder crania and smaller faces than earlier hominins had, as illustrated by this skull from a man who lived about 25 kya near the Don River in Russia. (Figure courtesy of Richard Klein.)

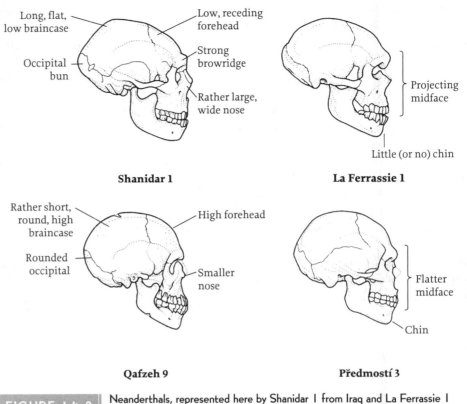

FIGURE 14.2 Neanderthals, represented here by Shanidar 1 from Iraq and La Ferrassie 1 from France, differ from modern *H. sapiens*, like Qafzeh 9 from Israel and Předmostí 3 from the Czech Republic. Modern humans had higher foreheads, smaller browridges, smaller noses, more rounded skulls, and more prominent chins than Neanderthals had.

- *Small face with protruding chin.* These people had smaller faces and smaller teeth than earlier hominins had, and the lower jaw bore a jutting chin for the first time (Figure 14.2). Some anthropologists believe that the smaller face and teeth were favored by natural selection because these people did not use their teeth as tools as much as earlier people had. There is no agreement about the functional significance of the chin.
- *Rounded skull.* Like modern people, these people had high foreheads, a distinctive rounded back of the cranium, and greatly reduced browridges (see Figure 14.2).
- *Less robust postcranial skeleton.* The skeleton of these people was much less robust than Neanderthal skeletons. These people had longer limbs with thinner-walled bones; longer, more lightly built hands; shorter, thicker pubic bones; and distinctive shoulder blades. Although these people were less robust than Neanderthals, they were still more heavily built than any contemporary human population. Eric Trinkaus of Washington University, St. Louis, argues that these people relied less on body strength and more on elaborate tools and other technological innovations to do their work.

Modern humans also differ from other living primates genetically in numerous ways. Because we lack genetic information about extinct hominins, we cannot say when these differences arose. See Box 14.1 for more details.

The Evolution of the Human Genome

BOX 14.1

The genome of an organism is all the genetic information carried on chromosomes in that species. For many years our knowledge of the genome was indirect: we could study the protein products of genes, and we could use specialized molecular techniques to track particular DNA segments called "genetic markers." In the last decade or so, technical progress has made it easier and cheaper to sequence large chunks of the genome. In 2002, a first cut at sequencing the entire human genome was announced with great fanfare. More quietly, geneticists have worked on sequencing the genomes of other organisms, including fruit flies, yeast, and mice. Of particular interest to us is the genome of one of our closest relatives, the chimpanzee. At this writing, a rough draft of the entire genome and a complete sequence of chimpanzee chromosome 22 have been produced. This genetic information gives us a new window on the kinds of evolutionary changes that have occurred in the human lineage.

Chromosome 22 contains about 33 million nucleotides and makes up about 7% of the entire chimpanzee genome. The chimpanzee chromosome 22 is homologous to the human chromosome 21. By comparing these two chromosomes, geneticists can construct a reasonable picture of the genetic similarities and differences between humans and chimpanzees.

Geneticists were able to estimate the number of positions at which one nucleotide was substituted for another by lining up the two chromosomes and comparing the sequences nucleotide by nucleotide. In about 1.4% of the nucleotides, one nucleotide has been substituted for another. There have also been many (68,000) insertions and deletions of bits of DNA in or out of the human genome or the chimpanzee genome. Most of these insertions and deletions involve a small number of nucleotides, and they add only a small percentage to the difference between the two genomes.

Many people find this fact puzzling. Humans and chimpanzees are really different, and it seems implausible that such a puny genetic difference could produce the sizable differences between the two. This would be very hard to explain if we assumed that if x percent of the DNA differed, then x percent of the genes would also differ. However, this conclusion doesn't follow. If DNA differences were distributed evenly across the genome, then even a 1% difference could cause every gene in the two species to differ.

This is where we benefit from having sequenced a sizable chunk of the genome of humans and chimpanzees. Geneticists identified 231 homologous structural genes (DNA sequences that code for proteins) on chromosome 22 in chimpanzees and chromosome 21 in humans. Only 39 of these 231 structural genes had exactly the same amino acid sequences. Among those that differed, 140 showed substitution of one or more amino acids but conserved overall length, and 47 of the genes showed significant structural changes. Thus, even though the DNA sequences of chimpanzees and humans differ by only a small percentage, 84% of the proteins produced by their genes differ.

Many of the differences in morphology and behavior between humans and chimpanzees are likely to be the result of natural selection, not just random mutations. But which ones? Another recent study provides a fascinating answer to this question. A team of geneticists determined the DNA sequence for 7645 homologous structural genes in the human, chimpanzee, and mouse genomes. Most of these genes showed some difference in DNA sequence.

To determine which changes were due to selection, the geneticists made use of the fact that the DNA code is redundant (see Chapter 2). This means that some nucleotide substitutions (**synonymous substitutions**) do not produce any change in the amino acid sequence of the protein that results from the gene, while **nonsynonymous substitutions** do produce a change in the amino acid sequence. Directional selection typically favors a particular protein that produces a particular phenotype. Thus, structural genes that have been subjected to directional selection are expected to show fewer nonsynonymous substitutions than synonymous ones show, and random change is expected to affect synonymous and nonsynonymous substitutions to the same extent.

Data on the mouse genome were included because that information allows us to determine which differences between humans and chimpanzees arose in the human lineage since our last common ancestor with chimpanzees, and which changes arose in the chimpanzee lineage after this point. When the mouse and the chimpanzee are the same and humans differ, it is likely that mice and chimpanzees have the ancestral DNA sequence, and humans have the derived one. Similarly, when mice and humans are the same and chimpanzees differ, the chimpanzee sequence is derived.

The results of these comparisons indicate that about 20% of the changes in the structural genes of humans and chimpanzees are the product of natural selection. These genes code for proteins with a number of different functions. The kinds of selective changes that have occurred in these 7645 structural genes are related mainly to functional differences in olfaction, hearing, amino acid metabolism, and development:

- *Olfaction*. Of the 7645 structural genes that code for proteins, 48 are involved in the human sense of smell, and 27 show significant change since the last common ancestor with chimpanzees. Most of this change seems to be due to a loss of function in the human lineage; apparently humans rely much less on their sense of smell than do chimpanzees.

- *Hearing*. About 15% of the proteins that affect human hearing have been subject to selection. These changes may be due to the necessity to process spoken language.
- *Amino acid metabolism*. A number of proteins that have been subjected to selection are involved in the metabolism of amino acids, including amino acids that are consumed in the form of meat. Amino acid metabolism is likely to reflect changes in the human diet and the increased importance of hunting and scavenging.
- *Development*. A number of proteins that control skeletal development and early embryonic development also show evidence of selection.

Many geneticists suspect that changes in regulatory genes are likely to be more important than changes in structural genes in the evolution of human morphology and behavior. However, it is not yet possible to identify regulatory genes from DNA sequences, so geneticists can't study the changes in regulatory genes in the same way that they study changes in structural genes.

FIGURE 14.3 Trees representing the differences between humans, chimpanzees, and macaques in gene expression in brain, liver, and white blood cells. The difference between humans and chimps in gene expression in liver and white blood cells is small, about the same as the overall genetic difference between the two species. Gene expression in human brain tissue, however, is very different from that in chimpanzees. This fact suggests that there has been substantial change in how regulatory genes affect gene expression in human brains.

A team of geneticists at the Max Planck Institute for Evolutionary Anthropology, led by Svante Pääbo, has studied the sequences of messenger RNA. Their work indicates that the levels of gene expression in the human brain are very different from those of chimpanzees, and this, in turn, suggests that there have been important changes in gene regulation during human evolution. The team used an array of 21,504 DNA segments, each about 1000 bases long. These were taken from a library of coding sequences for human genes, so that each DNA segment encoded a substantial part of a structural gene. Then they extracted messenger RNA from the brain tissue, liver tissue, and white blood cells of humans, chimpanzees, and rhesus macaques. When a particular gene is expressed, messenger RNA with the coding sequence for that gene will be present, and it will bind to the complementary DNA sequence on the array. Thus, Pääbo and his colleagues could determine which of the 21,504 genes were expressed in each tissue in each species.

The results from this study are shown in Figure 14.3. The three trees depict the distances (or differences) between humans, chimpanzees, and rhesus macaques based on the genes expressed in the brain, liver, and white blood cells. For the liver and blood, chimpanzees and humans have both changed about the same amount since their last common ancestor. Morever, this is about the amount of change we would expect based on the overall genetic difference between the two species. The story for the brain is very different: there has been much more change in the patterns of gene expression in human brains than in chimpanzee brains since we diverged from our last common ancestor. These results suggest that gene expression in human brains has changed much more than gene expression in other tissues.

ARCHAEOLOGICAL EVIDENCE FOR MODERN HUMAN BEHAVIOR

Archaeological evidence indicates that early modern humans in Europe were able to accumulate complex adaptive and symbolic behavior in the same way as people living today.

Modern human behavior is extraordinarily complex and varied. Remember that *H. ergaster* and *H. heidelbergensis* used Acheulean tools throughout Africa and western Eurasia for more than a million years. Thus the same tools, and presumably much the same adaptive strategies, were used over a wide range of habitats for a very long time. In contrast, present-day foragers use a vast range of different, highly specialized tools and techniques to adapt to a very large range of environments. They also engage in elaborate and varied symbolic, artistic, and religious behavior that is unparalleled among other creatures. The extraordinary geographic range and sophistication of modern humans is due partly to our cognitive abilities. Individual people can solve problems that would completely stump other creatures (see Chapter 9). However, being smarter than the average bear (or primate) is only part of our secret. Our other trick is having the ability to accumulate and transmit complex adaptive and symbolic behavior over successive generations. People rarely solve difficult problems on their own. Even the most brilliant of us couldn't construct a seaworthy kayak or invent perspective drawing from scratch. Instead, we gain skills, knowledge, and techniques from watching and being instructed by others. The variety and sophistication of modern human behavior is a product of our ability to acquire information in this way (see Chapter 16).

The archaeological record has numerous indications that the first *H. sapiens* in Europe had achieved this kind of complex and varied behavior:

- *Ecological range.* They were able to occupy a difficult, cold, dry habitat and extended their range farther north and east than previous hominins did.
- *Technology.* They assembled more sophisticated and more highly standardized tools made from a wider variety of materials, including antler, ivory, and bone. They also constructed elaborate shelters.
- *Social organization.* They used raw materials that came from sources hundreds of kilometers away for toolmaking, suggesting that they had long-distance exchange networks.
- *Symbolic expression.* They created art and ornamentation, performed ritual burials, and practiced other forms of symbolic behavior.

As we will explain more fully later in this chapter, the first modern humans in western Eurasia created a number of different tool industries in different parts of their range. Archaeologists refer to these tool industries collectively as **Upper Paleolithic** industries to distinguish them from the earlier tool industries associated with Neanderthals and other earlier hominins. The earliest Upper Paleolithic tools appear in the Near East about 45 kya, and they disappear from the archaeological record about 10 kya. Archaeologists refer to this period in western Eurasia as the Upper Paleolithic period, and the people who made the tools as Upper Paleolithic peoples.

Modern humans first entered Australia at least 40 kya, bringing technology similar to that of the Upper Paleolithic people in Europe.

The fossil and archaeological record in Australia is also quite good. Numerous well-dated archaeological sites indicate that modern *H. sapiens* entered Australia at least 40 kya. Several sites may be older, but the dates for each are controversial. What is certain is that people occupied the entire continent by 30 kya. Although the fossil record for the earliest sites is poor, there are good data for sites dated to 30 kya. The most complete early site is in southeastern Australia at Lake Mungo. The finds here include three hominin skulls, hearths, and ovens that have been dated to 32 kya using carbon-14 dating. The skull specimens are fully modern and well within the range of variation of contemporary Australian aborigines.

The earliest Australians seem to have practiced some of the same kinds of cultural behaviors as the Upper Paleolithic Europeans did. Some of the tools found at these early sites were made from bone, there are cave paintings dated to 17 kya, and there is evidence of both ceremonial burials and cremation. About 15 kya, Australians seem to have been the first people to use polished stone tools, which are made by grinding rather than flaking. In other parts of the world, polished tools do not appear in the record until agriculture is introduced, about 7 kya.

The fact that people got to Australia at all is evidence of their technological sophistication. Much of the world's water was tied up in continental glaciers 40 kya, so New Guinea, Australia, and Tasmania formed a single continent that geologists call Sahul. However, there was still at least 100 km (62 miles) of open ocean lying between Asia and Sahul, a gap wide enough to prevent nearly all movement of terrestrial mammals across it and thus to preserve the unique, largely marsupial fauna of Australia and New Guinea. The colonization of Sahul cannot be dismissed as a single lucky event, because people also crossed another 100 km of ocean to reach the nearby islands of New Britain and New Ireland at about the same time. Thus the people who first settled these islands must have been able to build seaworthy boats, a sophisticated form of technology.

More sophisticated stone tools appeared in eastern Asia around the same time.

Modern humans must have come to Australia by way of southern Asia, but signs of modern humans in southern Asia are scarce. Only one site there contains evidence of the kind of sophisticated artifacts seen in Upper Paleolithic Europe. The Batadomba-lena Cave in Sri Lanka, is dated to about 28 kya, and it has yielded modern human remains, elaborate stone tools, and tools made from bone.

Upper Paleolithic tools have been found at a number of sites in northern China, Mongolia, and Siberia. Especially notable is Berelekh, a site 500 km (about 300 miles) north of the Arctic Circle where the Yana River empties into the Arctic Ocean. Here archaeologists have recovered sophisticated stone tools and a number of artifacts made from bone, ivory, and horn (Figure 14.4). Radiocarbon methods indicate that these tools were made about 30,000 years ago. Pollen data tell us that this area then had a cool, dry climate in which grasslands were mixed with stands of larch and birch trees. Numerous processed bones of horse, musk ox, bison, and mammoth indicate that big game was plentiful. Nonetheless, life at this site must have been challenging for a recent African emigrant. Today the winters are long and dark, and January temperatures average −50°C (about −60°F)—a bracing thought, given that the world was much colder 30,000 years ago than it is today.

There is controversy over what was happening in Africa between 60 and 30 kya.

The fossil record during this period is very sparse, and there is disagreement among paleonthropologists about how modern human behavior evolved in Africa. Some researchers believe that modern human behavior came to Africa and Europe at about the same time. Others believe that modern human behavior evolved slowly in Africa over several hundred thousand years. We will return to this question at the end of the chapter.

Upper Paleolithic Technology and Culture

Upper Paleolithic peoples manufactured blade tools, which made efficient use of stone resources.

During this period, humans shifted from the manufacture of round flakes to the manufacture of blade tools. **Blades** are stone flakes that look like modern knife blades: they are long, thin, and flat and have a sharp edge. Blades have a longer cutting edge than flakes do, so blade technology made more efficient use of raw materials than older tool technologies did. However, there was a cost: although blades made more efficient use of materials, they also took more time to manufacture, requiring more preparation and more finishing strokes. Archaeologists label tool kits that emphasize blades as **Mode 4** technologies.

FIGURE 14.4 Spear foreshafts found at Yana, a site 500 km (about 300 miles) north of the Arctic Circle in eastern Siberia. These rhino horn foreshafts were fitted to the front end of the spear. If a hunter struck an animal without killing it, he could remove his spear, fit a second foreshaft to the spear, and reuse it. (From V. V. Pitulko et al., 2004, The Yana RHS site: Humans in the Arctic before the last glacial maximum, *Science*, 303: 52–56.)

The Upper Paleolithic tool kit includes a large number of distinctive, standardized tool types.

Upper Paleolithic peoples made many more kinds of tools than earlier hominins had made. Chisels, various types of scrapers, a number of different kinds of points, knives, burins (pointed tools used for engraving), drills, borers, and throwing sticks are just some of the items from the Upper Paleolithic tool kit.

Even more striking is the fact that the different tool types have distinctive, stereotyped shapes. It is as if the Upper Paleolithic toolmakers had a sheaf of engineering drawings on which they recorded their plans for various tools. When the toolmaker needed a new 10-cm (4-in.) burin, for example, she would consult the plan and produce one just like all the other 10-cm burins. Of course, these toolmakers didn't really use drawings as modern engineers do, but the fact that we find standardized tools suggests that they carried these plans in their minds. The final shape of Upper Paleolithic tools was not determined by the shape of the raw material; instead, the toolmakers seem to have had a mental model of what the tool was supposed to look like, and they imposed that form on the stone by careful flaking. The craft approach to toolmaking reached a peak in the Solutrean tool tradition, which predominated in southern France between 21 and 16 kya (Figure 14.5). Solutrean toolmakers crafted exquisite blades shaped like laurel leaves that were sometimes 28 cm (about 1 ft) long, 1 cm (about ½ in.) thick, and perfectly symmetrical.

FIGURE 14.5 Long, thin, and delicate blades characterized the Solutrean tool tradition.

Upper Paleolithic people were also the first to shape tools from bones, antlers, and teeth. Earlier hominins had made limited use of bone, but Upper Paleolithic people transformed bone, ivory, and antler into barbed spear points, awls, sewing needles, and beads.

Upper Paleolithic industries also varied in time and space.

The first Upper Paleolithic industry in Europe, the Aurignacian, was widespread in Europe by 35 kya (Figure 14.6). It is characterized by certain types of large blades, burins, and bone points. About 27 kya the Aurignacian was replaced in southern France by a new tool kit, the Gravettian, in which small, parallel-sided blades predominated and bone points were replaced by bone awls. Then about 21 kya, the Solutrean, with its beautiful leaf-shaped points, developed in the region. And 16 kya, the Solutrean gave way to the Magdalenian, a tool kit dominated by carved, decorated bone and antler points. Other parts of Europe are characterized by different sequences of tool complexes, so after the Aurignacian, each region typically has a distinctive material culture. Over roughly 25,000 years of the Upper Paleolithic in Europe there were dozens of distinctive tool kits emphasizing Mode 4 tools. This diversity stands in striking contrast to the Acheulean tool kit, which remained unchanged throughout more than half of the Old World for over a million years.

FIGURE 14.6 The Aurignacian tool kit, the earliest of several tool industries in the Upper Paleolithic of Europe, contains a wide variety of standardized tool types: 1, 2, 3, 9 = scrapers; 4, 5 = edged, retouched blades; 6, 10 = bladelets; 7 = a burin (a tool now used for engraving); 8, 11, 12 = bone points.

Stones and other raw materials for toolmaking were often transported hundreds of kilometers from their place of origin.

At Bacho Kiro, a 40,000-year-old Aurignacian site in Bulgaria, more than half of the flint used to make blades was brought from a source 120 km (about 75 miles) away. Distinctive, high-quality flint quarried in Poland has been found in archaeological sites more than 400 km (about 250 miles) away. Seashells, ivory, soapstone, and amber used in ornaments were especially likely to be transported long distances. By comparison, most of the stone used at a Mousterian site in France was transported less than 5 km (3 miles). The long-distance movements of these resources may mean that Upper Paleolithic peoples ranged over long distances, or that they participated in long-distance trade networks.

Modern humans exploited a wider range of prey species than did the Neanderthals, but the subsistence economies of the two populations were similar.

The Upper Paleolithic spanned the depths of the last ice age. The area in Europe that contains the richest archaeological sites was a cold, dry grassland that supported large populations of a diverse assemblage of large herbivores, including reindeer (called "caribou" in North America), horse, mammoth, bison, woolly rhinoceros, and a variety of predators, such as cave bears and wolves.

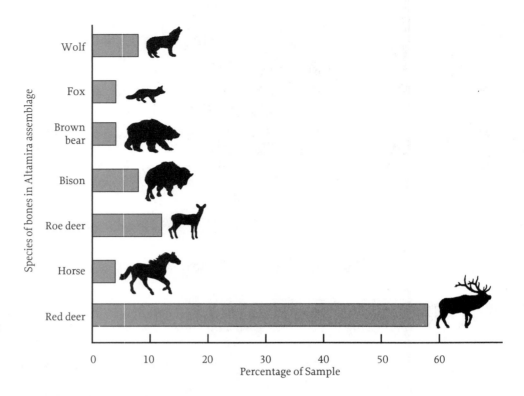

FIGURE 14.7 The bones of red deer dominate the assemblage at Altamira in northern Spain, as illustrated by these data, which come from a Magdalenian site dated to 15 to 13 kya.

Bones found at Upper Paleolithic sites indicate that large herbivores played an important role in the diets of Upper Paleolithic peoples. Everywhere, Upper Paleolithic peoples hunted herbivores living in large herds, fished, and hunted birds. In some places they concentrated on a single species—reindeer in France, red deer in Spain (Figure 14.7), bison in southern Russia, and mammoths farther north and east. In some areas, such as the southern coast of France, rich salmon runs may have been an important source of food. There are also places where these peoples harvested several different kinds of animals.

The peoples of the Upper Paleolithic developed more complex forms of shelter and clothing than the Neanderthals had.

In what is now western and central Europe, Russia, and the Ukraine, the remains of small villages have been found. Living on a frigid, treeless plain, Upper Paleolithic peoples either hunted or scavenged mammoth and used the hairy beasts for food, shelter, and warmth. At the site of Předmostí in the Czech Republic, the remains of almost 100,000 mammoths have been discovered. These peoples constructed huts by arranging mammoth bones in an interlocking pattern and then draping them with skins. [Temperatures of about −45°C (−50°F) outside provided a strong incentive for chinking the cracks!] The huge quantities of bone ash that have been found at these sites indicate that the mammoth bones were also used for fuel. A site about 470 km (about 300 miles) southeast of Moscow contains the remains of even larger shelters. They were built around a pit about a meter deep and were covered with hides supported by mammoth bones. Some of these huts had many hearths, suggesting that a number of families may have lived together (Figure 14.8).

Hearths
Large bones
Mammoth teeth

Mammoth crania
Mammoth crania
and scapulae

N

0   1 m

FIGURE 14.8 On the Russian plain, early humans had to cope with harsh climatic conditions. They may have used mammoth bones to construct shelters. Mammoth bones and teeth litter this Upper Paleolithic site of Moldova. The presence of multiple hearths suggests that this site may have been occupied by several families.

Several lines of evidence indicate that Upper Paleolithic peoples living in glacial Europe manufactured fur clothing. First, when modern hunters skin a fur-bearing animal, they usually leave the feet attached to the pelt and discard the rest of the carcass. Numerous skeletons of foxes and wolves that are complete except for their feet have been found at several Upper Paleolithic sites in Russia and the Ukraine, suggesting that early modern humans kept warm in sumptuous fur coats. Second, bone awls and bone needles are common at Upper Paleolithic sites, so sewing may have been a common activity. Finally, three individuals at a burial site in Russia seem to have been buried in caps, shirts, pants, and shoes lavishly decorated with beads.

Upper Paleolithic peoples were better able to cope with their environment than the Neanderthals were.

The richness of the fossil and archaeological record in Europe provides a detailed comparison of Neanderthal and Upper Paleolithic peoples. Three kinds of data suggest that Upper Paleolithic peoples were better adapted to their environment than Neanderthals were:

1. Upper Paleolithic peoples lived at higher population densities in Europe than Neanderthals did. Archaeologists estimate the relative population size of vanished peoples by comparing the density of archaeological sites per unit of time. Thus, if one group of people occupied a particular valley for 10,000 years and

left 10 sites, and a second group occupied the same valley for 1000 years and left 5 sites, then archaeologists would estimate that the second group had five times as many people. (In using this method it is important to be sure that the sites were occupied for approximately the same lengths of time.) By these criteria, Upper Paleolithic peoples had far higher population densities in Europe than the Neanderthals did.

2. Upper Paleolithic peoples lived longer than Neanderthals. Anthropologists Rachel Caspari of the University of Michigan and Sang-Hee Lee of the University of California Riverside have estimated that Upper Paleolithic peoples lived much longer than the Neanderthals. About a third of their sample of 113 Neanderthals reached twice the age of first reproduction, which is about 30 years of age in modern hunter-gatherer populations. In contrast, two-thirds of a sample of 74 Upper Paleolithic fossil individuals reached that age. The fact that Upper Paleolithic populations included a substantial fraction of older individuals, while Neanderthals were dominated by the young, may have allowed Upper Paleolithic peoples to retain and transmit more complex cultural knowledge than Neanderthals could.

3. Upper Paleolithic peoples were less likely to suffer serious injury or disease than were Neanderthals. In sharp contrast to the Neanderthals, the skeletons of Upper Paleolithic people rarely show evidence of injury or disease. Among the few injuries that do show up in the fossil record, there is a child buried with a stone projectile point embedded in its spine, and a young man with a projectile point in his abdomen and a healed bone fracture on his right forearm. Evidence of disease is slightly more prevalent than evidence of injury among the remains of Upper Paleolithic peoples; affected specimens include a young woman who probably died as the result of an abscessed tooth, and a child whose skull seems to have been deformed by hydrocephaly (a condition in which fluid accumulates in the cranial cavity and the brain atrophies). Nonetheless, there is still less evidence for disease among these peoples than among Neanderthals.

There is good evidence for ritual burials during the Upper Paleolithic period.

Like the Neanderthals, Upper Paleolithic peoples frequently buried their dead. Upper Paleolithic sites provide the first unambiguous evidence of both multiple burials and burials outside of caves. Unlike the Neanderthals, Upper Paleolithic burials appear to have been accompanied by ritual. The people frequently buried their dead with tools, ornaments, and other objects that suggest they had some concept of life after death. Figure 14.9 diagrams the grave of a child who died about 15 kya at the Siberian site of Mal'ta. The child was buried with a number of items, including a necklace, a crown (diadem), a figurine of a bird, a bone point, and a number of stone tools.

Upper Paleolithic peoples were skilled artisans, sculpting statues of animals and humans and creating sophisticated cave paintings.

It is their art that distinguishes Upper Paleolithic peoples most dramatically from the hominins who preceded them. They engraved decorations on their bone and antler tools and weapons, and they sculpted statues of animals and female figures (Figure 14.10). The female statues are generally believed to be fertility figures because they usually emphasize female sexual characteristics. Upper Paleolithic peoples also

Diadem

Necklace

Bracelet

Limestone
slabs

Retouched
blade

Bone
"button"

Bird
figurine

N

Bone
point

Borer

Blade

Blade

FIGURE 14.9 Diagram of a child's grave from the Upper Paleolithic illustrating the rich collection of goods frequently included in Upper Paleolithic burials. (Figure courtesy of Richard Klein.)

adorned themselves with beads, necklaces, pendants, and bracelets and may have decorated their clothing with beads.

All of these artistic efforts are remarkable, but it is their cave art that seems most amazing now. Upper Paleolithic peoples painted, sculpted, and engraved the walls of caves with a variety of animal and human figures. They used natural substances that included red and yellow ocher, iron oxides, and manganese to create a variety of paint colors. They used horsehair, sticks, and their fingers to apply the paint. Their cave paintings frequently depict animals that they must have hunted: reindeer, mammoths, horses, and bison. Some figures are half human and half animal. Sometimes the creators incorporated the natural contours of the cave walls in their work, and sometimes they drew one set of figures on top of others. Some of their work is spectacular: the perspective is accurate, the characterization of behavior is lifelike, and the scenes are complex. We don't know precisely why or under what circumstances these cave paintings were made, but they represent a remarkable cultural achievement that sets the people of this period apart from earlier hominins.

Recently developed techniques for dating pigments have allowed scientists to determine the age of the Upper Paleolithic cave paintings. Many of the famous caves,

FIGURE 14.10 Small animal figures were carved from mammoth tusks during the Aurignacian period.

3 cm

such as Lascaux, are dated to the end of the Upper Paleolithic, about 17 kya, but spectacular paintings in the Le Chauvet Cave in France are about 30,000 years old (Figure 14.11). Most of the famous carved figurines are also less than 20,000 years old, but there are good examples of representational sculpture that date to the earliest Aurignacian. For example, Figure 14.12 shows an ivory figure with a human body and a lion's head that was found at a site in Germany dated to 32 kya. There is also abundant evidence of the manufacture of beads, pendants, and other body ornaments at Aurignacian sites in France. The beads are standardized and often manufactured from materials that had been transported hundreds of kilometers. Archaeologists have found a well-preserved musical instrument that looks like a flute at an Aurignacian site in southwestern France. It is 10 cm (4 in.) long and has four holes on one side and two on the other. When this instrument was played by a professional flutist, it produced musical sounds.

THE ORIGIN AND SPREAD OF MODERN HUMANS

A dramatic shift in hominin morphology occurred during the last glacial epoch. About 100 kya the world was inhabited by a morphologically heterogeneous collection of hominins: Neanderthals in Europe; other robust hominins in East Asia; and more modern humans in the Middle East and Africa. By about 30 kya, most of this morphological diversity had disappeared; modern humans occupied all of the Old World. Obviously, inquiring minds want to know, how did this transition occur?

Thirty years ago most paleoanthropologists would have given the same answer: the robust hominins of the late Middle Pleistocene formed a single morphologically variable species—"archaic *Homo sapiens*"—from which a more modern morphology gradually evolved throughout the world. New evidence, however, both from the fossil record and from molecular genetics, has cast substantial doubt on this hypothesis. The new evidence indicates that the genes that gave rise to modern human morphology evolved in an African population sometime between 200 and 100 kya. People carrying these genes subsequently spread throughout Africa and differentiated into a number of morphologically modern but genetically variable populations. Then about 50 kya, people from one of these regional populations left Africa and spread across the world, replacing other hominin populations with little gene flow between them.

In the rest of this chapter, we will describe the genetic, paleontological, and archaeological evidence pertaining to the origin and spread of modern humans. As you will see, researchers working in a diverse set of academic disciplines have brought a wide range of methods to bear on this problem.

FIGURE 14.11 This image from Le Chauvet in France was created about 30 kya. At the upper left, several lions are depicted. On the other side are a number of rhinoceroses. At the top right, the multiple outlines suggest a rhinoceros in motion.

Genetic Data

Contemporary patterns of genetic variation, particularly in genes carried on mitochondria, provide information about the origin of modern humans.

The patterns of genetic variation within living people and genetic material extracted from fossils tell us a lot about the history of human populations. Much of the information used in such studies comes from genes that are carried on mitochondria. Eukaryotic cells, including those of humans, contain small cellular organelles called **mitochondria** (singular *mitochondrion*), which are responsible for the basic energy processing that goes on in the cells. Mitochondria contain small amounts of DNA (about 0.05% of the DNA contained in chromosomes), called, appropriately, **mitochondrial DNA (mtDNA)**. In humans and other primates, mtDNA codes for 13 proteins used in the mitochondria, for some of the RNA that makes up the structure of ribosomes, and for several kinds of transfer RNA. There are also two major noncoding regions on mtDNA.

Mitochondrial genes have three properties that make them especially useful for reconstructing the recent evolutionary history of human populations:

1. *Maternal inheritance.* Mitochondrial genes are inherited maternally. Both males and females get their mitochondria from their mother's egg cell. The mitochondria present in sperm are not transferred to the fertilized ovum. Therefore, there is no recombination in mtDNA, so a child has exactly the same mitochondrial genes as the mother, unless the child's mitochondria carry a novel mutation. This makes it possible to construct phylogenetic trees for mitochondria that can tell us a lot about human demographic history.

FIGURE 14.12 This ivory figure depicts a human body with a lion's head. It comes from an Aurignacian site in southern Germany and is 32,000 years old.

2. *High mutation rate.* Mitochondrial genes accumulate mutations faster than genes carried on chromosomes do. This means that the mitochondrial genetic clock provides more accurate dating of events in the last few hundred thousand years than do clocks based on nuclear genes. The mitochondrial clock is like a stopwatch that keeps track of hundredths of seconds, but the genes on chromosomes are like a clock with only a second hand. The mitochondrial genetic clock is particularly useful for dating recent events, for the same reason that a digital stopwatch is more useful than an ordinary watch for timing Justin Gatlin in the 100-m run; the mitochondrial clock changes rapidly enough to distinguish events that aren't very far apart in time.

3. *High copy number.* In each cell there are only two copies of each gene carried on chromosomes, but there are hundreds of mitochondria, each with its own copy of each mitochondrial gene. The larger number of gene copies makes it much easier to recover mitochondrial genes than nuclear genes from the tiny amounts of DNA that remain in fossils.

The human species is less genetically variable than are other species.

One measure of genetic variation is the average number of genetic differences per base pair (nucleotide) in a particular bit of DNA within a population. To compute this measure for mtDNA, geneticists collect tissue samples from members of a population and assess the same part of the DNA sequence of each individual's mitochondria. Then, for each pair of individuals in the sample, they check whether mtDNA at each position is the same or different. They repeat this for all pairs of individuals in the sample and then compute the average number of differences per nucleotide across the sample. As populations become more diverse genetically, the average number of genetic differences per nucleotide increases.

By this measure, humans are less genetically variable than chimpanzees, in two quite different ways. Figure 14.13 plots the amount of genetic variation within and between three geographically separated human populations—Africans, Asians, and Europeans—and the amount of genetic variation within and between chimpanzee populations in eastern, central, and western Africa. The bars on the diagonal (red) show that the amount of variation within each of these human populations is much lower than that within any of the chimpanzee populations. These data tell us that any two humans taken at random from a single population are much more similar to one another than are any two chimpanzees taken at random from a single population. The off-diagonal bars (blue) plot the average differences between human populations and between chimpanzee populations. The differences between chimpanzee populations are also much greater than the differences between human populations. This tells us that any two humans taken at random from *different* human populations are more similar to one another than any two chimpanzees taken from different chimpanzee populations are.

The most likely explanation for the small amount of genetic variation observed within the human species is that we have undergone a population explosion.

The data on genetic distance suggest that much of the human genome evolved mainly under the influence of drift and mutation. Remember that mutation introduces new genes at a very low rate, and that genetic drift eliminates genetic variation at a rate that depends on the size of the population. In large populations, drift removes genetic variants slowly, but in small populations, drift eliminates variation more

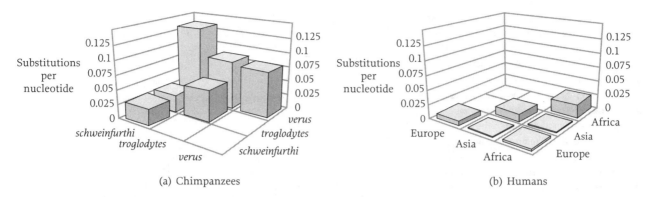

(a) Chimpanzees   (b) Humans

FIGURE 14.13 Humans are less genetically variable than chimpanzees. (a) Plotted here is the mean number of differences per nucleotide in one region of mtDNA for three geographically separated chimpanzee populations: *Pan troglodytes schweinfurthi* (from East Africa), *P. t. troglodytes* (from central Africa), and *P. t. verus* (from West Africa). (b) Here the same data are plotted for three geographically separated human populations (in Asia, Europe, and Africa). In both graphs, each red bar at the intersection of a row and a column gives data for comparing the population(s) identified at the ends of that row and column. Thus the height of each red bar represents the mean number of differences between pairs of individuals drawn from the same population. For example, each pair of chimpanzees belonging to the *verus* population differs at about 7.5% of the nucleotides sampled. Each pair of individuals drawn from the most variable human population, Africans, differs at only about 2.5% of the nucleotides assessed. The height of the blue bars represents the mean number of differences between pairs of populations. On average, an individual drawn from the *verus* population differs from an individual drawn from the *schweinfurthi* population at about 13% of the nucleotides, while Africans and Europeans, the most different pair of human populations, differ at less than 0.3% of the nucleotides. Thus the two graphs show that there is more variation within each of the chimpanzee populations than within any of the human populations, and human populations on the average are more similar to one another than chimpanzee populations are.

quickly. The effects of mutation and genetic drift will eventually balance (Figure 14.14), as the amount of variation arrives at an equilibrium. The amount of variation, which we label m, at equilibrium will depend on the size of the population. For a given mutation rate, bigger populations will have larger amounts of genetic variation at equilibrium. Population genetic theory says that $m = 2Nu$, where N is the number of females and u is the rate at which mutations occur.

We can substitute the measured values of m and u into the formula for m, to calculate N. Using an estimate for the mutation rate of mtDNA of $u \approx 0.0015$, and the average of the values for m given in Figure 14.13, we get $N \approx 5000$. This means that the existing amount of genetic variation within human populations today is consistent with the drift–mutation equilibrium value for a population of 5000 women. Obviously this estimate of N is far lower than the size of human populations today or even in the recent past. How can that be?

The simplest answer is that a small human population must have expanded very rapidly sometime in the past. When a population grows, the equilibrium amount of genetic variation also grows because genetic drift removes variation more slowly in large populations than it does in smaller ones. If the population expands rapidly, however, it may take a long time to reach a new equilibrium level because mutation adds variation very slowly. Thus the low levels of genetic variation in contemporary human populations may be the result of a rapid expansion from a small population sometime in the past.

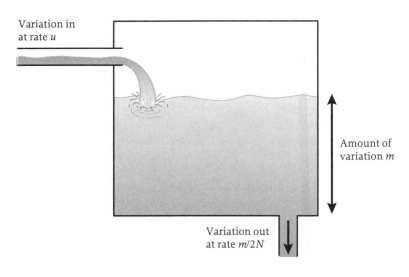

FIGURE 14.14 A physical analogy for the mutation–drift equilibrium can help explain why large populations have more genetic variation at equilibrium than small ones do. Mutation introduces new genetic variants at a constant rate u, much like a stream of water entering a tank. Genetic drift removes variants, like a drain at the bottom of the tank. The amount of variation (m) is analogous to the volume of water in the tank: as the level of water in the tank rises, the pressure increases and the water drains out more rapidly. Eventually the rate of outflow equals the rate of inflow, and the depth of the water remains constant. In the same way, as the amount of variation in a population increases, drift removes variation faster; eventually a steady state is reached at which the amount of variation is constant. To calculate the equilibrium amount of variation, set the rate of inflow (u) equal to the rate of outflow ($m/2N$), and solve for m.

Variation in at rate u

Amount of variation m

Variation out at rate $m/2N$

This conclusion supports any hypothesis that suggests that all contemporary people are descended from a small local population living sometime in the past. A population of 5000 adult women corresponds to an overall population of roughly 20,000 men, women, and children. It is very difficult to see how much a small population could have been spread across all of Africa and Eurasia. It is much more plausible that the human population at the time was much larger, but that modern humans are descended from members of a single local population.

Natural selection provides an alternative explanation for the lack of genetic diversity in mitochondrial genes. If a strongly beneficial mutation arose in the mitochondrial genome, it would rapidly sweep through the human population. Because there is no recombination, the particular mitochondrial genotype in which the beneficial mutation occurred would also spread, and all other mitochondrial genotypes would disappear. In this way, natural selection could reduce the number of distinct mitochondrial genotypes without any reduction in the number of people. However, studies of the X and Y chromosomes are consistent with results of analyses of mtDNA and suggest that there was a bottleneck between 200 and 100 kya. Natural selection could account for these data only if a number of separate beneficial mutations occurred throughout the nuclear genome at about the same time. This seems implausible but cannot be ruled out as a possibility.

The fact that modern African populations are genetically more variable than other populations is consistent with the idea that the population explosion began in an African population.

Notice in Figure 14.13 that the amount of mitochondrial genetic variation within contemporary African populations is greater than the variation within European or Asian populations. Data from studies of ordinary nuclear genes tell the same story: Africans are more genetically variable than other peoples.

This pattern of genetic variation is consistent with the hypothesis that modern humans first evolved in Africa. Suppose that populations in different parts of Africa were isolated from each other. If that were the case, they would have diverged genetically (Figure 14.15). If emigrants to Europe and Asia were drawn from one local African population, they would carry with them only a fraction of the total genetic

100 kya: Modern humans evolve and disperse throughout Africa.

100–50 kya: Dispersed human populations diverge within Africa.

50 kya: People from one African population migrate to Eurasia and Australasia.

50 kya–present: Dispersed human populations diverge.

FIGURE 14.15 A late African origin for modern humans explains why African populations today have greater genetic variation than modern human populations in other parts of the world have: (a) Modern humans evolved and dispersed throughout Africa approximately 100 kya. (b) Over the next 50,000 years, dispersed populations were isolated from each other by distance, and these populations became genetically different. (c) About 50 kya, people from one of the local African populations dispersed throughout Eurasia. Because these emigrants were from one local population, they were less variable than African populations taken as a whole. (d) Over the next 50,000 years, dispersed populations in Africa and Asia continued to diverge. Modern Eurasian populations are less variable than African populations today because Eurasian populations are descended from a single localized African population that migrated northward 50 kya. Modern African populations are more variable because they are the descendants of a number of local African populations that were spread across most of the continent.

variation present in Africa. Then the European and Asian descendants of this regional African population would be less variable than modern populations across Africa are. As we will see, phylogenetic trees for mitochondria are consistent with this scenario.

The fact that mitochondria are inherited maternally means that the mitochondria of every living person are copies of the mitochondrion of a single woman who lived in ages past.

This incredible idea is a simple consequence of asexual inheritance. The logic is based on the fact that, in each generation, some women leave no female descendants. (Because mitochondria are transmitted through the female line, sons are irrelevant.) If females leave no surviving female descendants, then no copies of their mitochondria survive into the next generation. As the generations go on, more and more mitochondrial lineages are lost, until eventually everyone carries the mitochondrion of a single woman, the most recent common ancestor—who is sometimes given the colorful but misleading name "Eve." (Box 14.2 gives a more detailed version of this argument.) Note that the most recent common ancestor is not the mother of us all, but only the mother of our mitochondria. Because genes carried on chromosomes recombine, it is likely that we have ordinary chromosomal genes from many of the women in the population containing the most recent common ancestor. And it is important to realize that this woman was not the first human woman. She may have been a

BOX 14.2

Mitochondrial Eve

To see why everyone carries the mitochondrion of a single woman, consider Figure 14.16. Each colored circle represents one woman, and each row of circles represents a population of 12 women during a given generation. The circles in row 1 represent the women in generation 1, the circles in the second row are women in generation 2—all of whom are daughters of women in generation 1—and so on. (We ignore men because their mitochondria are not transmitted to their children.) To keep things simple, we assume that population size is constant, so women must produce on average just one daughter. However, the number of daughters born to any particular woman varies; here we will assume that some have no daughters, some have one, and some have two. For the moment, we will also assume that there is no mutation.

To indicate that daughters inherit their mother's mitochondria, mothers and their daughters are assigned the same color. Thus, in any generation, all of the women with the same color carry copies of the mitochondrion of the same woman in generation 1. (This color scheme does not imply that the mitochondria carried by different women have different mtDNA sequences; they could all be genetically identical or all unique.)

In generation 1 there are three women (black, dark gray, and light gray) who have no daughters. As a result, after one generation, only 9 of the original 12 women and their mitochondria have descendants. However, three of the mitochondria in the first generation have two descendants in generation 2. During the second generation, three women have no daughters. However, because one of the women

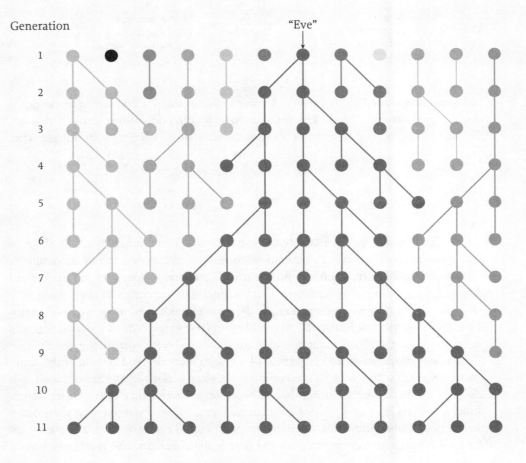

FIGURE 14.16 This mtDNA tree for a hypothetical population of 12 women shows why all the mitochondria in any population are descended from a single woman's mitochondria sometime in the past.

without a daughter has a sister who produced a daughter, copies of that woman's mitochondria are not lost. This means that, by generation 3, the number of women's mitochondria present in the population is reduced from 12 to 7. The final outcome should be evident: as long as there are copies of mitochondria from more than one of the original women present, there is a chance that one of them will be lost because all the descendants of one of the women will have no daughters. Eventually the mitochondria of all but one of the original women will disappear. At this point, all members of the population will be descendants of one of the original females. We have run this argument forward in time, but it can also be run backward. That is to say, we can pick any generation and then move backward through time to find the single mitochondrial ancestor of every individual in that generation.

In this example, there are only 12 women in the population, but exactly the same thing will happen in all populations.

modern human, or she may have been an earlier form of hominin. Eve was an otherwise unremarkable member of a (perhaps large) population whose only claim to fame is that her mitochondrion happened to survive while the mitochondria of other women did not.

The accumulation of mutations allows us to derive the phylogenetic relationships of the mtDNA of modern humans.

Even though the mitochondria of all living people are replicas of Eve's mitochondrion, they are not identical, because mutation occasionally introduces new mitochondrial variants. Since there is no recombination, once a mutation occurs in a particular woman, it is carried by all of her descendants. The existence of mutation has two important consequences. First, anthropologists can use the methods of phylogenetic reconstruction discussed in Chapter 4 to reconstruct a tree of descent among mitochondria based on derived similarities. To make such reconstructions (sometimes called **gene trees**) feasible, mutations must occur frequently to allow the branches of the gene tree to be distinguished. It turns out that mitochondria are particularly well suited to this sort of genetic reconstruction. Second, mutation makes it possible to estimate the time that has passed since our common mitochondrial ancestor lived, using genetic-distance measures (also discussed in Chapter 4).

Gene trees based on mtDNA support an African origin for modern humans.

Beginning with the pioneering work of the late Alan Wilson and Rebecca Cann, now at the University of Hawaii, numerous studies have attempted to construct gene trees from the patterning of variation in human mtDNA. These early studies were based on a relatively short noncoding section of the mtDNA, called the "D-loop," that has a highly variable mutation rate across sites. As a result, different mitochondrial lineages often experienced the same mutation, and this made it hard to construct and interpret gene trees. Newer data based on the entire mitochondrial genome yield highly consistent gene trees, like the one in Figure 14.17.

This tree supports the idea that modern humans originated in Africa and then migrated out of Africa and spread across the rest of the world. Notice that all of the deepest branches of the tree represent African populations, and all non-Africans are descendants of a single node in the tree. This indicates that humans originated in Africa and their mitochondrial lineages diversified. Later, one group left Africa and

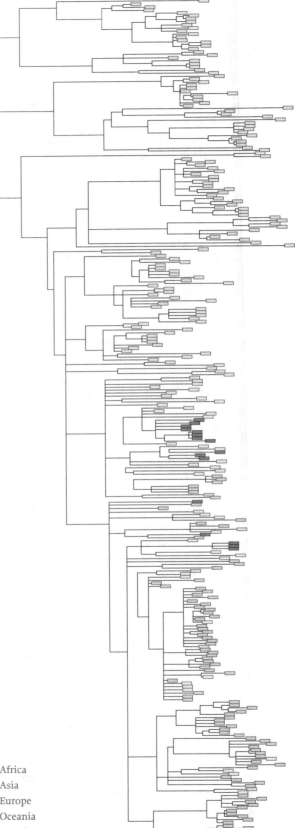

FIGURE 14.17 This gene tree for the complete mitochondrial genomes of 277 people from all over the world indicates that all modern humans are descended from an African population. Each branch represents the mtDNA sequence of a single individual, and the length of the branch represents the number of mutations along that branch. Thus the longer branches for Africans reflect the greater genetic variation on that continent. Almost all non-Africans are descended from a single node in the tree and from a more recent common ancestor than many Africans are. (Redrawn from L. Cavalli-Sforza and M. Feldman, 2003, The application of molecular genetic approaches to the study of human evolution, *Nature Genetics Supplement*, 33: 271.)

Africa
Asia
Europe
Oceania
America

gave rise to the mitochondrial lineages we observe today in the rest of the world. One group of Africans is more closely related to non-Africans than to other Africans. These could be the descendants of the African population that originally emigrated and settled the rest of the world. You can also see in Figure 14.17 that the branches that separate different African groups are much longer than the branches that separate non-African groups, indicating that non-African populations have grown rapidly. Finally, analysis of two different mtDNA gene trees tells us that the most recent common ancestor lived between 220 and 120 kya.

Trees based on the Y chromosome support the conclusion of mtDNA studies.

It is worrisome to depend completely on mtDNA data for our understanding of human demographic history, even though these data have been extremely useful. Mitochondrial genes are transmitted only by women, so mtDNA trees tell us only about the population dynamics of half of our species. Moreover, the fact that mitochondrial genes are not subject to recombination means that natural selection on even one mitochondrial gene could have strong effects on the rest of the mitochondrial genome. For example, a new beneficial mutant that arose about 150 kya and swept through the population would generate much the same pattern as a population bottleneck because only those initially rare individuals carrying the beneficial mutant would leave descendants.

Genes on the Y chromosome provide an independent source of information about human origins. Y chromosomes are carried only by men, and most of the Y chromosome does not experience any recombination. Thus, Y chromosome genes give us the same kind of information about the demographic history of men as mitochondrial genes give us for women. Because there is no linkage of genes on the Y chromosome and those on mitochondria, it is unlikely that selection would affect mtDNA and the Y chromosome in the same way. Mutation rates on the Y chromosome are lower than those on mtDNA. However, the Y chromosome is roughly 20 million DNA bases long, while mtDNA contains only about 16,000 bases. This means that there are enough detectable mutations on the Y chromosome, even though the rate of mutation is much lower, to construct accurate gene trees.

Two different gene trees for the Y chromosome have been constructed, based on two different sets of mutations. Both trees are consistent with trees based on mtDNA (Figure 14.18). The deepest branch occurs in Africa, and all but one of the non-Africans in the sample are the descendants of a more recently derived lineage. The estimated age of the most recent common ancestor is between 40,000 and 140,000 years old, and that of the most recent common ancestor of all non-Africans is between 35,000 and 89,000 years old. These ages are somewhat younger than those derived from the mtDNA, probably because the number of males who left children was smaller than the number of females who had descendants, as is typical in most mammalian populations (see Chapter 7).

Mitochondrial DNA extracted from a number of Neanderthals indicates that the last common mitochondrial ancestor of Neanderthals and modern humans lived about 500 kya.

In the film *Jurassic Park*, scientists extract dinosaur DNA from the bodies of bloodsucking insects trapped in amber and use the DNA to clone living dinosaurs. The gap between science fiction and science has narrowed in the laboratory of Svante

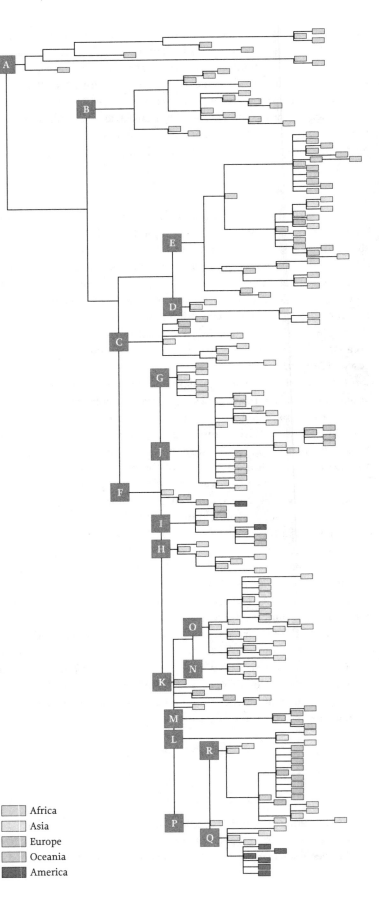

FIGURE 14.18 A gene tree for the human Y chromosome based on 167 genetic loci, and more than 1062 individual men. (Redrawn from L. Cavalli-Sforza and M. Feldman, 2003, The application of molecular genetic approaches to the study of human evolution, *Nature Genetics Supplement*, 33: 271.)

Africa
Asia
Europe
Oceania
America

Pääbo at the Max Planck Institute for Evolutionary Anthropology in Leipzig, Germany. Pääbo and his colleagues extracted and sequenced mtDNA from the original Neanderthal fossil found in the Neander Valley of Germany in 1856. More recently, Pääbo and his team sequenced mtDNA from several other Neanderthal fossils, and attempted to extract mtDNA from four early modern *Homo sapiens* from Europe.

These data allow researchers to construct gene trees and to compute the amount of genetic variation within and between populations. Figure 14.19 shows the tree for three of the Neanderthals and a large sample of modern humans from around the globe. The tree indicates that all modern humans are equally distant from Neanderthals. This is consistent with the idea that the modern human lineage diversified *after* it split from the lineage leading to the Neanderthals.

Researchers from Pääbo's laboratory have also computed the genetic distance within and between Neanderthal, modern human, and ape populations. These values indicate that the genetic distance between modern humans and Neanderthals is much greater than the distances among modern humans or among the Neanderthals. The magnitude of the differences between the Neanderthals and modern humans suggests that the last common mitochondrial ancestor of humans and Neanderthals lived between 690 and 357 kya. The data also indicate that Neanderthals, like modern humans, were much less variable genetically than other primates, such as chimpanzees. The relatively small genetic distances between the three Neanderthals in Figure 14.19 indicates that their last common ancestor lived between 352 and 151 kya.

These findings are consistent with the fossil and archaeological records of the Middle Pleistocene. Recall from Chapter 13 that the fossils from Sima de los Huesos suggest that the ancestors of Neanderthals had reached Europe and begun to evolve the distinctive Neanderthal morphology by about 300 kya. What we know about the climate and biogeography of Middle Pleistocene Eurasia and Africa suggests that these proto-Neanderthals colonized Europe during one of the interglacial periods and were subsequently isolated from African hominin populations. Morphologically and behaviorally, modern people gradually evolved in Africa between 200 and 100 kya.

These data do not exclude the possibility that there was some interbreeding between Neanderthals and modern humans. Mathematical models suggest that all

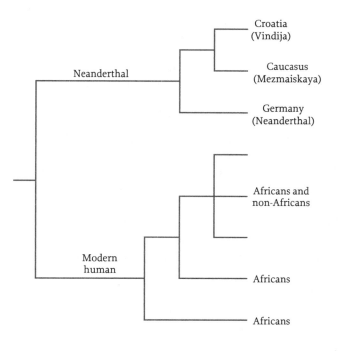

FIGURE 14.19 The phylogenetic relationships of mtDNA from three Neanderthals and modern humans are plotted. The length of each horizontal branch symbolizes the genetic distance between individuals or groups. The branches leading to modern humans represent a complex branching tree, each tip ending at a unique mtDNA genotype of at least one modern human. This tree indicates that the three Neanderthals are much more closely related to each other than any one of them is to any modern human.

modern human mitochondria are descended from about five individuals living 30,000 years ago. It is quite possible that there was a modest amount of interbreeding but the Neanderthal mitochondria were subsequently lost by chance. However, attempts to extract DNA from early modern human fossils didn't turn up any of the mtDNA sequences that characterize Neanderthals. This suggests that the Neanderthals and early humans did not interbreed.

Although we can say with some confidence that the DNA extracted from early modern human fossils does not match the DNA extracted from Neanderthals, it is harder to say how closely the DNA of early modern humans resembles the DNA of present-day humans or the DNA of Neanderthals. The problem is that the samples have apparently been contaminated. After 30,000 years in the ground, only minuscule amounts of DNA remain in fossilized bone. When archaeologists, museum curators, and molecular biologists handle bones, they inadvertently leave traces of their own DNA on the bones, and this modern DNA may swamp the DNA in the fossils. When scientists try to amplify the DNA from the fossils, they may inadvertently be amplifying modern DNA instead. This possibility is supported by the results of studies of DNA extracted from the fossilized bones of cave bears from the same period of time. These samples also yield modern human DNA, which must be the product of contamination rather than common ancestry!

Evidence from Fossils and Tool Kits

The oldest modern human fossils have been found in Africa and date to about 190 kya.

The oldest modern human fossil were unearthed in 1963 at Omo-Kibish a site in southern Ethiopia. One of the skulls found there was relatively modern, while the other was similar to *H. heidelbergensis*. Originally the dates for this site were uncertain, but new methods now indicate a date of 190 kya. More recently a number of fossils were uncovered at Herto, a site in Ethiopia. A team led by University of California anthropologist Tim White found the fossilized crania of two adults and one immature individual along with a number of other fragments. These skulls are intermediate between those of modern humans and older African hominins classified as *Homo heidelbergensis*. The skulls are longer and more robust than those of most living people. They also have prominent browridges, pointed occipital bones, and other features that link them to earlier African hominins. In addition, however, they have some very modern features—most notably a high, rounded braincase (Figure 14.20). Argon–argon dating was used to date these fossils to about 160 kya.

In those days the Herto site was on the shores of a lake, and there is ample evidence that hominins butchered hippopotamuses. The Middle Stone Age stone tools found at the site are much like those found in association with earlier African *H. heidelbergensis*. Multiple, unambiguous cut marks give evidence that the skulls were defleshed by stone tools, and polished surfaces are consistent with repeated handling by other hominins. White and his coworkers point out that the mortuary practices used by some contemporary peoples in New Guinea leave a similar combination of marks on skulls, and they suggest that the Herto fossils may provide early evidence of similar ritual behavior.

There is evidence that modern humans also lived in other parts of Africa around the same time, but the fossils are too fragmentary to be completely conclusive. The

FIGURE 14.20 Side and front views of one of the hominin crania found at Herto, Ethiopia. This specimen (BOU-VP-16/1) is intermediate between *H. heidelbergensis* and modern *H. sapiens*, displaying prominent browridges but a high, rounded braincase.

most extensive finds come from the mouth of the Klasies River in South Africa. Excavations at this site have yielded five lower jaws, one upper jaw, part of a forehead, and numerous smaller skeletal fragments. Electron-spin-resonance dating indicates that the site is 74,000 to 134,000 years old. Although one of the lower jaws clearly has a modern jutting chin and the forehead has modern-looking browridges, the fragmentary nature of the fossils makes it difficult to be sure that these are modern humans.

Modern people appeared in the Middle East and probably in Africa long before the Neanderthals disappeared in Europe.

Even more modern fossils have been found at the Qafzeh and Skhul caves in Israel. Thermoluminescence and electron-spin-resonance dating techniques have shown that these fossils are 115,000 years old. This was during a relatively warm, wet period when animals would have been able to move from Africa to the Middle East. This inference is supported by the fact that other fossilized animals found at these sites are primarily African species.

Neanderthal fossils also have been found at three other sites located quite close to Qafzeh and Skhul, named Kebara, Tabun, and Amud. For many years there were no reliable absolute dates for any of these sites because they are too young for potassium–argon dating and too old for carbon-14 dating. However, most anthropologists assumed that the Neanderthals came first and were succeeded by the modern hominins at Qafzeh and Skhul. When the sites were dated by thermoluminescence and electron-spin-resonance methods, the results were a big surprise. The Neanderthals occupied Tabun about 110 kya, around the same time that modern humans lived nearby. However, the Neanderthals at Kebara and Amud lived 60 to 55 kya, which is about 30,000 years *after* anatomically modern peoples inhabited Skhul and Qafzeh.

The long period of overlap between Neanderthals and modern humans in the Middle East means that modern humans cannot be descended from Neanderthals. If anatomically modern people appeared 60,000 years before the Neanderthals disappeared, then it can hardly be true that all Neanderthals evolved into modern humans in that area. Some paleoanthropologists, most notably Milford Wolpoff of the University of Michigan, deny that the Skhul and Qafzeh fossils are really morphologically modern. Instead, they believe that they and the more robust fossils from Kebara, Amud, and Tabun are part of a variable population that is unrelated to either European Neanderthals or modern human populations. However, most anthropologists believe that Skhul and Qafzeh fossils are modern, because the skulls from these sites have relatively high, rounded crania and small faces, while a cranium found at Tabun is very similar to that of European Neanderthals. Similarly, postcranial fossils from Qafzeh are modern, but the pelvis and femur from Tabun show all the features of classic Neanderthals (see Figure 14.2).

Archaeological data suggest that Upper Paleolithic industries spread rapidly across western Eurasia.

Additional support for the idea that Neanderthals overlapped with and were later replaced by modern peoples comes from archaeological data indicating that Neanderthals and modern people overlapped in Europe, as well as in the Middle East. Recall that the earliest *Homo sapiens* fossils in Europe are associated with the Aurignacian tool kit. Moreover, no Aurignacian tools have been found with Neanderthal fossils. Aurignacian tools appear in Europe about 40 kya—4000 years before the Neanderthals disappeared. This brief overlap suggests that the modern humans using Aurignacian tools appeared and rapidly replaced Neanderthals. This transition seems too rapid to be the result of genetic change.

However, the situation is not quite so simple. In southern France, the transition between the Mousterian and the Aurignacian is marked by the presence of a third industry, called the **Châtelperronian**, which is intermediate between the Mousterian and the Aurignacian. Many anthropologists believe that the Châtelperronian is the result of Neanderthals' borrowing ideas and technology from modern humans. Cambridge University archaeologist Paul Mellars argues that three kinds of evidence support this view. First, Châtelperronian tools are associated with Neanderthal fossils at Saint Césaire and Arcy-sur-Cure in France. Second, archaeological data indicate that the Châtelperronian and Aurignacian industries coexisted in southern France for hundreds of years. Finally, other transitional tool kits have been found. As Figure 14.21 shows, each of these transitional industries is localized: the Châtelperronian in southern France, the Uluzzian in northern Italy, and the Szeletian in central Europe. Mellars points out that each of these transitional industries is quite distinctive, and he argues that it is not likely that the very widespread Aurignacian evolved from several distinctive localized transitional industries.

MODERN HUMAN BEHAVIOR: REVOLUTION OR EVOLUTION?

Anthropologists differ sharply about the causes of the striking shift that we see in the European archaeological record 40 kya. The debate turns on what was going on in Africa between 250 and 50 kya. According to one view, championed by Richard Klein, the African archaeological record is very similar to that in Europe. Between 250 and

FIGURE 14.21 The earliest Upper Paleolithic industry, the Aurignacian, is found throughout Europe; three industries intermediate between the Mousterian and the Aurignacian (the Châtelperronian, the Uluzzian, and the Szeletian) are found in localized areas. Because each of these transitional industries is distinctive, some scientists believe it unlikely that the Aurignacian evolved from one of them.

Map legend: Uluzzian, Chatelperronian, Szeletian/Jerzmanovician, Aurignacian. Scale: 0 — 500 km

50 kya, African hominins had bodies much like those of modern people, but they behaved more like their European contemporaries, the Neanderthals. Then, about 50 kya there was a rapid transition to much more modern behavior in Africa, just as in Europe. Klein believes that this behavioral transition marks the appearance of cognitively modern people. About 50 kya some key cognitive innovation evolved in at least one human population and allowed for the rapid development of modern human behavior—a transition that is commonly called the "human revolution." More recently, Sally McBrearty and Alison Brooks have challenged the idea that there was a human revolution at all. Instead, they argue that the archaeological record from Africa shows that the complex behaviors that appeared suddenly in Europe 40 kya was gradually evolving in Africa between 250 and 50 kya. What seems like a revolutionary event in Europe actually was due to the rapid replacement of Neanderthals by African immigrants. It wasn't a revolution; it was an occupation by a technologically advanced people.

The African Archaeological Record during the Later Pleistocene

Human behavior increased in complexity at about the same time in Africa and Europe.

From about 250 to 40 kya, the African archaeological record is dominated by a variety of stone tool kits that, for the most part, emphasize Mode 3 tools. These industries are collectively labeled the **Middle Stone Age (MSA)**. Until recently, most archaeologists saw the MSA in Africa as qualitatively similar to the much better known Mousterian tool industries associated with Neanderthals in Europe. Although there is some evidence for blade production in the MSA, it was thought that the other signatures of modern human behavior seen in Upper Paleolithic Europe were rare or absent in Africa. According to this view, MSA peoples in Africa produced few bone tools, developed little regional variation in tools, engaged in little long-distance trade, didn't bury their dead, and had no important symbolic behavior. As we will see, this view of the MSA has been challenged, by McBrearty and Brooks.

About 40 kya, new tool industries came to predominate in Africa. These industries, labeled the **Later Stone Age** (**LSA**), emphasize very small, carefully shaped flakes called **microliths** (literally "tiny stones") that are thought to have been mounted on wood and bone handles to form complex, composite tools—spears, axes, and so on. Industries of this kind are referred to as **Mode 5** technology. There is also ample evidence of ornaments, intentional burial, long-distance trade, and more intensive foraging activity. The Mode 5 tools; the associated evidence for hunting large, dangerous game; and the clear proof of symbolic expression have led many archaeologists to regard the LSA as qualitatively similar to the Upper Paleolithic in Europe.

Some evidence suggests that LSA peoples were more proficient foragers than MSA peoples.

MSA deposits at the mouth of the Klasies River in South Africa and LSA deposits at nearby Nelson Bay Cave provide a "natural experiment" that allows us to compare the behavioral complexity of MSA and LSA peoples. The MSA peoples occupied this area between 130 and 115 kya during a warm, moist interglacial period; and LSA peoples occupied the same area about 12 kya at the beginning of the present warm, moist interglacial period. Richard Klein argues that several features of this comparison support a qualitative difference between the behavior of MSA and LSA peoples.

- *LSA peoples hunted larger, more dangerous game.* The MSA peoples hunted large game, particularly eland, a cow-sized antelope. They also consumed other species, mainly buffalo and bushpig. LSA peoples also hunted large game, but they concentrated more on buffalo and bushpig, species that are more common but more dangerous than eland.
- *LSA peoples engaged in more sophisticated planning.* MSA peoples hunted for fur seals throughout the year, but LSA humans hunted them only seasonally. They killed mainly young seal pups, which were available only during the short period when the mothers and pups were on the beach. This behavior suggests that LSA peoples could keep track of the seasons and timed their visits to the coast to coincide with the availability of seal pups.
- *LSA peoples engaged in more intensive foraging.* The presence of artifacts that archaeologists interpret as sinkers and fish gorges suggests that LSA peoples fished. There is no evidence of fishing for MSA peoples.

Not all archaeologists accept these conclusions. It has been pointed out that MSA peoples did take dangerous creatures, both at the Klasies River mouth and elsewhere. The quantitative difference could be due to the fact that higher population densities forced LSA peoples to take less desirable prey. There is also evidence from sites in the Sudan, Congo, and Botswana that MSA peoples captured fish and shellfish.

Several of the signatures of modern human behavior appear in association with MSA archaeological sites.

Recently, Sally McBrearty and Alison Brooks argued that the MSA is *not* qualitatively similar to the Mousterian in Europe. According to their reading of the

African archaeological record, most of the signatures of modern human behavior gradually appear between 250 mya and 50 kya, when the transition is complete. Here is the kind of evidence they cite:

- *Blades appear early in the MSA.* At the Kapthurin Formation in Kenya, roughly 25% of the tools are blades. Archaeologists can show that the knappers at this site were highly skilled at blade production, wasting little raw material and making few mistakes. This site has been dated to between 280 and 240 kya by the argon–argon technique. Blades have also been found at a number of other MSA sites that date between 250 and 50 kya.

- *There is regional variation in MSA industries.* On a continental scale there is quite a bit of variation within MSA industries (Figure 14.22). In North Africa the Aterian industry is characterized by tanged projectile points; the Lupemban industry of the Congo basin is characterized by thin, long, lanceolate points; and in South Africa the Howieson's Poort industry is dominated by small points that foreshadow the LSA. We do not know whether the kind of regional variability that characterizes the Upper Paleolithic in Europe is also characteristic of Africa, because many fewer sites in Africa have been excavated.

- *Refined bone tools occur at several MSA sites.* Brooks and her coworkers have recovered a number of exquisite bone points, some of them elaborately barbed, from a site on the northeastern border of the Republic of the Congo called Katanda (Figure 14.23). The MSA layer containing the points has been dated to between 174 and 82 kya by three independent dating methods. At Blombos Cave

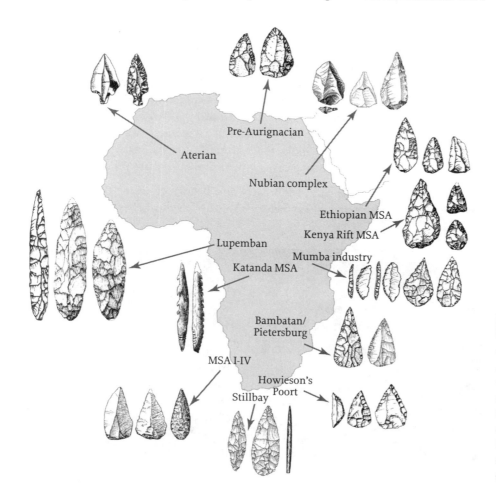

Pre-Aurignacian

Aterian

Nubian complex

Ethiopian MSA

Kenya Rift MSA

Lupemban

Mumba industry

Katanda MSA

Bambatan/
Pietersburg

MSA I-IV

Howieson's
Poort

Stillbay

FIGURE 14.22 There was substantial variation in tool industries across Africa during the Middle Stone Age (MSA). Compare the large, leaf-shaped blades of the Lupemban industry with the tanged points of the Aterian industry or the small blades of the Howieson's Poort industry. It is not known whether similar variation existed on smaller scales.

FIGURE 14.23 Beautiful bone points like this one found at Katanda in the Republic of the Congo have been dated to between 174 and 82 kya. If these dates are correct, then Middle Stone Age peoples were capable of producing bone tools that rival the best of the European Upper Paleolithic tools.

in South Africa, a number of polished bone points have been found in association with MSA tools and date to about 72 kya.

- *MSA peoples sometimes transported raw material great distances.* Most of the stone used to make tools at MSA sites comes from a short distance away. At several MSA sites, however, small amounts of raw materials were transported much farther. At several sites in East Africa, for example, tools were made from obsidian carried 140 to 240 km (about 90 to 150 miles).

- *Evidence for shelters and hearths appears in the MSA.* At several sites, MSA peoples built shelters. At the Mumbwa caves in Zambia, for example, there are three arcs of stone blocks that probably served as windbreaks. Elaborate stone hearths were constructed inside these structures. There are many more MSA sites at which people seem to have constructed hearths and built huts, but for each of these it is impossible to rule out the possibility that natural processes produced the features that archaeologists have documented.

- *There is some evidence of decorative carving, beads, and pigment use.* Recently, a team of archaeologists led by Christopher Henshilwood of the Iziko Museums of Cape Town discovered two elaborately engraved pieces of red ocher at Blombos Cave in South Africa (Figure 14.24). These artifacts were found in association with MSA tools and date to 77 kya. Ostrich shell beads that have been found at several sites dated to the very end of the MSA, 50 to 40 kya. There is good evidence for the use of red ocher at a number of sites. The earliest evidence comes from the Kapthurin Formation, which dates between 280 and 240 kya. Many present-day African peoples use red ocher to decorate themselves and for symbolic purposes, but some archaeologists have argued that red ocher might be used for utilitarian purposes, such as tanning hides. Few images are associated with MSA sites, but McBrearty and Brooks suggest that this lack of artwork may be due to the absence of deep limestone caves in which pigments are preserved.

On the basis of these data, McBrearty and Brooks conclude that there was no human revolution in Africa. They believe that the various behavioral elements that

FIGURE 14.24 One of two engraved pieces of red ocher found at Blombos Cave in South Africa. The artifact is dated to 77 kya and is associated with MSA tools. The engravings are similar to cave art found in other parts of the world.

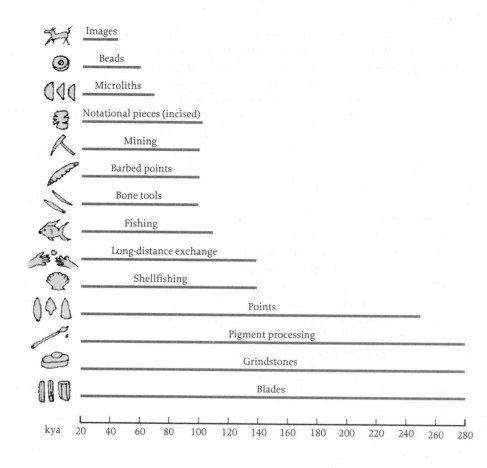

kya   20   40   60   80   100   120   140   160   180   200   220   240   260   280

FIGURE 14.25 McBrearty and Brooks believe that many of the archaeological signatures of modern behavior in Europe appeared gradually in Africa between 280 and 40 kya. If they are correct, then the genetic and cultural changes that underlie modern human behavior accumulated gradually in Africa during this period.

suddenly appear with modern humans in Europe were assembled piecemeal over a period of 200,000 years in Africa (Figure 14.25). They argue that archaeologists have been misled about what happened because the archaeological record from Europe is much more complete than the archaeological record from Africa. Remember, there are over 1000 archaeological sites in France alone, but just 100 sites in all of Africa.

Others, like Klein, interpret the same evidence differently. He argues that for the most part the MSA *is* like the Mousterian. There is evidence of a little long-distance trade, as well as a few bone points and rare examples of shelters and art. Most MSA sites lack these features, suggesting, he argues, that the spectacular exceptions, such as the bone points and the ostrich shell beads, are likely to be intrusions from more modern sites. If they really were part of the typical behaviors of MSA peoples, he argues, they would be more common, appearing at numerous MSA sites instead of only a couple.

How Modern Human Behavior Evolved

If there was a human revolution, it may have been caused by a shift in cognitive ability that did not lead to any detectable changes in the skeleton.

Remember that, in the fossil record, the first anatomically modern humans appeared about 100 kya. This means that if there was a human revolution, it occurred long after the first appearance of people who *look* fully modern. However, we need to remember that morphology and behavior can be decoupled. People who look fully modern could have evolved new cognitive abilities that were not reflected in their skeletal anatomy. For example, Richard Klein has suggested that the human revolution may have been caused by a mutation that allowed fully modern speech. It could be that this linguistic ability evolved late in the human lineage and gave rise to the technological sophistication and symbolic behavior of the Upper Paleolithic peoples.

One problem with this explanation is that it requires very rapid genetic change. Spoken language relies on a number of quite complicated features, such as rules of grammar and specialized production and processing of sound. There is considerable evidence that the brain is specially adapted for language. The cognitive and morphological adaptations underlying human speech are likely to be every bit as complicated as specialized adaptations such as the eye. Remember from Chapter 1 that most biologists think complex, beneficial adaptations are unlikely to arise by chance. Instead, complex adaptations usually require the accumulation of many small changes. It is not so easy to see how such adaptations could have arisen in just a few thousand years.

Another problem is that it is difficult to reconcile the idea that modern humans had unique, innate abilities that gave rise to modern behavior, with recent work suggesting that Neanderthals adopted some of the technological innovations of modern humans after they came into contact with them (Box 14.3).

If there was a human revolution, it may have been caused by a technological advance that gave rise to larger human groups.

Alternatively, the human revolution may have resulted from cultural, not genetic, changes. We know that something like this happened later in human history. About 10 kya an equally profound transformation was associated with the adoption of agriculture. Agriculture led to sedentary villages, social inequality, large-scale societies, monumental architecture, writing, and many other innovations that we see in the archaeological record. Harvard archaeologist Ofer-Bar Yosef has suggested that the rapid transition we see in the archaeological record in Europe about 40 kya could have been caused by a similar kind of technological innovation that allowed for much more efficient food acquisition, which in turn led to a greater economic surplus, more economic specialization, and greater symbolic and ritual activity.

There are two related problems with this explanation. First, there is no obvious technological change, analogous to plant domestication, that could cause such a shift in a subsistence economy. Second, morphologically modern people appeared at least 100 kya. If these people were also cognitively modern, why did it take so long for the human revolution to occur? It is possible that environmental conditions were not conducive to innovation. It seems likely that the stabilization of the climate at the end of the Pleistocene gave rise to agriculture. Perhaps an analogous change created conditions that facilitated the human revolution 50 kya. The problem with this idea is that there is no obvious candidate for such a factor.

Modern human behavior could have evolved gradually in Africa through a combination of genetic and cultural changes.

The gradual evolution of human behavior in Africa is more easily reconciled with the usual picture of adaptive evolution, which is based on the gradual accumulation of small changes. Such a process requires no special macromutations or unlikely

BOX 14.3

Arcy-sur-Cure and the Causes of Modern Human Behavior

The Grotte du Renne, a site at the French town of Arcy-sur-Cure, provides important clues about whether the human revolution resulted from biological or cultural change in human populations. When the site was excavated between 1947 and 1963, archaeologists uncovered many layers that showed evidence of human activity. The lowest, and therefore oldest, levels yielded many Mousterian tools, and the highest and most recent levels contained Upper Paleolithic artifacts. In between, archaeologists found Châtelperronian tools and hominin fossils, including a small part of a cranium. More significantly, they also unearthed a large number of worked bone tools and 36 personal ornaments, artifacts typically associated with Upper Paleolithic peoples (Figure 14.26). However, it was not clear whether the hominins should be classified as Neanderthal or as anatomically modern humans. Thus it was not clear what kind of hominin made the ornaments and bone tools.

Recently, two clever bits of detective work have shown that the tools and ornaments at the Grotte du Renne were made by Neanderthals. The first piece of evidence was provided by Fred Spoor and his colleagues at the University of Liverpool. They used **computed tomography** (CT scan) to show that the shape of the semicircular canals of the inner ear differed between Neanderthals and modern humans.

Using this diagnostic feature, they were able to establish that the Grotte du Renne cranium was from a young Neanderthal child. This means that bone tools and ornaments were used at a site *occupied* by Neanderthals. It was still possible, however, that the tools and ornaments were manufactured by anatomically modern humans and subsequently acquired by Neanderthals, perhaps by trade or by scrounging.

This possibility was effectively eliminated by the evidence provided by a French team that completed a detailed reanalysis of the Grotte du Renne record. They discovered that the tools and ornaments were manufactured at the site while Neanderthals were living there. This conclusion is based partly on one piece of bone that was clearly the product of an unsuccessful effort to make an awl (a sharp tool used to punch holes in leather), the most common bone tool found at the site. There were also several ornaments made from the ends of swan bones, along with the matching piece of bone from which the ornament was cut. Taken together, these data show that the tools were made by the people who lived at the site, and these people were Neanderthals.

Thus we are reasonably certain that both Neanderthals and anatomically modern humans carved ornaments and tools out of bone. This conclusion affects our thinking

FIGURE 14.26 These personal ornaments found at Arcy-sur-Cure were likely manufactured by Neanderthals living at the site about 33 kya. The fact that Neanderthals could learn to make and use personal ornaments suggests that the absence of ornaments at most Mousterian sites is not due to some biologically transmitted, cognitive deficit among Neanderthals.

about the causes of the human revolution. The fact that the Neanderthals who lived at Arcy-sur-Cure made and used both bone artifacts and personal adornments is not consistent with the idea that modern behavior is caused by a cognitive innovation that Neanderthals lacked. It seems unlikely that Neanderthals would have been able to borrow ideas from their neighbors if they themselves lacked symbolic abilities. On the other hand, it is plausible that they might have adopted more sophisticated technology from neighboring peoples. The ethnographic record tells us that technological accomplishments do not provide a good measure of social or cognitive complexity. There are many cases in the historical record of technologically more advanced peoples coming in contact with technologically less advanced peoples. In such cases, it is common for the technologically less advanced to adopt ideas and techniques from the more advanced without completely abandoning their own way of life.

chance events. As we explained in Chapters 7 and 8, behavior is subject to the same kinds of evolutionary forces that shape morphology and physiology.

Klein, a strong advocate of the human revolution, has argued that the difficulty with this gradualist account is that it provides no ready explanation of why modern humans waited until 40 kya to leave Africa. If, as we have seen, most of the package of modern behavior was already assembled 100 kya, why didn't modern humans move north and east then, when the climate was relatively warm and moist? Instead, they waited until Europe was cold and dry and they had to cross something like the modern Sahara to get there.

FURTHER READING

Bahn, P. 1998. Neanderthals emancipated. *Nature* 394: 719–721.

Carrol, S. 2003. Genetics and the making of *Homo sapiens. Nature* 422: 849–857.

Jobling, M. A., M. E. Hurles, and C. Tyler-Smith. 2004. *Human Evolutionary Genetics*. Garland, New York.

Klein, R. 1999. *The Human Career* (2nd ed.). University of Chicago Press, Chicago.

McBrearty, S., and A. Brooks. 2000. The revolution that wasn't: A new interpretation of modern human behavior. *Journal of Human Evolution* 39: 453–563.

Stringer, C. 1997. *African Exodus: The Origins of Modern Humanity*. Holt, New York.

STUDY QUESTIONS

1. What derived anatomical features distinguish modern humans from other hominins?
2. Describe what the archaeological record tells us about the pattern of human behavior 100 kya and 30 kya. What facts are widely accepted? Which are in dispute?
3. Describe the main differences between the tools of Upper Paleolithic peoples and those of their predecessors.

4. What evidence suggests that Upper Paleolithic peoples were better able to cope with their environments?

5. Explain why it is possible to make phylogenetic trees for mitochondrial DNA and the Y chromosome, but not for other chromosomes.

6. Explain why the mitochondrial DNA and Y chromosome trees are consistent with the hypothesis that modern humans evolved in Africa and then later spread across the rest of the globe.

7. Suppose that you were able to choose three more fossils to extract DNA from and that your goal was to test the hypothesis that humans evolved in Africa. Which three would you pick? Explain why.

8. Describe the two extreme hypotheses that have been put forward to explain the evolution of modern human behavior. Describe and evaluate the evidence and arguments for and against both.

9. How do we know that Neanderthals made the personal ornaments found at Arcy-sur-Cure? How does this fact affect different hypotheses about the evolution of modern human behavior?

KEY TERMS

Upper Paleolithic
blades
Mode 4
mitochrondria
mitochrondrial DNA/mtDNA
Châttelperronian

Middle Stone Age/MSA
Later Stone Age/LSA
Mode 5
synonymous substitutions
nonsynonymous substitutions

CONTENT FROM *HUMAN EVOLUTION: A MULTI-MEDIA GUIDE TO THE FOSSIL RECORD*

Modern Homo sapiens
   Overview
   Transition to Modernity
   Genetic Evidence
   Upper Paleolithic Cultures

PART FOUR

EVOLUTION AND MODERN HUMANS

Explaining Human Variation

*Variation in Traits Influenced
by Single Genes*

   *Causes of Genetic Variation within
   Groups*

   *Causes of Genetic Variation among
   Groups*

Variation in Complex Phenotypic Traits

   Genetic Variation within Groups

   Genetic Variation among Groups

The Race Concept

HUMAN GENETIC DIVERSITY

EXPLAINING HUMAN VARIATION

Human beings vary in myriad ways. In any sizable group of people, there is variation in height, weight, hair color, eye color, food preferences, hobbies, musical tastes, skills, interests, and so on. Some people you know are tall enough to dunk a basketball, some have to roll up the hems of all their pants; some have blue eyes and freckle in the sun, others have dark eyes and can get a terrific tan; some people have perfect pitch, others can't tell a flat from a sharp. Your friends may include heavy drinkers and teetotalers, great cooks and people who can't microwave popcorn, skilled gardeners and some who can't keep a geranium alive, some who play classical music and others who prefer heavy metal.

If we look around the world, we encounter an even wider range of variation. Some of the variation is easy to observe. Language, fashions, customs, religion, technology, architecture, and other aspects of behavior differ among societies. People in different parts of the world also look very different. For example, most of the people in northern Europe have blond hair and pale skin, and most of the people in southern Asia have dark hair and dark skin. As we described in Chapter 13, Arctic peoples are generally shorter and stockier than people who live in the savannas of East Africa. Groups also differ in ways that cannot be detected so readily. For instance, the peoples of the world vary in blood type and the incidence of many genetically transmitted diseases. Figure 15.1 shows that the distributions of three debilitating diseases—PKU (phenylketonuria, introduced in Chapter 3), cystic fibrosis, and Tay-Sachs disease—vary considerably among populations. Tay-Sachs, for example, is nearly 10 times more common among Ashkenazi Jews in New York than among other New Yorkers.

In this chapter we will consider how much of this variation is due to genetic differences among people. We want to know how people vary genetically within and

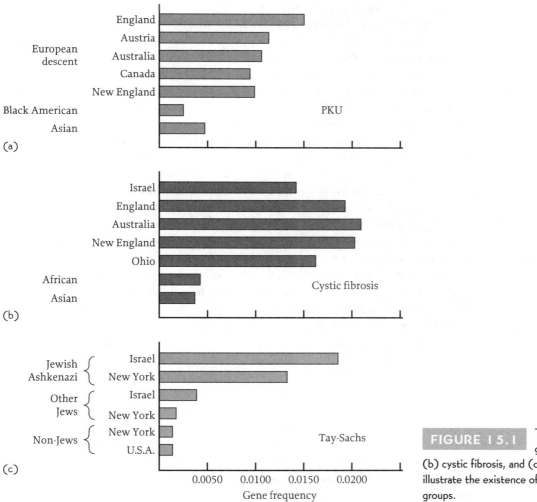

FIGURE 15.1 The distributions of three genetic diseases—(a) PKU, (b) cystic fibrosis, and (c) Tay-Sachs disease— illustrate the existence of variation among human groups.

among societies, and to understand the processes that create and sustain this variation. We'll begin by describing the nature of variation in traits that are influenced by single genes with large effects. Next we'll consider variation in traits that are influenced by many genes. As you will see, the methods that are used to assess variation in traits caused by single genes and multiple genes are quite different. In both cases, we will consider the processes that give rise to variation within and among populations. Finally, we will use our understanding of human genetic diversity to explore the significance and meaning of a concept that plays an important, albeit often negative, role in modern society: race. We will argue that a clear understanding of the nature and source of human genetic variation demonstrates that race is not a valid scientific construct.

Scientists distinguish two sources of human variation: genetic and environmental.

Scientists conventionally divide the causes of human variation into two categories: **Genetic variation** refers to differences between individuals that are caused by the genes they inherited from their parents. **Environmental variation** refers to differences between individuals caused by environmental factors (such as climate, habitat, and competing species) on the organisms' phenotypes. For humans, culture is an important source of environmental variation.

A practical example—variation in body weight—will clarify this distinction. Many environmental factors affect body weight. Some factors, such as the availability of food, have an obvious and direct impact on body weight. The majority of people living under siege in Sarajevo in the mid-1990s were undoubtedly leaner than they were a decade earlier when Sarajevo was a rich, cosmopolitan city. Other environmental effects are more subtle. For example, culture can affect body weight because it influences our ideas about what constitutes an appropriate diet and shapes our standards of physical beauty. In the United States, many young women adopt strict diets and rigorous exercise regimens in order to maintain a slim figure because thinness is considered desirable. But in a number of West African societies, young women are secluded and force-fed large meals several times a day for the express purpose of gaining weight and becoming fat. In these societies, obesity is extremely desirable, and fat women are thought to be very beautiful. Body weight also appears to have an important genetic component. Recent research has shown that individuals with some genotypes are predisposed to be heavier than others, even when diet and levels of activity are controlled.

Genetic and environmental causes of variation may also interact in complicated ways. Consider, for example, two people who have inherited quite different genes affecting body weight. One is easily sated while the other craves food constantly. Both individuals may be thin if they have to subsist on one cup of porridge a day, but only the one who is unconcerned about being thin will gain weight when Big Macs and fries are readily available.

It is difficult to determine the relative importance of genetic and environmental influences for particular phenotypic traits.

It is often difficult to separate the genetic and environmental causes of human variation in real situations. The problem is that both genetic transmission and shared environments cause parents and offspring to be similar. For example, suppose we were to measure the weights of parents and offspring in a series of families living in a range of environments. It is likely that the weight of parents and offspring (corrected for age) would be closely related. However, we would not know whether the association was an effect of genes or environment. Children might resemble their parents because they inherited genes that affect fat metabolism or because they learned eating habits and acquired food preferences from their parents.

Quite different processes create and maintain genetic and environmental variation among groups, and identifying the source of human differences will help us understand why people are the way they are. Genetic variation is governed by the processes of organic evolution: mutation, drift, recombination, and selection. Biologists and anthropologists know a great deal about how the various processes work to shape the living world and how evolutionary processes explain genetic differences among contemporary humans in particular cases.

It is important to distinguish variation within human groups from variation among human groups.

Variation within groups refers to differences between individuals within a given group of people. In the National Basketball Association (NBA), for example, 1.65-m (5-ft 5-in.) Earl Boykins of the Denver Nuggets competes against much larger players, like 2.3-m (7-ft 6-in.) Yao Ming of the Houston Rockets (Figure 15.2). **Variation among groups** refers to differences between entire groups of people. For instance, the average height of NBA players [exemplified in Figure 15.3 by the late, great 2.15-m (7-ft 1-in.) Wilt Chamberlain] is much greater than the average height of professional jockeys [exemplified in the figure by the equally late and equally great 1.5-m (4-ft 11-in.) Willy Shoemaker]. It is important to distinguish these two levels of variation because, as we will see, the causes of the variation within groups can be very different from the causes of variation among groups.

FIGURE 15.2 Variation in stature within the NBA is illustrated by the difference in height between Yao Ming (2.3 m, or 7 ft 6 in.) and Earl Boykins (1.65 m, or 5 ft 5 in.).

FIGURE 15.3 Variation in stature between professional basketball players and professional jockeys is illustrated here by the difference in height between Willy Shoemaker (1.5 m, or 4 ft 11 in.) and Wilt Chamberlain (2.15 m, or 7 ft 1 in.).

VARIATION IN TRAITS INFLUENCED BY SINGLE GENES

By establishing the connection between particular DNA sequences and specific traits, scientists have shown that variation in some traits is genetic.

Although it is sometimes difficult to establish the source of variation in human traits, in some cases we can be certain that variation arises from genetic differences between individuals. For example, recall from Chapter 2 that in West Africa many people suffer from sickle-cell anemia, a disease that causes their red blood cells to have a sickle shape instead of the more typical rounded shape. We know that people with this debilitating disease are homozygous for a gene that codes for one variant of hemoglobin, the protein that transports oxygen molecules in red blood cells. Hemoglobin is made up of two different protein subunits, labeled α (the Greek letter alpha) and β (the Greek letter beta). The DNA sequence of the most common hemoglobin allele, hemoglobin A, specifies the amino acid glutamic acid in the sixth position of the protein chain of the β subunit. But there is another hemoglobin allele, hemoglobin S, which specifies the amino acid valine at this position. People who suffer from sickle-cell anemia are homozygous for the hemoglobin S allele.

We can prove that traits are controlled by genes at a single genetic locus by showing that their patterns of inheritance conform to Mendel's principles.

Although it is often difficult to distinguish between genetic and environmental sources of variation, we can sometimes make this distinction when traits are affected by genes at a single genetic locus. In such cases, Mendel's laws make very detailed predictions about the patterns of inheritance (see Chapter 2). If scientists suspect that a trait is controlled by genes at a single genetic locus, they can test this idea by collecting data on the occurrence of the trait in families. If the pattern of inheritance shows a close fit to the pattern predicted by Mendel's principles (conventionally called "laws"), then we can be confident that the trait is affected by a single genetic locus.

Research on the genetic basis of a language disorder called **specific language impairment** (**SLI**) illustrates the strengths and weaknesses of this approach. Children with SLI have difficulty learning to speak, and in some cases they have small vocabularies and make frequent grammatical errors as adults. SLI is known to run in families, but the genetic basis of the condition is unclear in most cases.

The pattern of inheritance of SLI in one family suggests that at least some cases of SLI are caused by a dominant allele at a single genetic locus. A group of researchers at the Wellcome Trust Centre for Human Genetics in Oxford, England, has studied the expression of SLI in three generations of one family (known as the "KE family"; Figure 15.4). The members of this family who suffer from SLI have severe problems learning grammatical rules, and they also have difficulty with fine motor control of the tongue and jaws. The grandmother (shown as a blue circle) had SLI, but her husband (a yellow triangle) did not. Four of her five children and 11 of her 24 grandchildren also had SLI. Suppose that SLI is caused by a dominant gene. Then because SLI is rare in the population as a whole, the Hardy–Weinberg equations tell us that almost all SLI sufferers will be heterozygotes. Of course, anyone not having SLI must be a homozygote for the normal allele at this locus. From Mendel's laws, on average half of the offspring of a mating between a person with SLI and one without will have SLI and half will have normal linguistic skills. The KE family fits this prediction very well. Both

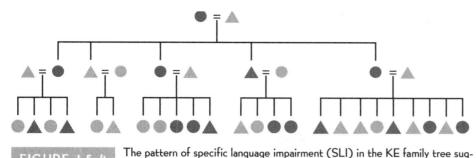

FIGURE 15.4 The pattern of specific language impairment (SLI) in the KE family tree suggests that some cases of SLI are caused by a single dominant gene. Circles represent women, triangles represent men, and blue symbols represent people with SLI. If SLI is caused by a dominant gene, then because SLI is rare in the population as a whole, we know from the Hardy–Weinberg equations that almost all people with SLI will be heterozygotes. Thus, Mendel's principles tell us that, on average, half of the offspring of a mating between a person with SLI and a person without it will have SLI, and half of the offspring will have normal linguistic skills. Notice how well the family shown in this tree fits this prediction.

of the children of the son without SLI are normal, and the rest of the matings produced approximately equal numbers of normal and language-impaired children.

Although the pattern in the KE family is consistent with the idea that SLI is caused by a single dominant gene, it is possible that an environmental factor causes SLI to run in families and that the observed pattern arose by chance. Scientists search for two kinds of data to clinch the case. First, they collect data on more families. The larger the number of families that fit the pattern associated with the inheritance of a single-locus dominant gene, the more confident researchers can be that this pattern did not occur by chance. Second, researchers search for genetic markers (genes whose location in the genome is known) that show the same pattern of inheritance. Thus, if every individual who has SLI also has a specific marker on a particular chromosome, we can be confident that the gene that causes SLI lies close to that genetic marker.

In 1998, the Wellcome Trust researchers demonstrated that SLI in the KE family is closely linked to a genetic marker on chromosome 7, and so it seems likely that SLI in this family is controlled by a gene closely linked to this marker. Even more remarkably, the subsequent discovery of an unrelated person with the same symptoms allowed the researchers to identify the specific gene that causes the disorder in the KE family. The same allele of this gene, named *FOXP2*, was found in all affected members of the KE family and not in 364 unrelated people without SLI. Interestingly, molecular evidence suggests that the *FOXP2* gene has undergone strong directional selection since the divergence of humans and chimpanzees.

The fact that SLI is caused by a single gene does not mean that the gene is responsible for all of the psychological machinery in the human brain that gives rise to language. It means only that damage to the *FOXP2* gene prevents the normal development of some of the psychological machinery necessary for language. If you cut the wire connecting the hard disk to the power supply in your computer, the hard disk will stop working, but that does not mean the wire contains all of the machinery necessary for operation of the hard disk. This argument is supported by the fact that the *FOXP2* gene codes for a transcription factor belonging to a family of genes that play an important role in regulating gene expression during development. *FOXP2* itself is strongly expressed in the brains of developing fetuses. By the same reasoning, SLI in other families may be caused by other genes whose expression is necessary for normal brain development. Just as there are many ways to wreck your hard disk, there may be many mutants at many loci that damage the parts of the brain necessary for language.

Causes of Genetic Variation within Groups

Mutation can maintain deleterious genes in populations, but only at a low frequency.

Many diseases are caused by recessive genes. For example, only people who are homozygous for hemoglobin S are afflicted with sickle-cell anemia. Other diseases caused by recessive alleles include PKU, Tay-Sachs disease, and cystic fibrosis. All of these diseases are caused by mutant genes that code for proteins that do not serve their normal function, and all produce severe debilitation and sometimes death. Why haven't such deleterious genes been eliminated by natural selection?

One answer to this question is that natural selection steadily removes such genes, but they are constantly being reintroduced by mutation. Very low rates of mutation can maintain these deleterious genes because they are recessive traits, so most individuals who carry the gene are heterozygous for the deleterious genes and do not suffer the disastrous consequences that homozygotes suffer. The observed frequency of many deleterious recessive genes is about 1 in 1000. According to the Hardy–Weinberg equations, then, the frequency of newborns homozygous for the recessive allele will be $0.001 \times 0.001 = 0.000001$! Thus, only one in a million babies will carry the disease. This means that even if the disease is fatal, selection will remove only two copies of the deleterious gene for every 1 million people born. Because mutation rates for such deleterious genes are estimated to be a few mutations per million gametes produced, mutation will introduce enough new mutants to maintain a constant frequency of the gene. When this is true, we say that there is **selection–mutation balance**.

Selection can maintain variation within populations if heterozygotes have higher fitness than either of the two homozygotes.

Some lethal genes are too common to be the result of selection–mutation balance. In West African populations, for example, the frequency of the hemoglobin S allele is typically about 1 in 10. How can we account for this? The answer in the case of hemoglobin S is that this allele increases the fitness of heterozygotes. It turns out that individuals who carry one copy of the sickling allele, *S*, and one copy of the normal allele, *A*, are partially protected against the most dangerous form of malaria, called **falciparum malaria** (Figure 15.5). As a consequence, where falciparum malaria is prevalent, heterozygous *AS* newborns are about 15% more likely to reach adulthood than *AA* infants.

When heterozygotes have a higher fitness than either homozygote has, natural selection will maintain a **balanced polymorphism**, a steady state in which both alleles persist in the population. To see why balanced polymorphisms exist, first consider what happens when the *S* allele is introduced into a population and is very rare. Suppose that its frequency is 0.001. The frequency of *SS* individuals will be 0.001×0.001, or about 1 in 1 million, and the frequency of *AS* individuals will be $2 \times 0.001 \times 0.999$, or about 2 in 1000. This means that, for every individual who suffers the debilitating effects of sickle-cell anemia, there will be about 2000 heterozygotes who are partially immune to malaria. Thus, when the S allele is rare, most S alleles will occur in heterozygotes, and the S allele will increase in frequency. However, this trend will not lead to the elimination of the A allele. To see why, let's consider what happens when the S allele is common and the A allele is rare. Now almost all of the A alleles will occur in AS heterozygotes and be partially resistant to malaria, but almost all of the S alleles will occur in SS homozygotes and suffer debilitating anemia. The A allele has higher fitness than the S allele when the S allele is common (Box 15.1). The balance between these two processes depends on the fitness advantage of the heterozygotes and the disadvantage of the homozygotes. In this case, the equilibrium frequency for the hemoglobin S allele is about 0.1, approximately the frequency actually observed in West Africa.

Scientists suspect that the relatively high frequencies of genes that cause a number of other genetic diseases may also be the result of heterozygote advantage. For example, the gene that causes Tay-Sachs disease has a frequency as high as 0.05 in some eastern European Jewish populations. Children who are homozygous for this gene seem normal for about the first six months of life. Then, over the next few years a gradual deterioration takes place, leading to blindness, convulsions, and finally death, usually by age four. There is some evidence that individuals who are heterozygous for the Tay-Sachs allele are partially resistant to tuberculosis. Jared Diamond of the University of California Los Angeles points out that tuberculosis was much more prevalent in cities than in rural areas of Europe over the last 400 years. Confined to the crowded urban ghettos of eastern Europe, Jews may have benefited more from increased resistance to tuberculosis than did other Europeans, most of whom lived in rural settings.

Variation may exist because environments have recently changed and genes that were previously beneficial have not yet been eliminated.

Some genetic diseases may be common because the symptoms they create have not always been deleterious. One form of diabetes, **non-insulin-dependent diabetes (NIDD)**, may be an example of such a disease. **Insulin** is a protein that controls the uptake of blood sugar by cells. In NIDD sufferers, blood-sugar levels rise above normal levels because the cells of the body do not respond properly to insulin in the blood. High blood-sugar levels cause a number of problems, including heart disease, kidney damage, and impaired vision. NIDD is also known to have a genetic basis. (The other form of diabetes, insulin-dependent diabetes, occurs because the insulin-producing cells in the pancreas have been destroyed by the body's own immune system. It is unlikely that insulin-dependent diabetes was ever adaptive.)

In some contemporary populations the occurrence of NIDD is very high. On the Micronesian island of Nauru, for example, more than 30% of people over 15 years old now have the disease. Such high rates of NIDD are a recent phenomenon, although the genes that cause the disease are not new. The late human geneticist J. V. Neel of the University of Michigan suggested that the genes now leading to NIDD were beneficial in the past because they caused a rapid buildup of fat reserves during periods of plenty—fat reserves that would help people survive periods of famine in harsh environments. Traditionally, life on Nauru was very difficult. The inhabitants subsisted by fishing and farming, and famine was common. NIDD was virtually unknown during this period. However, Nauru was colonized by Britain, Australia, and New Zealand in recent times, and these influxes brought many changes in the residents'

(a)

(b)

FIGURE 15.5 (a) Sufferers of sickle-cell anemia have abnormal red blood cells with a sickle shape. (b) Normal red blood cells are round. Sickle-cell anemia partially protects against falciparum malaria.

BOX 15.1

Calculating Gene Frequencies for a Balanced Polymorphism

It is easy to calculate the frequency of hemoglobin S when selection has reached a stable, balanced polymorphism. Suppose the fitness of AA homozygotes is 1.0, the fitness of AS heterozygotes is 1.15, and the fitness of SS homozygotes is 0, and let p be the equilibrium frequency of the allele S. If individuals mate at random, a fraction p of the S alleles will unite with another S allele to form an SS heterozygote, and a fraction $1 - p$ will unite with an A allele to form an AS heterozygote. Thus the average fitness of the S allele will be

$$0p + 1.15(1 - p)$$

By the same reasoning, the average fitness of the A allele will be

$$1.15p + 1(1 - p)$$

The relationship between the average fitness of each allele and the frequency of hemoglobin S, shown in Figure 15.6, confirms the reasoning given in the text. When S is common, so that p is close to 1, the average fitness of the S allele is close to zero; but when S is rare, its average fitness is almost 1.15. If one gene has a higher fitness than the other, natural selection will increase the frequency of that gene. Thus a steady state will occur when the average fitnesses of the two alleles are equal—that is, when

$$1.15(1 - p) = 1.15p + (1 - p)$$

If you solve for p, you will find that

$$p = \frac{1.15 - 1.10}{1.15 + 1.15 - 1.0}$$

$$= \frac{0.15}{1.30} \approx 0.1$$

which is about the observed frequency of the sickle-cell allele in West Africa.

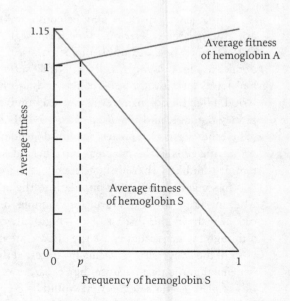

FIGURE 15.6 The average fitness of the S allele of hemoglobin S declines as the frequency of S increases because more and more S alleles are found in SS homozygotes. Similarly, the average fitness of the A allele of hemoglobin A increases as the frequency of S increases because more and more A alleles are found in AS heterozygotes. A balanced polymorphism occurs when the average fitness of the two alleles is equal.

lives. They obtained access to Western food, and prosperity derived from the island's phosphate deposits allowed them to adopt a sedentary lifestyle. NIDD became common. Genes that formerly conferred an advantage on the residents of Nauru now lead to NIDD, the primary cause of nonaccidental death there.

Causes of Genetic Variation among Groups

There are many genetic differences between groups of people living in different parts of the world. The existence of genetic variation among groups is intriguing because we know that all living people are members of a single species, and, as we saw in Chapter 4, gene flow between different populations within a single species tends to make them genetically uniform. In this section we consider several processes that oppose the homogenizing effects of such gene flow and thereby create and maintain genetic variation among human populations.

Selection that favors different genes in different environments creates and maintains variation among groups.

The human species inhabits a wider range of environments than any other mammal. We know that natural selection in different environments may favor different genes, and that natural selection can maintain genetic differences in the face of the homogenizing influence of gene flow if selection is strong enough. Variation in the distribution of hemoglobin genes provides a good example of this process. Hemoglobin S is most common in tropical Africa, around the Mediterranean Sea, and in southern India (Figure 15.7a). Elsewhere it is almost unknown. Generally, hemoglobin S is prevalent where falciparum malaria is common, and hemoglobin A is prevalent where this form of malaria is absent (Figure 15.7b). Southeast Asia represents an exception to this pattern, and it is possible that hemoglobin E, a hemoglobin allele that is common in that region, also provides resistance to malaria.

The gene that controls the digestion of **lactose**, a sugar found in mammalian milk, provides another interesting example of genetic variation maintained by natural selection. Lactose is synthesized in the mammary glands and occurs in large amounts only in mammalian milk. Most mammals have the ability to digest lactose as infants but gradually lose this ability after they are weaned. The vast majority of humans follow the mammalian pattern and cannot digest lactose after the age of five. Such people are said to lack lactase persistence. When people who lack lactase persistence drink more than about half a liter (just over 1 pint) of fresh milk at once, they suffer gastric distress that ranges from mild discomfort to quite severe pain. However, most northern Europeans and members of a number of North African and Arabian populations retain the ability to digest lactose as adults and are said to have lactase persistence. Evidence from family studies indicates that the ability to digest lactose as an adult is controlled by a single dominant gene, labeled **LTC*P**. People who have one copy of LTC*P continue to synthesize lactase as adults, but people who are homozygous for the alternative allele, labeled **LTC*R**, do not. The relationship between genotype and phenotype for the trait of lactase persistence is summarized in Table 15.1. Recent molecular studies indicate that the difference between the two alleles lies in a regulatory region close to the structural gene that codes for lactase.

The prevalence of LTC*P in the deserts of North Africa and Arabia is probably the result of natural selection for the ability to digest large amounts of fresh milk.

(a)

(b)

FIGURE 15.7   Hemoglobin S is common only in areas of the world in which falciparum malaria is prevalent. (a) The colors show the frequency of hemoglobin S throughout the world. (b) The regions of the Old World in which falciparum malaria is prevalent are in red.

TABLE 15.1	The ability to digest lactose is controlled by a single genetic locus with two alleles, *LTC*P* and *LTC*R*.

Genotype	Phenotype
LTC*P/LTC*P	Synthesize lactase and are able to digest lactose as adults
LTC*P/LTC*R	Synthesize lactase and are able to digest lactose as adults
LTC*R/LTC*R	Do not synthesize lactase and are unable to digest lactose as adults

Traditionally, nomadic pastoralism has been the main mode of subsistence in this part of the world, and fresh milk plays a crucial role in this way of life. Gebhard Flatz of the Medizinische Hochschule of Hannover, Germany, studied the Beja, a people who wander with their herds of camels and goats in the desert lands between the Nile and the Red Sea (Figure 15.8). During the nine-month dry season, the Beja rely almost entirely on the milk of their camels and goats. They drink about 3 liters of fresh milk a day, and they obtain virtually all of their energy, protein, and water from milk. Moreover, the milk must be consumed when it is fresh. High desert temperatures prevent the Beja from storing milk, and their nomadic lifestyle makes it difficult to produce dairy products, such as cheese and yogurt, that lack lactose. The Beja probably could not survive without the ability to digest fresh milk. Thus it comes as no surprise that *LTC*P* is common among them; 84% of the Beja are able to digest lactose.

Scientists are less sure about why *LTC*P* is common in northern Europe. Frequencies of *LTC*P* are highest in Scandinavia and Great Britain, decline steadily to the south, and reach lower values around the Mediterranean Sea. Traditionally, large amounts of fresh milk have not been an important part of the diet of the peoples in this region. Low temperatures make milk storage practical, and northern Europeans have long made use of cheese and other processed-milk products. Thus it does not seem likely that the ability to digest fresh milk would provide a big enough advantage to account for the high frequency of *LTC*P*. One possibility is that lactose

 FIGURE 15.8 Pastoralists in northern Africa, such as the Beja, herd camels, and during some parts of the year they obtain virtually all of their nourishment from fresh milk. A high proportion of the Beja are able to digest lactose as adults.

digestion is favored in northern Europe because it enhances absorption of vitamin D. When sunlight penetrates the fatty tissue in human skin, vitamin D is synthesized. Consequently, in sunny environments humans rarely suffer vitamin D deficiency. In northern Europe, long, dark, cloudy winters create a potential for vitamin D deficiency. Laboratory studies suggest that the ability to digest lactose increases vitamin D absorption. Thus the ability to digest lactose might be common in northern Europe because it helps prevent vitamin D deficiency.

Many people think of evolution by natural selection as a glacially slow process that acts only over millions of years. The correlation of lactase persistence with dairying, however, suggests that the ability to digest lactose has evolved since people began domesticating livestock in the Middle East and North Africa about 7 kya. This hypothesis is supported by molecular evidence that indicates that the lactase gene has been subjected to recent strong selection. Joel Hirschhorn and his colleagues at Harvard Medical School have identified 101 **single nucleotide polymorphisms (SNPs)** in the lactase gene and surrounding noncoding DNA. SNPs are single nucleotide sites in which the base varies within a population. It turns out that if you identify the base at one site for an individual, then you can predict the base that the same individual will have at the other 100 sites. This is the pattern that we would expect to find if there had been recent strong selection on the lactase gene because selection will tend to increase the frequency of both the beneficial DNA segment and all of the closely linked DNA, even if the latter are not directly beneficial. Over time, though, recombination will tend to destroy these patterns. Thus the pattern of variation in these SNPs suggests that the ability to digest lactose in adulthood evolved relatively recently. We don't need to imagine that selection has huge effects on fitness in order to account for the rapid evolution of this trait. Figure 15.9 shows how fast the frequency of lactase persistence could increase if the ability to digest lactose increased fitness by just 3%. As you can see, even this relatively small benefit could easily explain the high frequencies of persistence that we now find in some parts of the world.

Genetic drift creates variation among isolated populations.

In Chapter 3 we saw that genetic drift causes random changes in gene frequencies. This means that if two populations become isolated from each other, both will change randomly, and over time the two populations will become genetically distinct. Because drift occurs more rapidly in small populations than in large ones, small populations will diverge from one another faster than large ones will. Genetic drift caused by the expansion of a small founding population is sometimes called the **founder effect**.

Genetic differences among members of three religious communities in North America demonstrate how this process can create variation among human groups. Two of these groups are Anabaptist sects—the Old Order Amish (Figure 15.10) and Hutterites—and the third group is the Utah Mormons. Each of these groups forms a well-defined population. About 2000 Mormons first arrived in the area of what is now Salt Lake City in 1847, but members of the church continued to arrive until 1890. Virtually all of the immigrants were of northern European descent. At the turn of the twentieth century, there were about 250,000 people in this area, and about 70% of them belonged to the Mormon church. In contrast, the two Anabaptist groups were much smaller. The founding population of the Old Order Amish was only 200 people, and gene flow from

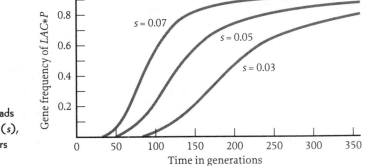

FIGURE 15.9 If the ability to digest lactose as an adult leads to even as little as a 3% increase in fitness (s), then it is possible that the *LTC·P* gene has spread in the 7000 years (300 to 350 generations) since the origin of dairying.

outside the group has been very limited. Contemporary Hutterites are all descended from a population of only 443 people and, like the Amish, have been almost closed to immigration.

Researchers studying the genetic composition of each of these populations have found that Mormons are genetically similar to other European populations. Thus, even though Mormon populations have been partly isolated from other European populations for over 150 years, genetic drift has led to very little change. This is just what we would expect, given the size of the Mormon population. In contrast, the two Anabaptist populations are quite distinct from other European populations. Because their founding populations were small and the communities were genetically isolated, drift has created substantial genetic changes in the same period of time.

Genetic drift can also explain why certain genetic diseases are common in some populations

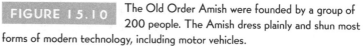

FIGURE 15.10 The Old Order Amish were founded by a group of 200 people. The Amish dress plainly and shun most forms of modern technology, including motor vehicles.

but not in others. For example, Afrikaners in what is now the Republic of South Africa are the descendants of Dutch immigrants who arrived in the seventeenth century. By chance, this small group of early immigrants carried a number of rare genetic diseases, and these genes occurred at much higher frequency among members of the colonizing population than in the Dutch populations from which the immigrants were originally drawn. The Afrikaner population grew very rapidly and preserved these initially high frequencies, causing these genes to occur in higher frequencies among modern Afrikaners than in other populations. For example, sufferers of the genetic disease **porphyria variegata** develop a severe reaction to certain anesthetics. About 30,000 Afrikaners now carry the dominant gene that causes this disease, and every one of these people is descended from a single couple who arrived from Holland in the 1680s.

Current patterns of genetic variation reflect the history of migration and population growth in the human species.

Some of the genetic variation among human groups reflects the history of the peoples of the Earth. In Chapter 14 we explained that the pattern of genetic variation in mitochondrial DNA indicates that the human species underwent a worldwide population expansion about 100,000 years ago. This was only one of several expansions of the world's population. The invention of agriculture led to expansions of farming peoples from the Middle East into Europe, from Southeast Asia into **Oceania** (the Pacific island groups of Polynesia, Melanesia, and Micronesia), and from west-cental Africa to most of the rest of the continent between 4000 and 1000 years ago; the domestication of the horse and associated military innovations led to several expansions of peoples living in the steppes of central Asia between 3000 and 500 years ago; and improvements in ships, navigation, and military organization led to the expansion of European populations during the last 500 years.

L. L. Cavalli-Sforza, a human geneticist at Stanford University, has argued that patterns of genetic variation preserve a record of these expansions. As human populations grow, they often expand into new geographic regions. As the distance grows between parts of the population, they become genetically isolated from one another and begin to accumulate genetic differences. If the population expansion continues, the initial "parent" population may eventually be split into several isolated and genetically differentiated "daughter" populations. If the daughter populations remained completely isolated from all other human populations, they would be just like new species, and we could use the techniques of phylogenetic reconstruction described in Chapter 4 to reconstruct the demographic history of the daughter populations. Such complete isolation is very rare, though. Instead, daughter populations usually experience gene flow with each other and with other human populations they encounter during their expansion, and such gene flow tends to obscure the history of the populations. Nonetheless, Cavalli-Sforza argues, if there is not too much gene flow, the present patterns of genetic variation can help us reconstruct the pattern of past migrations.

Cavalli-Sforza and his colleagues believe that the worldwide pattern of genetic variation results from the expansion of modern humans about 100,000 years ago. Recall from Chapter 14 that supporters of the replacement model believe this expansion began in Africa, and then spread north and east to the rest of Eurasia and Australasia, and finally reached the New World. Cavalli-Sforza and his colleagues have collected data on gene frequencies in populations across the world. Figure 15.11 shows a tree based on the frequencies of 120 genes in 42 populations from every part of the globe. These data are based on what geneticists call "classical markers" because they have been detectable by geneticists for decades. This result was constructed using the genetic-distance methods described in Chapter 4, and it assumes that the rate of genetic change along each branch of the tree has been constant. It is consistent with the view that modern humans originated in Africa and spread to the rest of the world, and that the patterns of genetic variation we see in today's world are the result of that expansion. A simplified version of the tree (Figure 15.12) tells us that African populations first expanded into southern Asia. Then southern Asian populations expanded into northern Asia and Oceania. Finally, northern Asian populations spread into Europe.

The higher resolution allowed by analysis of Y chromosomes and mitochondrial DNA leads to a more complicated picture (Figure 15.13). As with the classical mark-

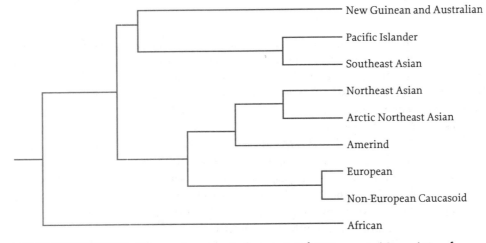

FIGURE 15.11 This tree, based on the frequencies of 120 genes in 42 populations from every part of the globe, is consistent with the hypothesis that humans originated in Africa and spread from there to the rest of the globe.

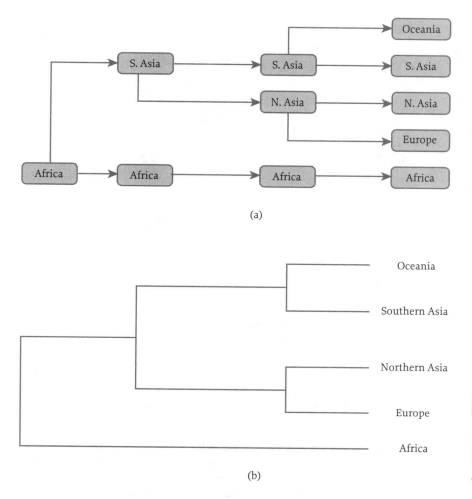

(a)

(b)

FIGURE 15.12 (a) This model of the expansion of early anatomically modern human populations generates the phylogenetic tree shown in (b) if geographically separate populations remain genetically isolated.

ers, the geographic pattern suggests that modern humans are all descended from African populations that moved out of African into southern Asia and subsequently to Europe, northern Asia, and the New World. However, now the results of later population movements can also be seen. Notice for example that Y chromosomes from group C are common in Australia but not elsewhere in Southeast Asia. A more detailed examination of the Y chromosome types common among aboriginal Australians indicates that these C-type chromosomes are most similar to those found in India, and that individuals bearing these chromosomes probably arrived in Australia less than 10,000 years ago. This date coincides with the introduction of the dingo to Australia and with archaeological evidence for new plant-processing techniques. The genetic and archaeological evidence suggests that a new group of foragers arrived in Australia about 10,000 years ago and brought domesticated dogs with them.

VARIATION IN COMPLEX PHENOTYPIC TRAITS

As we saw in Chapter 3, the vast majority of human traits are influenced by many genes, each alone having a relatively small effect. For such traits, it is usually impossible to detect the effects of single genes or to trace the patterns of Mendelian inheri-

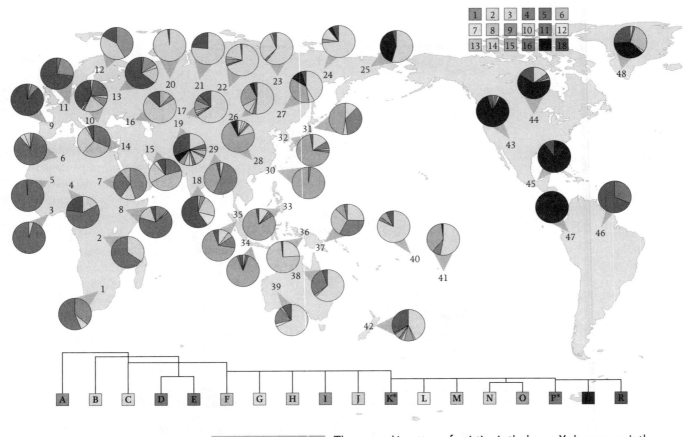

FIGURE 15.13 The geographic pattern of variation in the human Y chromosome is the result of the spread of humans from Africa to Asia and then Australia, the Pacific, and the New World. The tree at the bottom is a simplified version of Figure 14.18, in which the main labeled groups of terminal branches are color-coded. With three exceptions, these groups are all the Y chromosome genotypes that share a particular mutation. The exceptions are groups F*, K*, and P*, which share a mutation with other groups descended from F, K, and P, respectively. The pie graphs indicate the fraction of the Y chromosomes at each site that belong to the various groups labeled on the tree.

tance. Nonetheless, it is still possible to assess the influence of genes on such traits. Geneticists have developed statistical methods that enable them to estimate the relative importance of genetic and environmental components of variation within groups. Because the relative importance of genetic variation and environmental variation will affect the resemblance between parents and offspring, the measure that computes the proportion of variation due to the effects of genes is referred to as the **heritability** of phenotypic traits.

This material will be easier to understand if we have a concrete example in mind. Height is an ideal trait: it is quite easy to measure, it is quite variable within and between populations, it is relatively stable once individuals reach adulthood, and there is a wealth of data on height of individuals in different populations. In any moderately large sample of people there will be a wide range of variation in height. For example, the data in Figure 15.14 are taken from men who joined the British Army in 1939. Some of these young recruits were more than 2 m (around 7 ft) tall; others were less than 1.5 m (5 ft) tall.

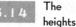 The heights of men joining the British rmy in 1939 varied considerably, illustrating the range of variation in morphological characters within populations. The tallest men joining the army were more than 2 m (around 84 in., or 7 ft) tall, and others were less than 1.5 m (60 in., or 5 ft) tall.

Genetic Variation within Groups

Under certain conditions, measuring the phenotypic similarities among relatives such as twins allows us to estimate the fraction of the variation within the population that is due to genes.

In Part One we saw that the transmission of genes from parents to offspring causes children and parents to be phenotypically similar. If parents who are taller than average tend to have offspring who are taller than average, and parents who are shorter than average tend to have children who are shorter than average, you might think that height is determined by genes. In contrast, if parents and offspring are no more similar to each other than to other individuals in the population, you might think that genes have little effect on height. The problem with this reasoning is that nongenetic factors may also cause parents and offspring to be similar. It is known that many environmental factors, such as nutritional levels and the prevalence of infectious diseases, also affect height. Human parents directly affect their offspring's environment in many ways: they provide food and shelter, arrange for their children to be inoculated against diseases, and shape their children's beliefs about nutrition. Similarity between the environments of parents and their offspring is called **environmental covariation** and is a serious complication in computing heritability.

Data from studies of twins can be used to separate the effects of genetic transmission from environmental covariation. The technique involves comparing the similarity between monozygotic and dizygotic twins. **Monozygotic** (identical) **twins** begin life when the union of a sperm and an egg produces a single zygote. Then, very early in development, this embryo divides to form two separate, genetically identical individuals. **Dizygotic** (fraternal) **twins** begin life when two different eggs are fertilized by two different sperm to form two independent zygotes. Dizygotic twins share approximately one-half of their genetic material, and they are just like other pairs of full siblings except that they were conceived at the same time. Both monozygotic and dizygotic twins share a womb and experience the same intrauterine environment. After they are born, most twins grow up together in the same family. Thus, if most of the variation in stature has a genetic origin, monozygotic twins are likely to be more similar to one another than dizygotic twins are because monozygotic twins are genetically identical. On the other hand, if most of the variation is due to the environment, and

FIGURE 15.15 Identical, or monozygotic, twins are produced when an embryo splits at an early stage and produces two genetically identical individuals.

the similarity between parents and offspring is due to having a common family environment, then monozygotic twins will be no more similar to one another than dizygotic twins are. Population genetic theory provides a way to use comparisons of the similarity among dizygotic and monozygotic twins to adjust estimates of heritability for the effects of correlated environments.

Twin studies are useful in trying to estimate the relative magnitude of the effects of genetic variation and environmental variation on phenotypic characters, but the data may be biased in certain ways. For example, twin studies will overestimate heritability if the environments of monozygotic twins are more similar than the environments of dizygotic twins. There are several reasons why this may be the case. In the uterus, some monozygotic twins are more intimately associated than dizygotic twins are. Monozygotic twins are always the same sex. After they are born, monozygotic twins may be treated differently by their parents, family, teachers, and friends than dizygotic twins are treated. It is not uncommon to see monozygotic twins dressed in identical outfits or given rhyming names, and it is inevitable that their physical similarities to one another will be pointed out to them over and over (Figure 15.15).

Studies of monozygotic and dizygotic twins suggest that somewhat more than half of the variation in height in most human populations is due to genetic similarities between parents and their children.

Genetic Variation among Groups

Stature varies among human populations.

Just as people within groups vary in many ways, groups of people collectively vary in certain characteristics. For example, there is a considerable amount of variation in average height among populations. People from northwestern Europe are tall, averaging about 1.75 m (5 ft 9 in.) in height. People in Italy and other parts of southern Europe are about 12 cm (5 in.) shorter on the average. African populations include very tall peoples like the Nuer and the Maasai, and very short peoples like the !Kung. Within the Western Hemisphere, Native Americans living on the Great Plains of North America and in Patagonia are relatively tall, and peoples in tropical regions of both continents are relatively short.

Some of the variation in body size among human groups appears to be adaptive.

In Chapter 13 we learned that larger body size is favored by natural selection in colder climates. Tall peoples, such as the indigenous people of Patagonia in South America and of the Great Plains in North America, usually live in relatively cold parts of the world, but shorter peoples typically live in warmer areas, like southern Europe or the New World tropics. This pattern suggests that variation in body size among groups may be adaptive, a conjecture that is borne out by data on the relationship between body size and climate from a large number of human groups (Figure 15.16). Thus, at least some fraction of the variation in body size among groups is adaptive.

The fact that variation within populations has a genetic component does not mean that differences between groups are caused solely by genetic differences.

We have seen that a significant proportion of the variation in height and body size within some populations reflects genetic variation. We also know that the variation in height and body shape among populations seems to be adaptive. From these two facts, it might seem logical to conclude that the variation in body size among populations is genetic, and that this variation represents a response to natural selection.

However, this logic is wrong! All of the variation in height within populations could be genetic *and* all of the variation in height among populations could be adaptive, but this would not mean that there is variation among populations in the distribution of genes that influence height. In fact, all of the observed variation in height among groups could be due solely to differences in environmental conditions.

This point is frequently misunderstood, and this misunderstanding leads to serious misconceptions about the nature of genetic variation among human groups. A simple example may help you see why the existence of genetic variation within groups does not imply the existence of genetic variation among groups. Suppose Rob and his neighbor Pete both set out to plant a new lawn. They go to the garden store together, buy a big bag of seed, and divide the contents evenly. Pete, an avid gardener, goes home and plants the seed with great care. He fertilizes, balances the soil acidity, and provides just the right amount of water at just the right times. Rob, who lives next door, scatters the seed in his backyard, waters it infrequently and inadequately, and never even considers fertilizing it. After a few months, the two gardens are very different. Pete's lawn is thick, green, and vigorous, but Rob's lawn hardly justifies the name (Figure 15.17). We know that the difference between the two lawns cannot be due to the genetic characteristics of the grass seed, because Rob and Pete used seed from the same bag. Nonetheless, variation in the height and greenness of the grass within each lawn might be largely genetic because the seeds within each lawn experience very similar environmental conditions. All of the seeds in Pete's lawn get regular water and fertilizer, while all of the seeds in Rob's lawn are neglected to an equal extent. Thus, if the seed company has sold genetically

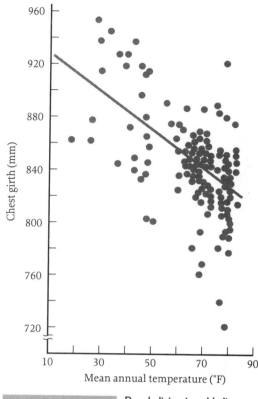

FIGURE 15.16 People living in cold climates have larger bodies than those who live in warm climates. The vertical axis plots mean chest girth for numerous human groups, and the horizontal axis plots the mean yearly temperature in the regions in which each group lives. Because chest girth is a measure of overall size, these data show that people living in colder climates have larger bodies.

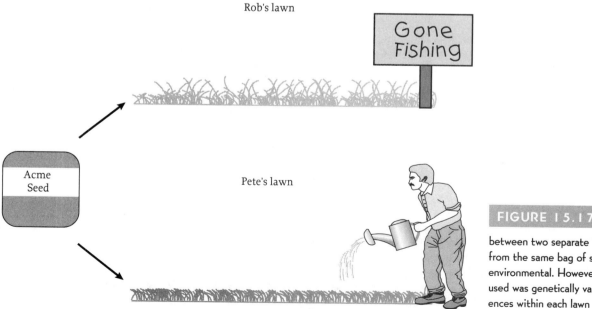

FIGURE 15.17 The differences between two separate lawns planted from the same bag of seed must be environmental. However, if the seed used was genetically variable, the differences within each lawn could be genetic.

variable seed, differences between individual plants within each lawn could be due mainly to genetic differences between the seeds themselves.

Exactly the same argument applies to variation in human stature. The fact that much of the variation in stature among Americans has a genetic component does not mean that stature is determined entirely by genes. It means there is genetic variation that affects stature, and these effects are relatively large in comparison with the effects of environmental differences among Americans. It does not follow that the differences in stature between Americans and other peoples are the result of genetic differences between them. For example, although Americans are taller on average than citizens of Japan, these differences in height are not necessarily genetic. That would be true only if two quite different conditions held: First, there would have to be a difference between Americans and Japanese in the distribution of genes affecting stature. Second, this genetic difference would have to be large compared with the differences in culture and environment between the two groups. The fact that there is genetic variation among Americans does not tell us whether or not Americans are genetically different from Japanese. The relatively small effect of environmental and cultural variation on height among Americans tells us nothing about the average difference in environment between Americans and Japanese.

The increase in stature that coincided with modernization is evidence for the influence of environmental variation on stature.

For height, there is good reason to believe that variation among groups is at least partly environmental. There has been a striking effect of modernization on the average heights of many peoples. For example, Figure 15.18 plots the heights of several groups of English boys between the ages of 5 and 21 in the nineteenth and twentieth centuries. In 1833, 19-year-old factory workers averaged about 160 cm (about 5 ft 3 in.). In 1874, laborers of the same age averaged about 167 cm (5 ft 6 in.). In 1958 the

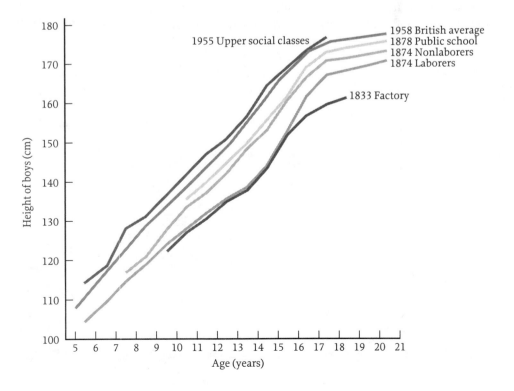

FIGURE 15.18 Height increases with time in English populations, but at any given time richer people are taller. Note that English "public schools" are the equivalent of American private schools.

TABLE 15.2	Japanese men who immigrated to Hawaii during the first part of the twentieth century were shorter than their children who had been born and raised in Hawaii. The immigrants were similar in height to the Japanese who remained in Japan, which indicates that the immigrants were a representative sample of the Japanese populations from which they came. The fact that the children of the immigrants were taller than their parents shows that environmental factors play an important role in creating variation in stature. (Data from Table 12.3 in G. A. Harrison, J. M. Tanner, D. R. Pilbeam, and P. T. Baker, 1988, Human Biology: An Introduction to Human Evolution, Variation, Growth, and Adaptability, 3rd ed., Oxford Science Publications, Oxford, England.)

	Average Height (cm)	Sample Size
Japanese immigrants to Hawaii	158.7	171
People from same regions of Japan who remained in Japan	158.4	178
The immigrants' children born in Hawaii	162.8	188

average British 19-year-old stood about 177 cm (5 ft 9 in.). Similar increases in height over the last hundred years can be seen among Swedish, German, Polish, and North American children. These changes have occurred very rapidly, probably too fast to be due solely to natural selection.

There also have been substantial changes in height among immigrants to the United States in the course of a few generations. During the first part of the twentieth century, when Japan had only begun to modernize, many Japanese came to Hawaii to work as laborers on sugar plantations. The immigrants were considerably shorter than their descendants who had been born in Hawaii (Table 15.2). This change in height among immigrants and their children was so rapid that it cannot be the result of genetic change. Instead, it must be due to some environmental difference between Japan and Hawaii in the early twentieth century. The underlying cause of this kind of environmental effect is not completely understood. In 1870s England, poverty was involved to some extent, because relatively wealthy public school boys were taller than less affluent nonlaborers, and nonlaborers were taller than poorer laborers. Observations like this have led some anthropologists to hypothesize that increases in the standard of living associated with modernization improve early childhood nutrition and increase children's growth rates. However, this cannot be the full explanation. Notice that even the richest people in England 120 years ago were shorter than the average person in England is today. Since it seems unlikely that wealthy Britons were malnourished in the 1870s, other factors must have contributed to the increase in stature during the last 120 years. Some authorities think that the control of childhood diseases may have played an important role in these changes.

THE RACE CONCEPT

Race plays an important role in modern life, but the popular conception of race is flawed.

Race is part of everyday life. For better or worse, our race affects how we see the world and how the world sees us; it affects our social relationships, our choice of marriage partners, our educational opportunities, and our employment prospects. We may decry discrimination, but we cannot deny that race plays a major role in many aspects of our lives.

Like any widely used word, *race* means different things to different people. However, the understanding of race held by many North Americans is based on three fundamentally flawed propositions:

1. *The human species can be naturally divided into a small number of distinct races.* According to this view, almost every person is a member of exactly one race; the only exceptions are the offspring of the members of different races. For example, many people in the United States think that people belong to one of three races: descendants of people from Europe, North Africa, and western Asia; descendants of people from sub-Saharan Africa; and descendants of people from eastern Asia.

2. *Members of different races are different in important ways, so knowing a person's race gives you important information about what he or she is like.* For example, biomedical researchers sometimes suggest that race predicts susceptibility to diseases like high blood pressure, heart disease, and infant mortality. Less benignly, some people believe that knowing a person's race reveals something about his or her intelligence or character.

3. *The differences between races are due to biological heritage.* Members of each race are genetically similar to each other, and genetically different from members of other races. Most Americans view African Americans and European Americans as members of different races because they are marked by genetically transmitted characters like skin color. In contrast, the Serbs and Croats of the former Yugoslavia are seen by most Americans as ethnic groups, rather than racial groups, because the differences between them are cultural rather than genetic.

Although many people believe these propositions to be true, they are not consistent with scientific knowledge about human variation. There are genetic differences between groups of people living in different parts of the world, but as we will see, these differences do not mean that the human species can be meaningfully divided into a set of nonoverlapping categories called races. *The common view of race is bad biology.*

Because people vary, it is possible to create classification schemes in which similar peoples are grouped together.

People tend to be more genetically and phenotypically similar to people who live near them than to people who live farther away. As we have seen already in this chapter, this is true for many genes. For example, the sickle-cell gene is common in central Africa and in India but is rare elsewhere; the $LTC*P$ gene, which allows adults to digest lactose, predominates in northern Europe and North Africa but is uncommon in the rest of the world. In general, overall genetic similarity is strongly associated with geographic proximity (Figure 15.19). Morphological similarities also link neighboring peoples. For example, most of the people who live near the equator have dark skin (Figure 15.20), and most of the people who live at high latitudes are stocky.

One consequence of these similarities between people is that it is possible to group people into geographically based categories on the basis of their genetic or phenotypic similarities. For example, a classification scheme based on the ability to digest lactose would place northern Europeans and North Africans in one group and the rest of the world in a second group. On the other hand, the overall genetic similarity shown in Figure 15.11 could be used to create a classification system that puts Africans in one

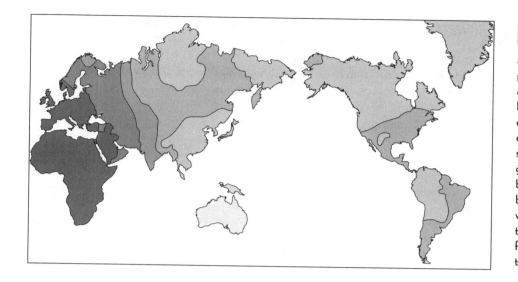

FIGURE 15.19 This contour map of overall genetic similarity is based on a sample of 120 genes from 42 populations assembled by Cavalli-Sforza and his colleagues. The fact that the contours of equal genetic similarity are roughly evenly spaced indicates that there is a smooth east-to-west gradient of overall genetic similarity; there are no sharp boundaries between groups. Sharp boundaries would produce a map in which many contour lines were positioned close together. This map is drawn from the same data used to construct the tree shown in Figure 15.11.

group; Europeans, northern Asians, and Native Americans in a second group; and southern Asians and people from Oceania in a third group.

However, such classification schemes do not support two properties required by the common concept of race. First, classification schemes based on different characters lead to radically different groupings, and the placement of individuals within any single category is often arbitrary. Second, classification schemes are not very informative. The average difference between groups of people living in different parts of the world is much smaller than the differences among individuals within each group.

There is no single natural classification of the human species.

In Chapter 4 we argued that species are distinctive entities that can be unambiguously identified in nature. Racial classifications for humans are quite different, and there is no natural classification scheme for categorizing us. To see what is meant by a natural classification scheme, consider the following analogy. Suppose you are a clerk

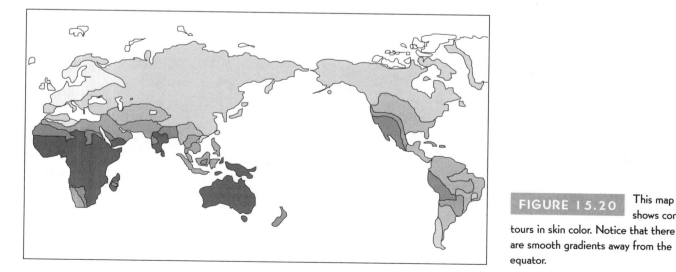

FIGURE 15.20 This map shows contours in skin color. Notice that there are smooth gradients away from the equator.

in a hardware store. Your boss assigns you to classify the contents of two large cabinets. The first cabinet contains power drills made by a number of different manufacturers; there are many drills but only one model per manufacturer. The second cabinet holds various different kinds of screws. The power drills vary in many ways: they have different colors, shapes, weights, and power ratings. The screws also vary: they have different lengths, diameters, pitches, and heads. You will have little trouble sorting the drills into piles according to manufacturer because all the drills made by a single manufacturer are similar in all of their dimensions: they are the same color, shape, and weight and have the same power rating. Moreover, each model is distinctly different; there are no intermediate types. This is a natural classification system. You will have a much harder time classifying the screws. Using length will produce one set of piles; diameter, a second set of piles; and screw pitch, a third set of piles. Moreover, even a classification based on a single characteristic like length will require arbitrary distinctions: Should there be three or four piles? Should the 1.5-inch screws be put in the pile with the smallest screws, or with the next bigger sizes? There is no natural way to classify the screws.

Racial classification schemes based on different sets of characters don't result in the same groupings for all characters. For example, a classification scheme based on the ability to digest lactose would yield very different groupings from one based on resistance to malaria. A classification based on skin color would produce a different grouping from one based on height. This problem cannot be solved by evaluating many different characters at the same time. As Figure 15.21 demonstrates, trees based on a large number of genes and trees based on a large number of morphological characters organize local groups in very different ways. The tree based on genetic traits groups aboriginal peoples from Australia and New Guinea together with people from Southeast Asia, but the one based on morphological features groups these aboriginal peoples with African Pygmies and the !Kung. Also notice that the genetic tree says that people from northern China are more similar to Europeans than they are to Southeast Asians.

This means that folk classification schemes based on skin color and facial morphology are not reliable predictors of overall genetic similarity. In Brazil, for example,

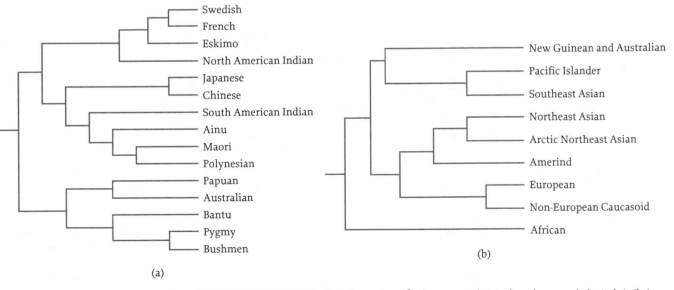

(a)

(b)

FIGURE 15.21   Evolutionary trees for human populations based on morphological similarity (a) look very different from trees based on genetic similarity (b).

people are classified according to what is called *cor* in Portugese. Although the literal translaton of *cor* is "color," the Brazilians' classification is based on more than skin color; it includes the morphology of the lips and eyes, and hair type. *Cor* plays a role in Brazilian society analogous to race in North America: there is substantial prejudice against those classified as "black," and people classified as black earn less money than other Brazilians on average. If the Brazilian folk classification is biologically meaningful, *cor* should be a good predictor of ancestry: "whites" should be of mainly European ancestry, and "blacks" of mainly African ancestry.

To test this idea, Flavia Parra and his colleagues at the Universidade Federal de Minas Gerais in Brazil assembled samples from three populations. They took blood samples from people on São Tomé, an island near the coast of Africa. This is near the area where the ancestors of most African Brazilians lived before being captured and transported to Brazil as slaves. Parra's group also took blood samples from people in Portugal, the area where the ancestors of most European Brazilians came from. It turns out that a small number of genetic loci differ between West African and European populations, and this pattern can be used to compute an index of African ancestry. Finally, these researchers collected two kinds of information from contemporary Brazilians. They assigned each of the individuals to one of three common Brazilian categories—"black," "white," and "intermediate"—on the basis of their phenotypes. They also took blood from each individual, extracted DNA, and typed each individual for genetic loci that differentiate West African and European populations. This analysis allowed them to compute the extent of African ancestry for each individual. The results are quite clear: there is very little correlation between phenotype and ancestry (Figure 15.22). People classified as "black" and people classified as "white" on the basis of their phenotypes are more or less indistinguishable genetically.

Racial classification schemes explain very little of the world's human genetic variation.

Geneticists have tried to account for the patterns of variation across the globe in biochemically detectable characters, such as blood-group loci and other genetic

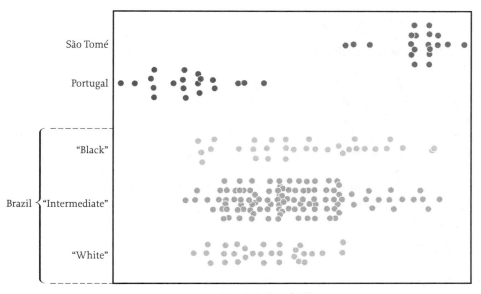

Genetic index of African ancestry

FIGURE 15.22 The genetic index of African ancestry for contemporary Africans living on São Tomé (an island just off the coast of Gabon that served as the entry point for the West African slave trade), contemporary Portuguese, and contemporary Brazilians classifed as "black," "white," and "intermediate" on the basis of skin color, facial morphology, and hair texture. These data indicate that the Brazilian folk classification system predicts little about overall genetic similarity.

polymorphisms. In these studies the human species was categorized first into local groups of people belonging to the same ethnic group, linguistic group, or nationality. Then local groups were collected into larger, geographically based categories that correspond roughly to the usual races. Geneticists computed the amount of variation in these characters within each local group, among groups within each race, and among races. They found that there is much more genetic variation *within* local groups than there is *among* local groups or among races themselves. Differences within local groups account for about 85% of all the variation in the human species. To put this another way, suppose that a malevolent extraterrestrial wiped out the entire human species except for one local group, which it preserved in an extraterrestrial zoo. The alien could pick any local group at random—the Efe, the Inuit, the citizens of Ames, Iowa, or the people of Patagonia—and then wipe out the rest of the humans on the planet. This group would still contain, on average, 85% of the genetic variation that exists in the entire human species. This means that standard racial classifications do not correspond to variation in genetic traits among the peoples of the world.

Racial classification schemes don't represent natural biological categories.

The bottom line is that people can be classified, and such classifications are not necessarily arbitrary, but they do not reflect any *natural* subdivision of the human species into biologically distinct groups. Nor does knowing a person's position in a classification reveal very much about what that person is like.

This conclusion is consistent with what we have learned about human evolution. It seems likely that anatomically modern humans are a very recently evolved species; the evidence from both mitochrondrial DNA and fossils suggests an age of less than 200,000 years. This means that it is less likely that natural selection and genetic drift have produced larger genetic differences within the human species than in other, older species. Recall that the genetic differences among different species of chimpanzees are much greater than among different groups of humans, probably because chimpanzees are a considerably older genus. Moreover, we know that gene flow tends to eliminate genetic differences between groups, and there has been extensive gene flow in human history.

Races represent cultural categories that play an important, but unfortunate, role in society.

Many people find the conclusion that races aren't real completely implausible. They "know" from experience that race is real. The late Martin Luther King Jr.'s dream that "my four little children will one day live in a nation where they will not be judged by the color of their skin, but by the content of their character" has not yet been realized. This is because racism is real and remains a pervasive problem in our society. But it's important to separate the reality of racism from the scientific understanding of the concept of race.

Many view the claim that race is not a valid scientific construct as another example of the "political correctness" that is now common in academia. This view has some support within anthropology. For example, in the November 1994 issue of *Discover* magazine, University of Colorado anthropologist Alice Brues stated,

> A popular political statement now is, "There is no such thing as race." I wonder what people think when they hear this. They would have to suppose that the speaker if he were dropped by parachute into downtown Nairobi, would

be unable to tell, by looking around him, whether he was in Nairobi or Stockholm. This could only damage his credibility. The visible differences between different populations tell everyone that *there is something here.* (p. 60)

But our intuitions sometimes lead us astray. Our eyes tell us that the Earth is flat, but it is really a sphere. Our intuition tells us that a bullet fired horizontally from a rifle will hit the ground long after a bullet dropped from the muzzle at the same instant, yet in reality they will hit the ground at the same time. Our mind tells us that it is impossible for an elephant to have descended from a shrewlike insectivore, even though that is exactly what happened. The intuition that race is real is also an illusion.

Professor Brues is undoubtedly correct that a parachute jumper who landed in Nairobi would be unlikely to think that he was in Stockholm, Tokyo, Bombay, or Honolulu. But would he be certain that he was in Nairobi, and not in Johannesburg, or Khartoum? Probably not. And what if we imagine an intrepid soul who attempts to bicycle from Nairobi to Stockholm? As she pedaled from Nairobi through Kinshasa, Khartoum, Cairo, Istanbul, and Budapest and finally reached Stockholm, she would observe that people change in many ways, but the change would always be subtle; there would be no sharp boundaries with one kind of people on one side and a different kind of people on the other side. The cyclist would see that people vary but this variation does not sort itself out into neat, discrete categories. Thus, our perception of race depends on which of these two metaphors we think captures the essential features of human variation. The scientific evidence demonstrates quite conclusively that there is considerably more variation within human groups than among them, and this is why our transcontinental bicyclist would not note any sharply defined changes as she made her way slowly north.

In our opinion, race is a culturally constructed category, not a meaningful biological concept. The characters that North Americans conventionally use to sort people into racial categories tend to be biologically transmitted traits, like skin color and facial features. But we could just as well use culturally transmitted traits like religion, dialect, or class. Classifications based on a small set of biologically transmitted traits have no more scientific validity than do classifications based on religion, language, or political affiliation. Although skin color and facial features are salient characteristics in the United States, in some societies other types of characters matter much more. Religion is the basis of bitter animosity in Northern Ireland, although the genetic differences between Protestant and Catholic Irish are even more microscopic than are the genetic differences between African Americans and European Americans. In the ethnic conflicts that have seared the globe in the last decade it is literally a matter of life and death whether you are Azeri or Armenian in Nagorno-Karabakh; Hutu or Tutsi in Rwanda; or Serb or Muslim in Bosnia. Yet in each case, people are divided by culture, not genes.

FURTHER READING

Bodmer, W., and L. L. Cavalli-Sforza. 1976. *Genetics, Evolution, and Man.* Freeman, New York.

Cavalli-Sforza, L. L., P. Menozzi, and A. Piazza. 1994. *The History and Geography of Human Genes.* Princeton University Press, Princeton, NJ.

Falconer, D. R. 1981. *Introduction to Quantitative Genetics.* Longman, London.

Flatz, G. 1987. The genetics of lactose digestion in humans. *Advances in Human Genetics* 16: 1–77.

Harrison, G. A., J. M. Tanner, D. R. Pilbeam, and P. T. Baker. 1988. *Human Biology: An Introduction to Human Evolution, Variation, Growth, and Adaptability* (3rd ed.). Oxford Science, Oxford, England.

Jobling, M. A., M. E. Hurles, and C. Tyler-Smith. 2004. *Human Evolutionary Genetics, Origins, Peoples & Disease*. Garland, New York.

STUDY QUESTIONS

1. What sources of human variation are described in this chapter? Why is it important to distinguish among them?

2. Consider the phenotype of human finger number. Most people have exactly five fingers on each hand, but some people have fewer. What is the source of variation in finger number?

3. Why is it hard to determine the source of variation in human phenotypes? Why might it be easier to determine the source of variation for other animals?

4. Explain how studies of human twins allow researchers to estimate the effects of genetic and environmental differences on phenotypic traits.

5. What kind of body size and shape is best in a humid climate? Why?

6. Suppose you are told that differences in IQ scores among white Americans have a genetic basis. What would that tell you about the differences in average scores between white Americans and Americans belonging to other ethnic groups? Why?

7. Explain why race is not a biologically meaningful category of classification.

KEY TERMS

genetic variation

environmental variation

variation within groups

variation among groups

specific language impairment/SLI

selection-mutation balance

falciparum malaria

balanced polymorphism

non-insulin-dependent diabetes/NIDD

insulin

lactose

*LCT*P*

*LTC*R*

single nucleotide polymorphisms/SNPs

founder effect

porphyria variegata

Oceania

heritability

environmental covariation

monozygotic twins

dizygotic twins

CHAPTER 16

EVOLUTION AND HUMAN BEHAVIOR

WHY EVOLUTION IS RELEVANT TO HUMAN BEHAVIOR

The application of evolutionary principles to understanding human behavior is controversial.

The theory of evolution is at the core of our understanding of the natural world. By studying how natural selection, recombination, mutation, genetic drift, and other evolutionary processes interact to produce evolutionary change, we come to understand why organisms are the way they are. Of course, our understanding of evolution is far from perfect, and other disciplines, most notably chemistry and physics, contribute greatly to our understanding of life. As the great geneticist Theodosius Dobzhansky once said, however, "Nothing in biology makes sense except in the light of evolution."

431

So far, the way we have applied evolutionary theory in this book is not controversial. We are principally interested in the evolutionary history of our own species, *Homo sapiens*, but we began by using evolutionary theory to understand the behavior of our closest relatives, the nonhuman primates. Twenty years ago, when evolutionary theory was new to primatology, this approach generated some controversy, but now most primatologists are committed to evolutionary explanations of behavior. In Part Three we used evolutionary theory to develop models of the patterns of behavior that might have characterized early hominins. Although some researchers might debate the fine points of this analysis, there is little disagreement about the value of adaptive reasoning in this context. Perhaps this is because the early hominins were simply "bipedal apes," with brains the size of modern chimpanzee brains. Not many people object to evolutionary analyses of physiological traits, such as lactose tolerance, but they may debate the merits of particular explanations for those traits. Similarly, most people accept evolutionary explanations about why we live so long and mature so slowly. These traits are clearly part of human biology, and there is a broad consensus that evolutionary theory provides an essential key for understanding them.

The consensus evaporates when we enter the the domain of contemporary human behavior. Most social scientists acknowledge that evolution has shaped our bodies, our minds, and our behavior to a limited extent. However, many social scientists have been very critical of attempts to apply evolutionary theory to contemporary human behavior because they think evolutionary analyses imply that behavior is genetically determined. Genetic determinism of behavior in humans seems inconsistent with the fact that so much of our behavior is acquired through learning, and that so much of our behavior and beliefs is strongly influenced by our culture and environment. The notion that evolutionary explanations imply genetic determinism is based on a fundamental misunderstanding about how the natural world works.

All phenotypic traits, including behavioral traits, reflect the interactions between genes and the environment.

Many people have the mistaken view that genetic transmission and learning are mutually exclusive. That is, they believe that behaviors are either genetic and therefore unchangeable, or learned and thereby controlled entirely by environmental contingencies. This assumption lies at the heart of the "nature–nurture question," a debate that has plagued the social sciences for many years.

The nature–nurture debate is based on a false dichotomy. It assumes that there is a clear distinction between the effects of genes (nature) and the effects of the environment (nurture). People often think that genes are like engineering drawings for a finished machine, and that individuals vary simply because their genes carry different specifications. For example, they imagine that basketball player Yao Ming is tall because his genes specified an adult height of 2.3 m (7 ft 6 in.), and Earl Boykins is short because his genes specified an adult height of 1.65 m (5 ft 5 in.).

However, genes are not like blueprints that specify phenotype. Every trait results from the *interaction* of a genetic program with the environment. Thus, genes are more like recipes in the hands of a creative cook, sets of instructions for the construction of an organism using materials available in the environment. At each step, this very complex process depends on the nature of local conditions. The expression of any genotype always depends on the environment. A person's adult height is shaped by the genes they inherited from their parents, how well nourished they were in childhood, and the nature of the diseases they were exposed to when they were growing up.

The expression of behavioral traits is usually more sensitive to environmental conditions than is the expression of morphological and physiological traits. As we saw in Chapter 3, traits that develop uniformly in a wide range of environments, such as finger number, are said to be "canalized." Traits that vary in response to environmental cues, such as subsistence strategies, are said to be "plastic." Every trait, however, whether plastic or canalized, results from the unfolding of a developmental program in a particular environment. Even highly canalized characters can be modified by environmental factors, such as fetal exposure to mutagenic agents or accidents.

Natural selection can shape developmental processes so that organisms develop different adaptive behaviors in different environments.

Some people understand that all traits are influenced by a combination of genes and environment, but they reject evolutionary explanations of human behavior because they have fallen prey to a second, more subtle, misunderstanding. Namely, they believe that natural selection cannot create adaptations unless behavioral differences between individuals are caused by genetic differences. If this were true, it would follow that adaptive explanations of human behavior must be invalid because there is no doubt that most of the variation in behavioral traits, such as foraging strategies, marriage practices, and values, is not due to genetic differences but is instead the product of learning and culture.

This belief is false, however, because natural selection shapes learning mechanisms so that organisms adjust their behavior to local conditions in an adaptive way. Recall from Chapter 3 that this is exactly what happens with soapberry bugs. Male soapberry bugs in Oklahoma guard their mates when females are scarce, but not when females are abundant. Individual males vary their behavior adaptively in response to the local sex ratio. In order for this kind of flexibility in male behavior to evolve, there had to be small genetic differences in the male propensity to guard a mated female, and small genetic differences in how mate guarding is influenced by the local sex ratio. If such variation exists, then natural selection can mold the responses of males so that they are locally adaptive. In any given population, however, most of the observed behavioral variation is due to the fact that individual males respond adaptively to environmental cues.

Behavior in the soapberry bug is relatively simple. Human learning and decision making are immensely more complex and flexible. We know much less about the mechanisms that produce behavioral flexibility in humans than we do about the mechanisms that produce flexibility in mate guarding among soapberry bugs. Nonetheless, such mechanisms must exist, and it is reasonable to assume that they have been shaped by natural selection. (Note that we are not arguing that all behavioral variation in human societies is adaptive. We know that evolution does not produce adaptation in every case, as we discussed in Chapter 3.) The crucial point here is that evolutionary approaches do not imply that differences in behavior among humans are the product of genetic differences between individuals.

In the remainder of this chapter we will consider two ways that evolutionary theory can be used to understand the minds and behavior of modern humans. As you will see, researchers from different academic disciplines have followed different approaches in their efforts to understand how evolution has shaped human behavior. Some have focused on how natural selection has shaped the design of the human brain. Others have tried to understand how the human capacity for culture, and the ability to acquire ideas, beliefs, and values from other group members, have influenced the evolution of human behavior. In the remainder of this chapter and the next we will illustrate how these approaches can be used to gain insights about the behavior of contemporary humans.

UNDERSTANDING HOW WE THINK

Evolutionary analyses provide important insights about how our brains are designed.

The adaptation that most clearly distinguishes humans from other primates is our large and very complex brain. Natural selection hasn't just made our brains big; it has shaped our cognitive abilities in very specific ways and molded the way we think.

Even the most flexible strategies are based on special-purpose psychological mechanisms.

Psychologists once thought that people and other animals had a few general-purpose learning mechanisms that allowed them to modify any aspect of their phenotypes adaptively. However, a considerable body of empirical evidence indicates that animals are predisposed to learn some things and not others. For example, rats quickly learn to avoid novel foods that make them ill. Moreover, rats' food aversions are based solely on the taste of a food that has made them sick, not the food's size, shape, color, or other attributes. This learning rule makes sense because rats live in a very wide range of environments, where they frequently encounter new foods, and usually forage at night when it is dark. In order to determine whether a new food is edible, they taste a small amount first and then wait several hours. If it is poisonous, they soon become ill, and they do not eat it again. Rats may pay attention to the taste of foods, instead of other attributes, because it is often too dark to see what they are eating (Figure 16.1). However, there are limits to the flexibility of this learning mechanism. There are certain items that rats will never sample, and in this way their diet is rigidly controlled by genes. Moreover, the learning process is not affected equally by all environmental contingencies. For example, rats are affected more by the association of novel tastes with gastric distress than they are with other possible associations.

Natural selection determines the kinds of problems that the brains of particular species are good at solving. To understand the psychology of any species, we must know what kinds of problems its members need to solve in nature.

FIGURE 16.1   Rats initially sample small amounts of unfamiliar foods, and if they become ill soon after eating something, they will not eat it again.

Our brains may be designed to solve the kinds of problems that our ancestors faced when they lived in small foraging bands.

We know that people lived in small-scale foraging societies for the vast majority of human history (Figure 16.2); stratified societies with agriculture and high population density have existed for only a few thousand years (Figure 16.3). John Tooby and

Leda Cosmides of the University of California Santa Barbara argue that complex adaptations like the brain evolve slowly, so our brains are designed for life in foraging societies. They use the term **environment of evolutionary adaptedness** (EEA) to refer to the social, technological, and ecological conditions under which human mental abilities evolved. Tooby and Cosmides and their colleagues envision the EEA as being much like the world of contemporary hunter-gatherers.

People living in foraging groups face certain kinds of problems that affect their fitness. For example, food sharing is an essential part of life in modern foraging groups. Although vegetable foods are typically distributed only to family members, meat is nearly always shared more widely. Food sharing is a form of reciprocal altruism. The big problem with reciprocal altruism is that it is costly to interact with individuals who do not reciprocate. Thus, Cosmides and Tooby hypothesized that human cognition should be finely tuned to detect cheaters, and they have accumulated a convincing body of experimental data suggesting that people are very attentive to imbalances in social exchange and violations of social contracts.

As we have seen, there is quite a bit of uncertainty about how early humans lived, and this adds ambiguity to predictions about human psychology based on evolutionary reasoning. Some authorities believe that early members of the genus *Homo* were much like contemporary human foragers. That is, they lived in small bands and subsisted by hunting and gathering. They controlled fire, had home bases, and shared food. They could talk to one another, and they shared cultural beliefs, ideas, and traditions. Other authorities think that the lives of the earliest species of *Homo* were completely unlike those of modern hunter-gatherers. They think that these hominins didn't hunt large game, share food, or have home bases. If early hominins lived like contemporary foragers, then it is reasonable to think that the human brain has evolved to solve the kinds of problems that confront modern foragers, such as detecting freeloaders in social exchange. On the other hand, if lifeways that characterize contemporary foragers did not emerge until 40 kya, then there might not have been enough time for selection to assemble specialized psychological mechanisms to manage the challenges that foragers face, such as food sharing.

FIGURE 16.2   Evolutionary psychologists believe that the human mind has evolved to solve the adaptive challenges that confront food foragers because this is the subsistence strategy that humans have practiced for most of our evolutionary history.

Evolved psychological mechanisms cause human societies to share many universal characteristics.

Much of anthropology (and other social sciences) is based on the assumption that human behavior is not effectively constrained by biology. People have to obtain food, shelter, and other resources necessary for their survival and reproduction. But beyond that, human behavior is not constrained by biology.

As we have just seen, however, this assumption is not very plausible from an evolutionary perspective. It is likely that evolved mechanisms in the human brain channel the evolution of human societies and human culture, making some outcomes much more likely than others. So the right question is, What kinds of mental mechanisms do humans have? We are likely to share some mental mechanisms with other animals, but we may also have certain mental mechanisms that differentiate us from other creatures. In the discussion that follows, we examine two examples of cognitive

FIGURE 16.3   Indigenous peoples of the Mississippi Delta constructed these mound structures about 2500 to 1300 years ago. Monumental architecture like this is based on the ability of one group of people to control the labor of others, a signal of social stratification.

mechanisms that are found in all human societies: one mechanism—inbreeding avoidance—that we may have inherited from our primate ancestors; and another—the capacity for language—that is derived.

Inbreeding Avoidance

The offspring of genetically related parents have lower fitness than the offspring of unrelated parents do.

Geneticists refer to matings between relatives as **inbred matings** and contrast them with **outbred matings** between unrelated individuals. The offspring of inbred matings are much more likely to be homozygous for deleterious recessive alleles than are the offspring of outbred matings. As a consequence, inbred offspring are less robust and have higher mortality than the offspring of outbred matings. In Chapter 15 we discussed a number of genetic diseases, such as PKU, Tay-Sachs disease, and cystic fibrosis, that are caused by a recessive gene. People who are heterozygous for such deleterious recessive alleles are completely normal, but people who are homozygous suffer severe, often fatal consequences. Recall that such alleles occur at low frequencies in most human populations. However, there are many loci in the human genome. Thus, even if the frequency of deleterious recessives at each locus is very small, there is a good chance that everybody has at least one lethal recessive gene somewhere in their genome. Geneticists have estimated that each person carries the equivalent of two to five lethal recessives. Mating with close relatives is deleterious because it greatly increases the chance that both partners will carry a deleterious recessive allele at the same locus. Inbreeding leads to substantial reductions in fitness (Box 16.1). This, in turn, suggests that natural selection should favor behavioral adaptations that reduce the chance of inbreeding.

Matings between close relatives are very rare among nonhuman primates.

Remember from Chapter 7 that in all species of nonhuman primates, members of one or both sexes leave their natal groups near the time of puberty. Adult males do not often remain in groups long enough to be able to mate with their own daughters. It is very likely that dispersal is an adaptation to prevent inbreeding. In principle, primates could remain in natal groups and simply avoid mating with close kin. However, this would limit the number of potential mates and might be unreliable if there were much uncertainty about paternity.

Natural selection has provided at least some primates with another form of protection against inbreeding: a strong inhibition against mating with close kin. In matrilineal macaque groups, some males acquire high rank and mate with adult females before they emigrate. However, matings among maternal kin are extremely uncommon.

Experimental studies conducted by Wendy Saltzman of the University of California Riverside and her colleagues suggest that reproductive inhibition in callitrichids is due partly to inbreeding aversion. Young females housed with their mothers and fathers do not reproduce; but when fathers are replaced with unrelated males, both mothers and daughters breed. Adult female chimpanzees often have opportunities to mate with their fathers (Figure 16.5). More than 30 years of research at Gombe Stream National Park indicates that, in fact, they rarely do. Female chimpanzees seem to have a general aversion to mating with males much older than they are, and males seem to

BOX 16.1

Why Inbred Matings Are Bad News

The following simple example illustrates why inbreeding increases the chance that offspring will be homozygous for a deleterious recessive gene. Suppose that Cleo has exactly one lethal recessive somewhere in her genome. If she mates with a nonrelative, Mark, the chance that he carries the same deleterious recessive is simply equal to the frequency of heterozygotes carrying that gene in the population. (We don't need to consider the frequency of individuals who are homozygous for the recessive allele, because the allele is lethal in homozygotes.) Let p be the frequency of deleterious recessives in the population. Using the Hardy–Weinberg law, we know that the frequency of heterozygotes is $2p(1 - p)$. The frequency of lethal recessives is typically about 0.001. Thus there is only about 1 chance in 500 that Mark and Cleo carry the same deleterious recessive.

If Cleo mates with her brother, Ptolemy, the story is quite different. Remember from Chapter 8 that r, the coefficient of relatedness, gives the probability that two individuals will inherit the same gene through common descent. For full siblings, $r = 0.5$. Thus if Cleo mates with her brother, there is 1 chance in 2 that he will carry the same lethal recessive that she does, a value that is about 100 times greater than for an outbred mating. Because Cleo and Ptolemy are both heterozygotes for the lethal recessive, Mendel's laws say that 25% of their offspring will be homozygotes and therefore will die. Thus, on average, Cleo will experience a 12.5% decrease in fitness by mating with her brother Ptolemy compared with an outbred mating with Mark.

This simple example actually understates the cost of inbreeding, because people often carry more than one deleterious recessive. Oxford University biologist Robert May derived the estimates in Figure 16.4 using a more realistic model. As you can see, inbreeding is quite bad. Matings between siblings or between parents and their offspring ($r = 0.5$) produce about 40% fewer offspring than do outbred matings. The effects for other inbred matings are smaller but still serious.

Empirical studies strongly support these predictions. Data from 38 species of captive mammals indicate that the offspring of matings among siblings and among parents and their offspring are 33% less likely to survive to adulthood than the offspring of outbred matings. Studies in wild populations, though less conclusive, tell the same story. Several studies suggest that humans are affected by inbreeding in the same way. For example, the 161 children of father–daughter or brother–sister matings studied by geneticist Eva Seemanová, of Charles University in the Czech Republic, were twice as likely to die during their first year as their maternal half-siblings were, and they were 10 times as likely to suffer serious congenital defects. Other evidence comes from studies of Moroccan Jews living in Israel who do not consider marriages between men and their nieces to be incestuous. A study of 131 children from such marriages indicates that they suffer a 20% reduction in fitness compared with a control group from the same population.

 Population genetic theory predicts that close inbreeding can lead to serious reductions in fitness. The vertical axis plots the percentage of reduction in fitness due to inbreeding, and the horizontal axis plots the coefficient of relatedness among spouses. The curve is based on the conservative assumption that people carry the equivalent of 2.2 lethal recessives.

be generally uninterested in females much younger than themselves. These mechanisms may protect females from mating with their fathers, and vice versa.

FIGURE 16.5 Female chimpanzees avoid mating with closely related males. Although mothers have close and affectionate relationships with their adult sons, matings between mothers and sons are quite uncommon.

Humans rarely mate with close relatives.

During the first half of the twentieth century, cultural anthropologists fanned out across the world to study the lives of exotic peoples. Their hard and sometimes dangerous work has given us an enormous trove of information about the spectacular variety of human lifeways. They found that domestic arrangements vary greatly across cultures: some groups are polygynous, some monogamous, and a few polyandrous. Some people reckon descent through the female line and are subject to the authority of their mother's brother. In some societies, married couples live with the husband's kin, in others they live with the wife's kin, and in some they set up their own households. Some people must marry their mother's brothers' children; others are not allowed to do so.

In all of this variety of domestic arrangements, there is not a *single* ethnographically documented case of a society in which brothers and sisters regularly marry, or one in which parents regularly mate with their own children. The only known case of regular brother–sister mating comes from census data collected by Roman governors of Egypt from A.D. 20 to 258. From the 172 census returns that have survived, it is possible to reconstruct the composition of 113 marriages: 12 were between full siblings and 8 between half-siblings. These marriages seem to have been both legal and socially approved, as both prenuptial agreements and wedding invitations survive.

The pattern for more distant kin is much more variable. Some societies permit both sex and marriage with nieces and nephews or between first cousins; other societies prohibit sex and marriage among even distant relatives. Moreover, the pattern of incest prohibitions in many societies does not conform to genetic categories. For example, even distant kin on the father's side may be taboo in a given society, while maternal cousins may be the most desirable marriage partners in the same society. Sometimes the rules about who can have sex are different from the rules governing who can marry.

Adults are not sexually attracted to the people with whom they grew up.

The fact that inbreeding avoidance is very common among primates suggests that our human ancestors probably also had psychological mechanisms preventing them from mating with close kin. These psychological mechanisms would disappear during human evolution only if they were selected against. However, mating with close relatives is highly deleterious in humans, as it is in other primates. Thus, both theory and data predict that modern humans will have psychological mechanisms that reduce the chance of close inbreeding, at least in the small-scale societies in which human psychology was shaped.

There is evidence that such psychological mechanisms exist. In the late nineteenth century the Finnish sociologist Edward Westermarck speculated that childhood propinquity stifles desire. By this he meant that people who live in intimate association as small children do not find each other sexually attractive as adults. A number of lines of evidence provide support for Westermarck's hypothesis:

- *Taiwanese minor marriage.* Until recently, an unusual form of marriage was widespread in China. In **minor marriages**, children were betrothed and the prospective bride was adopted into the family of her future husband during infancy. There the betrothed couple grew up together like brother and sister. According to Taiwanese informants interviewed by Stanford University anthropologist Arthur Wolf, the partners in minor marriages found each other sexually unexciting. Sexual disinterest was so great that fathers-in-law sometimes had to beat the newlyweds to convince them to consummate their marriage. Wolf's data indicate that minor marriages produced about 30% fewer children than did other arranged marriages (Figure 16.6a) and were much more likely to end in separation or divorce (Figure 16.6b). Infidelity was also more common in minor marriages. When modernization reduced parental authority, many young men and women who were betrothed in minor marriages broke their engagements and married others.

- *Kibbutz age-mates.* Before World War II, many Jewish immigrants to Israel organized themselves into utopian communities called *kibbutzim* (plural of **kibbutz**). In these communities, children were raised in communal nurseries, and they lived intimately with a small group of unrelated age-mates from infancy to adulthood. The ideology of the kibbutzim did not discourage sexual experimentation or marriage by children in such peer groups, but neither behavior occurred. Israeli sociologist Joseph Sepher, himself a kibbutznik, collected data on 2769 marriages in 211 kibbutzim. Only 14 of them were between members of the same peer group, and in all of these cases one partner joined the peer group after the age of six. From data collected in his own kibbutz, Sepher found no instances of premarital sex among members of the same peer group.

- *Third-party attitudes toward incest.* As you may have realized already, aversions to inbreeding extend beyond our attitudes toward our own mating behavior to include strong beliefs about appropriate mating behavior by other individuals. We are disgusted not only by the idea of having sex with our parents or our own

 In minor marriages, the age of the wife when she arrives in her future husband's household (age at adoption) affects both fertility and the likelihood of divorce. (a) The fertility of women adopted at young ages is depressed. (b) The younger a woman is when she arrives in her husband's household, the less likely it is that the marriage will survive.

children, but also by the idea of other people having sex with their children. Daniel Fessler and Carlos Navarette of the University of California Los Angeles think that these kinds of "third-party" aversions are a form of "egocentric empathy." Westermarck hypothesized that coresidence during childhood generates sexual aversions to particular partners. If that is the case, then the extent of exposure to siblings of the opposite sex during childhood might also be linked to the strength of feelings about one's own behavior and the strength of feelings about the behavior of others. Debra Lieberman, John Tooby, and Leda Cosmides at the University of California Santa Barbara, along with Fessler and Navarette, have tested these predictions by conducting experiments in which they asked subjects (university undergraduates) to contemplate consensual sibling incest involving hypothetical adults. The results from both studies largely confirmed Westermarck's hypothesis. Those who had grown up with opposite-sex siblings had stronger negative responses to the hypothetical scenario than those who had not. Moreover, women generally had stronger aversive responses to the hypothetical scenario than men did.

Evolutionary interpretations of inbreeding avoidance differ sharply from influential theories about incest and inbreeding avoidance in psychology and cultural anthropology.

Incest and inbreeding avoidance play a central role in many influential theories of human society. Thinkers as diverse as Sigmund Freud (the founder of psychoanalysis) and Claude Lévi-Strauss (the father of structuralist anthropology) have asserted that people harbor a deep desire to have sex with members of their immediate family. According to this view, the existence of culturally imposed rules against incest is all that saves society from these destructive passions. This view is not very plausible from an evolutionary perspective. There are compelling theoretical reasons to expect that natural selection will erect psychological barriers to incest, and good evidence that it has done so in humans and other primates. Both theory and observation suggest that the family is not the focus of desire; it's a tiny island of sexual indifference.

However, the evolutionary analysis we have outlined here is not quite complete. For example, we might expect the Westermarck effect and egocentric empathy to produce an aversion to minor marriage in China. Yet this practice has persisted for a long time. It is possible that psychological mechanisms are supplemented or perhaps superseded by conscious reasoning. People in many societies believe that incest leads to sickness and deformity, and their beliefs may guide their behavior and shape their cultural practices. Finally, it seems clear that attitudes about incest are not based solely on the deleterious effects of inbreeding. If they were, then all societies would have the same kinds of rules about who can have sexual relationships. Instead, we find considerable variation. For example, some societies encourage first cousins to marry, while others prohibit them from doing so.

Human Language

The cognitive capacities that give rise to language are universal.

Languages are clearly part of human culture; children learn to speak the language of the people around them. Although people in different parts of the world speak different languages, they share the morphological adaptations that make spoken language possible and the cognitive capacities that allow them to learn and to use language. The abilities to decode words and to extract meaning from combinations of words are based on highly specialized and derived cognitive mechanisms.

Humans can perceive speech sounds at a much more rapid rate than other sounds.

Phonemes are the basic unit of speech perception, the smallest bits of sound that we recognize as meaningful elements of language. Not all languages recognize the same phonetic distinctions. For example, English speakers hear the difference between "l" and "r" sounds, but Swahili and Japanese speakers lump them together in a single phoneme. Interestingly, infants can initially distinguish the full range of phonemes, but during the first year of life they become insensitive to distinctions that are not part of the language spoken around them.

We are able to decode very rapid streams of phonemes. When we speak normally, we utter about 10 phonemes per second. If we concentrate, we can understand people who bombard us with 25 phonemes per second. By contrast, even the best Morse code operators cannot keep up once the transmission rate exceeds about 5 clicks per second. In fact, if the rate of transmission of a simple sound like a Morse code click exceeds 20 sounds per second, we hear a continuous buzz rather than a sequence of discrete sounds.

It's not hard to imagine why the ability to communicate rapidly was favored by natural selection. The early human who could decode the hurried shout, "Look out, a lion is behind you," would have a substantial edge over the poor fellow who could only say, "Speak more slowly, I can't . . . "

We perceive speech as a sequence of discrete words, even though this is an auditory illusion.

We perceive speech the same way we write it down: as a sequence of discrete words separated by brief silences. However, this is not really the case. There are no periods of silence in ordinary speech. When researchers use an instrument that plots sound level against time, they note that sound level does not drop to zero between spoken words, and in fact, distinct words do not appear on the plot. You may have experienced this phenomenon yourself while listening to people speaking a language you don't understand. You probably couldn't tell when one word ended and another began. This is because there are no gaps between words.

Language is based on grammatical properties that allow us to interpret sequences of words.

Consider the following two sentences: *Org killed your brother* and *Your brother killed Org*. The words are the same, but the meanings produced in your brain are very different. One situation calls for revenge, and the other calls for keeping a close watch on Org's relatives. We hear speech as a sequence of words, like cars coming down an off-ramp. In order to create meaning, our brain interprets this information using rules that specify meaning. These rules are what we call **grammar**. These are not the obscure rules that modern Western people struggle to master in school, but unconscious rules that allow almost every person to speak and understand spoken language effortlessly.

The world's languages share a number of grammatical rules that allow people to use sequences of words to express useful ideas. Some of these rules were listed in a paper written by Steven Pinker, now at Harvard University, and Paul Bloom, now at Yale:

- Words must belong to categories such as "noun," "adjective," and "verb," which correspond to basic features of the world that people need to talk about—in this case, things, the qualities of things, and actions, respectively.

- Some rules allow the listener to figure out what the speaker intended to say about the relationship between things, qualities, and actions. These kinds of rules tell us that Org is a killer in the first sentence above and a corpse in the second. In English these rules are based on the order of the words: the actor comes before the verb, and the recipient of the act comes after the verb. In other languages these distinctions are made by modification of the nouns to indicate, for example, which person is the killer and which is the victim. Linguists refer to this part of grammar as **syntax**.

- Words are grouped into phrases that also belong to categories such as "noun phrase" and "verb phrase." By combining words in this way, language can express a wide range of thoughts with a small number of words. The noun *brother* by itself is not very informative. By combining *brother* with other words in noun phrases, however, you can refer to *my brother, your brother, your older brother, your husband's brother*, and so on.

- Some rules allow a listener to determine which words the speaker meant to group together in phrases. These rules allow us to distinguish between the sentences *Your brother killed my father* and *My brother killed your father* by telling us that *your* is to be grouped with *brother* in the first sentence, and with *father* in the second sentence.

- Verbs are modified to indicate when events occurred. For example, we can distinguish between the statements *Org killed your brother* and *Org will kill your brother*. Verbs are also modified to indicate the relative timing of two events. Thus, *Org had killed your brother before Thag showed up* tells the listener that Thag did not witness the killing.

There are other grammatical rules for forming questions, for indicating states of mind, and for reducing the amount of memory necessary to process a sentence.

This system is not perfect. Even with all the grammatical rules in action and with help from context, many sentences allow for more than one meaning. Wordplay such as double entendre relies on such ambiguity. Nonetheless, by combining discrete words using grammatical rules, humans can communicate an incredible range of useful information (and make very bad puns).

The psychological mechanisms that structure language are different from other cognitive abilities.

Many researchers think that language is a manifestation of a powerful general-purpose learning mechanism. Humans learn many complicated rule-bound skills, like playing the piano or long division. However, no one would argue that our brains evolved because of the selective advantages of learning to play the piano or doing long division. Instead, we must have a powerful and very general learning mechanism that allows us to acquire diverse skills. According to this view, language is not a specialized adaptation; it is just another complex skill acquired by the same general learning mechanism.

This point of view does not take into account several lines of evidence that suggest that we have special-purpose cognitive mechanisms specifically shaped by natural selection to allow people to learn and to use language. First, we would expect to find a direct relationship between cognitive abilities and linguistic skills if the ability to learn and to use language were based solely on general cognitive ability. However, this is not the case. Some stroke victims lose nearly all of their linguistic ability, but their intelligence is not diminished. These people are not fluent language users, and they have particular difficulty with syntax, but they do not show any other cognitive deficiencies. There are also people who speak grammatically but are otherwise mentally impaired. For example, many children suffering from spina bifida are severely retarded, and they cannot learn to read, write, or do simple arithmetic. Nonetheless, some of them speak fluently and at length, using grammatically correct sentences, but the content of their speech is nonsensical.

Second, if the ability to use language were like other complex skills, children would need considerable tutoring to learn grammatical rules. But children seem to know some universal grammatical principles without having to learn them. Most children begin to acquire the grammar of their native language when they are about two years old, and by the time they are three, most children make relatively few grammatical errors. Many linguists believe that children have to learn the surface grammar of their own language—how to speak properly in English, Spanish, or Farsi, for example—but they do not need to learn the deep, universal grammar that underlies all languages. This knowledge is innate. In fact, these linguists think that without some innate knowledge of the structure of language, children could not learn language at all.

Comparative evidence suggests that animals can associate concepts with arbitrary symbols but have only a limited mastery of syntax. Thus, human language capacities are derived traits.

Language is based on the ability to attach meaning to arbitrary sounds, and this ability allows us to communicate about things outside of our immediate experience. When one person smells smoke and yells "Fire!" in a crowded theater, the rest of the audience knows it's time to head for the exits, even if they can't smell the smoke themselves. Moreover, the audience knows that there is a fire in the theater—not a flood or an earthquake or a sighting of Elvis.

Robert Seyfarth and Dorothy Cheney of the University of Pennsylvania have demonstrated that alarm calls in vervet monkeys work in much the same way (Figure 16.7). Vervets give acoustically distinct calls when they encounter snakes, eagles, and leopards, and they also respond differently to each of these predators. When they see a leopard, they rush up into a tree; when they see an eagle, they dive into dense bushes; and when they see a snake, they look down at the ground around them. Cleverly designed playback experiments demonstrate that the monkeys associate particular kinds of calls with particular predators. When they hear a tape-recorded eagle call, for example, they dive into the bushes, even though there is no eagle to be seen (Table 16.1).

Great apes also demonstrate these kinds of abilities in laboratory studies. For example, a gorilla named Koko was taught to use American Sign Language to

FIGURE 16.7 Vervet monkeys associate particular calls with specific predators.

| TABLE 16.1 | Responses of vervet monkeys to playbacks of alarm calls. The data indicate that the monkeys recognize the meaning of different calls. (From Table 1 in R. M. Seyfarth, D. L. Cheney, and P. Marler, 1980, Monkey responses to three different alarm calls: Evidence of predator classification and semantic communication, Science, 210: 801–803.) |

| | **RESPONSE TO PLAYBACK** | | | |
Type of Alarm Call	Climb into Tree	Run into Bushes	Look Up	Look Down
Leopard	8	2	4	1
Eagle	2	6	7	4
Snake	2	2	2	14

Koko was trained by psychologist Francine Patterson, of the Gorilla Foundation, to use American Sign Language.

Kanzi, a bonobo trained by Sue Savage-Rumbaugh and Duane Rumbaugh (now at the Great Ape Trust in Des Moines, Iowa) uses abstract lexigrams to communicate.

communicate (Figure 16.8); and a bonobo named Kanzi points to abstract written symbols, or lexigrams, to tell his trainers when he wants a banana or a tickle (Figure 16.9). Surprisingly, these skills are not limited to primates. A gray parrot named Alex has learned to count, label, and categorize objects as "the same" or "different" in spoken English. These individuals, and several others, have extensive vocabularies and seem to grasp the relationship between objects and arbitrary symbols.

None of the language-trained animals have mastered the full complexity of human syntax. They can string symbols together to make requests ("Sue tickle"), create novel terms ("water bird"), and express thoughts ("surprise hide"). However, nearly all of the strings are either short or repetitive. For example, they might sign "give orange give give orange give orange orange." Chimpanzees have been taught to use simple rules that specify the order between elements, such as action–agent (for example, "hug Roger"). Kanzi, the bonobo trained by Sue Savage-Rumbaugh at Georgia State University, has gone one step further. Some of Kanzi's comments involve two lexigrams, or a lexigram and a gesture, and he has spontaneously generated simple rules to order these elements. For example, Kanzi is more likely to name an action ("keep away") first, and the agent or object second ("balloon"), than vice versa. He is also more likely to name something and then point to the object, than he is to point to the object and then name it.

However, syntax is more than word order. Kanzi's combinations of elements and those of the most fluent signing apes both fail to meet several of the criteria for syntax that were defined earlier in the chapter. For example, the elements are not grouped into phrases, they provide no information about the timing of events, and much of the meaning must be derived from context. What do we make of the apes' achievements and limitations? Patricia Greenfield of the

University of California Los Angeles emphasizes that ape abilities are comparable to those of very young children just beginning to acquire language, and she suggests that there is continuity between the linguistic abilities of apes and humans. Others, including Steven Pinker, emphasize differences between apes and young children in the ease with which they learn symbols, acquire grammatical rules, and naturally grasp the complexities of syntax. Those that emphasize this gap conclude that linguistic abilities in humans are derived traits.

EVOLUTION AND HUMAN CULTURE

For many anthropologists, culture is what makes us human. Each of us is immersed in a cultural milieu that influences the way we see the world, shapes our beliefs about right and wrong, and endows us with the knowledge and technical skills to get along in our own environment. Despite the central importance of culture in anthropology, there is little consensus about how or why culture arose in the evolution of the human lineage. In the discussion that follows, we present a view of the evolution of human culture developed by one of us (R. B.) and Peter Richerson at the University of California Davis. Although we believe strongly in this approach to understanding the evolution of culture, there is not a broad consensus among anthropologists that this, or any other particular view of the origins of culture, is correct.

Culture is information acquired by individuals by imitation, teaching, and other forms of social learning.

Before we begin, we must provide some definitions of terms. We define **culture** as information acquired by individuals through some form of social learning. Cultural variation is the product of differences among individuals that exist because they have acquired different behaviors as a result of some form of social learning. The properties of culture are sometimes quite different from the properties of other forms of environmental variation. If people acquire behavior from others through teaching or imitation, then culturally transmitted adaptations can gradually accumulate over many generations (Figures 16.10 and 16.11). For example, one man may learn to fletch his arrows and teach this skill to his sons. One of his sons may learn from his neighbor to dip his arrows in poison, and his sons may learn both of these behaviors by watching their father. To understand culture, we need to take its cumulative nature into account.

Culture Is a Derived Trait in Humans

Culture is common among other animals.

In the last few years, primatologists have documented a range of behavioral variation across groups in chimpanzees, orangutans, and *Cebus* monkeys. For example, chimpanzees living on the western shores of Lake Tanganyika raise their arms and clasp hands while they groom, but chimpanzees living on the eastern shores of the lake don't. Orangutans in some areas use sticks to pry seeds out of fruits, but at other sites, orangutans are unable to extract the seeds because they have not mastered this technique.

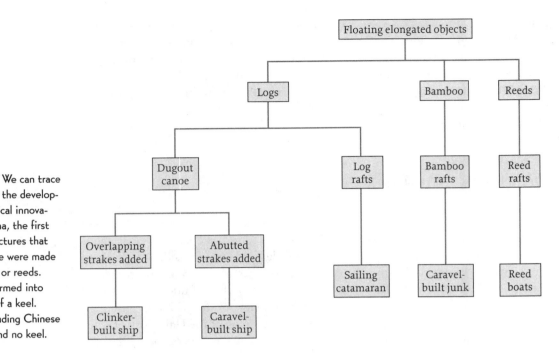

We can trace the development of certain technological innovations through time. In China, the first boats were elongated structures that floated on the water. Some were made of logs, others of bamboo or reeds. Floating logs were transformed into canoes with the addition of a keel. Other types of ships, including Chinese junks, have a square hull and no keel.

Cebus monkeys show considerable variation in foraging techniques and social conventions. For example, capuchins at some sites participate in long bouts of mutual hand sniffing (Figure 16.12), but capuchins at other sites never display this behavior. In some cases, scientists have documented the appearance, diffusion, and eventual extinction of behavioral variants.

(a)

(b)

Bamboo rafts like the one shown in (a) may have been the precursors of the great Chinese junks (b).

Cumulative cultural change is rare in nature.

These compendiums of behavioral traditions are important because they demonstrate that behavioral innovations can arise and spread through primate groups, but they neglect a question that is very important for understanding the evolution of the human capacity for culture: How are these behaviors acquired and transmitted? Do individuals learn these behaviors on their own, or do they learn them by observing others? There are at least two nongenetic transmission mechanisms that can account for persistent behavioral differences between populations.

FIGURE 16.12 Capuchin monkeys display a variety of behaviors that seem to vary from group to group. Here a capuchin monkey at Lomas Barbudal Biological Reserve in Costa Rica sniffs the hands of its partner. (Photograph courtesy of Susan Perry and Sharon Kessler.)

1. **Social facilitation** occurs when the activity of one animal indirectly increases the chance that other animals will learn the behavior on their own. Social facilitation would account for the persistence of tool use in the following scenario: Nuts are a greatly desired food, and young chimpanzees find eating nut meats highly reinforcing. Young chimpanzees accompany their mothers while they are foraging. This means that young animals spend a lot of time in proximity to nuts and hammer stones in populations in which females use stones to break open nuts. Young chimpanzees fool around with stone hammers and anvils until they master the skill of opening the nuts. They do not learn the skill by watching their mothers. In populations in which chimpanzees do not use stones to open nuts, young chimpanzees never spend enough time in proximity to both nuts and hammer stones to acquire the skill.

2. **Observational learning** occurs when "naïve" animals learn how to perform an action by watching the behavior of experienced, skilled animals. If this were the case, the tool tradition would be preserved because young chimpanzees actually imitate the behavior of older ones. (As we will see, evidence for imitation in apes is scant.)

Social facilitation and observational learning can both can lead to persistent behavioral differences between populations. However, there is an important distinction between the two processes. Social facilitation can only preserve variation in behavior that organisms can learn on their own. Observational learning allows cumulative cultural change. To see the difference, consider the following hypothetical example: Suppose that, in especially favorable circumstances, an early hominin learns to strike rocks together to make useful flakes. Her companions, who spend time near her, will be exposed to the same kinds of conditions, and some of them might learn to make flakes too, entirely on their own. This behavior will be preserved by social facilitation because groups in which tools are used will spend more time in proximity to the appropriate stones. However, that will be as far as it goes. If an especially talented individual finds a way to improve the flakes, this innovation will not spread to other members of the group; rather, each individual will have to learn the behavior by himself. With observational learning, on the other hand, innovations can persist as long as younger individuals are able to acquire the modified behavior by observing the actions of others. As a result, observational learning can lead to the cumulative evolution of behaviors that no single individual could invent on its own.

There is some debate about whether observational learning occurs in nonhuman primates. Many of the behavioral traditions described by primatologists are relatively simple and could be learned independently by individuals in each generation. Some behaviors, such as potato washing by Japanese macaques (Figure 16.13), were once thought to have been spread through imitation but are now thought to be the product of social facilitation and individual learning. But claims that nonhuman primates have "culture" continue to be debated.

In the field, it is always very difficult to know how behaviors are acquired and to distinguish between social facilitation and observational learning (Box 16.2). To sort this out, researchers turn to the laboratory, where they can carefully control animals' experience and their opportunities to learn novel skills. One of the most influential experiments was conducted by Elisabetta Visalberghi, of the Consiglio Nazionale delle Ricerche in Rome. Capuchins are extremely clever monkeys, well known for their manipulative abilities. In captivity, they are skilled tool users. Visalberghi gave several capuchins the opportunity to learn to use a stick to push a peanut out of a horizontal, clear plastic tube. She then allowed a second set of monkeys to watch the skilled monkeys get the peanut out of the tube. If capuchins learn by observing conspecifics, then we would expect monkeys housed with the skilled monkeys to learn faster than monkeys who did not have a chance to watch skilled models. However, exposure to skilled models didn't make any difference. So Visalberghi and her colleague Dorothy Fragaszy of the University of Georgia wryly concluded that "monkeys don't ape."

FIGURE 16.13 A young Japanese macaque learned to wash her sweet potatoes, and many members of her group subsequently began to wash their potatoes as well. For many years, this was thought to be a good example of observational learning. However, we now think each monkey learned the behavior by trial and error.

This experiment inspired many new experiments based on the same basic design: allow naïve individuals to observe an expert perform a rewarding task using a particular technique, and then find out whether the naïve individuals can master the task and if they use the same technique that they observed. For example, Andrew Whiten of St. Andrews University and his colleagues constructed an "artificial fruit." The fruit is really a box that can be opened in two different ways. Naïve chimpanzees in one group saw the box opened one way; naïve chimpanzees in another group saw the box opened the other way. The researchers observed that naïve chimpanzees tend to use the technique that they have seen demonstrated. On the other hand, a body of experiments conducted by Michael Tomasello and his colleagues suggest the opposite conclusion. That is, chimpanzees are quick to learn that tools can be used to obtain rewards, but they do not learn the same techniques that models use. Thus, important questions remain unresolved about how chimpanzees and other primates learn novel skills and behaviors.

But even if apes can learn new skills by watching others, there is still a huge gap between humans and other primates. No other primate relies on observational learning to the same extent that humans do, other primates have not elaborated behavioral traditions to the same extent as humans have, and the behavior of other primates is much less variable from group to group or from region to region than the behavior of humans is.

BOX 16.2

Understanding the Sources of Behavioral Variation

In the early 1960s, Jane Goodall reported that chimpanzees at Gombe stripped the leaves from slender twigs and used the twigs as probes to fish for termites. As Goodall continued her work, she documented a number of additional forms of tool use. For example, chimpanzees at Gombe also use long, slender twigs to collect ants, crumple leaves and use them as "sponges" to soak up water from tree hollows, and use leaves to wipe debris from their bodies. These observations made a huge impact in anthropology and the social sciences because tool use was thought to be a defining feature of the human species. Darwin himself thought that bipedal evolution had been favored by natural selection because it enabled early hominins to carry their tools from one place to another. But the discovery that tool use occurs in a wide range of species—from Caledonian crows that fashion hooks out of twigs (Figure 16.14), to sea otters that use rocks to bash open abalone shells, and *Cebus* monkeys that use large stones to crack hard-shelled nuts (Figure 16.15)—demonstrates that humans do not have a monopoly on technology.

When researchers began to study chimpanzees at other sites in Africa, they discovered new forms of tool use. Moreover, they began to realize that the behavioral repertoire of chimpanzees varied across groups. For example, in the Mahale Mountains, just miles away from Gombe, chimpanzees raise their arms and clasp hands while they groom (Figure 16.16), a position never adopted at Gombe. As more chimpanzee communities were habituated and studied, more and more examples of behavioral differences were accumulated.

In 1999, a group of researchers led by Andrew Whiten of St. Andrews University published an exhaustive catalogue of behavioral variants observed in seven well-studied wild

FIGURE 16.15 In northeastern Brazil, *Cebus* monkeys use large stones to smash open hard-shelled nuts on sandstone slabs. This behavior is now being studied by a group of researchers including Dorothy Fragaszy, Elisabetta Visalberghi, Patricia Iza, and Eduardo Ottoni of the Universidade de São Paulo, and Marino Gomes de Oliveira of Fundação BioBrasil. (Photo by Peter Oxford.)

FIGURE 16.14 Caledonian crows make and use tools in nature. Here a female has bent the end of a twig and is using the hooked end to retrieve a food reward. (Photo courtesy of the Behavioral Ecology Research Group, Department of Zoology, University of Oxford.)

Chimpanzees in the Mahale Mountains in Tanzania often hold their hands above their heads and clasp their partner's hands as they groom. This grooming posture has never been seen at Gombe, just 135 km (about 90 miles) away. (Photograph courtesy of William C. McGrew.)

der twigs (or wands) for ant dipping, but chimpanzees in the Ivory Coast's Taï Forest typically choose shorter sticks. Gombe chimpanzees hold the wand in one hand and pull it slowly through the other hand, and then pop the ants into the mouth. Taï chimpanzees hold the wand in one hand, then use their lips to wipe the ants directly off the wand.

Whiten and his colleagues note that "it is difficult to see how such behaviour patterns could be perpetuated by social learning processes simpler than imitation." According to this view, chimpanzees at Taï and Gombe use different techniques because they see others in their communities using those techniques, and they imitate the behaviors that they have observed. Close observation also seems to play a role in the development of termite fishing in chimpanzees. Elizabeth Lonsdorf and her colleagues at the University of Minnesota videotaped young chimpanzees while their mothers were fishing for termites. She found that young females watched their mothers carefully as they fished for termites, but young males were considerably less attentive (Figure 16.17). Lonsdorf also discovered that mothers varied in their fishing techniques, some consistently using longer twigs than others. Daughters tended to use the same kinds of tools that their mothers used, but sons did not.

You might be convinced that observational learning is the only plausible explanation for differences in ant-dipping techniques at Taï and Gombe. After all, it seems implausible that all the chimpanzees at Gombe would adopt one method, while all the chimpanzees at Taï would adopt a different method, if each chimpanzee figured out the technique for ant dipping on its own. This makes sense as long as there

chimpanzee communities. Their list includes 39 behaviors that are common in some communities but absent in others. These behaviors include various forms of tool use, distinctive grooming styles, and courtship gestures. Some behaviors, such as fishing for algae, occur in only one community; other behaviors, such as dipping for ants, occur in multiple communities. In some cases, behavioral variants seem to be regionally specific. Thus, chimpanzees use stones to hammer open hard-shelled nuts in West Africa but not in East Africa. Other behaviors, such as rain displays that are performed at the beginning of rainstorms, occur in widely separated locations.

In some cases, chimpanzees in different groups perform similar tasks in different ways. For example, chimpanzees use different techniques to collect safari ants. Safari ants live in subterranean nests and often migrate through the underbrush in dense swarms. Columns of marching ants, numbering hundreds of thousands of individuals, provide a mobile snack for chimpanzees. Safari ants aggressively defend themselves and have a painful bite. Chimpanzees apparently find ants tasty but don't like being bitten, so they use tools to gather them. Chimpanzees at Gombe choose long, slen-

Young female chimpanzees carefully watch their mothers termite fishing, and they tend to acquire the same kinds of techniques that their mothers use. Males are much less attentive to their mothers, and do not match their mother's techniques.

is no functional reason why one technique works better than another technique. However, Tatyana Humle, now at the University of Wisconsin, and Tesuro Matsuzawa of Kyoto University, have discovered that functional distinctions do underlie differences in ant-dipping techniques in a small community of chimpanzees in Boussou, Guinea. The Boussou chimpanzees are accomplished tool users. They use stones to hammer open nuts, they use sticks to scoop algae off the water surface, and they also dip for ants.

The Boussou chimpanzees' ant-dipping tools are intermediate in length between the tools used at Gombe and those used at Taï. Sometimes Boussou chimpanzees use the two-handed pull-and-wipe method like the Gombe chimpanzees, and sometimes they wipe the tool with their mouths like the chimpanzees at Taï do (Figure 16.18). Humle and Matsuzawa discovered that the chimpanzees at Boussou eat two different kinds of ants: red ones and black ones. The black ants are considerably more aggressive than the red ants, and their bite is more painful; both kinds of ants are more aggressive at their subterranean nests than when they are migrating. The chimpanzees use longer tools to dip for black ants than to dip for red ones, and they use longer tools when they dip at the entrance to the nest than when they dip into the migrating swarms. They are also more likely to dip from a position of safety off the ground when they dip at the nest site than when they dip on migrating ants. The chimpanzees used the pull-through technique mainly when they used long tools at ant nests. They tended to use the mouthing technique when they were feeding on migrating ants with shorter sticks. Thus the chimpanzees at Boussou apparently use safer techniques for more dangerous prey. Humle and Matsuzawa think that there is good reason to believe that the ants that chimpanzees eat at Gombe are like the black ants at Boussou, and the ants that

FIGURE 16.18 A chimpanzee in Boussou uses its mouth to collect ants from a wand.

the chimpanzees eat at Taï are like the milder red ants at Boussou.

Humle and Matsuzawa's observations are important because they remind us just how hard it is to figure out how behaviors are acquired and transmitted in natural settings. It is possible that behavioral differences across chimpanzee communities represent cultural traditions passed from one generation to the next as naïve youngsters observe skilled adults and imitate their behavior. However, it is also possible that behavioral differences arise as individuals within groups encounter similar conditions, gain exposure to the artifacts that others use, and then learn the skill on their own. Many different learning mechanisms could produce the kinds of stable differences in behavior that researchers have documented among different chimpanzee groups, and it takes careful work under controlled conditions to discriminate between them.

Culture Is an Adaptation

Observational learning is not a by-product of intelligence and social life.

Chimpanzees and capuchins are among the world's cleverest creatures. In nature, they use tools and perform many complex behaviors; in captivity, they can be taught extremely demanding tasks. Chimpanzees and capuchins live in social groups and have ample opportunity to observe the behavior of other individuals, and yet the best evidence suggests that neither chimpanzees nor capuchins make much use of observational learning. Thus, observational learning appears not to be simply a by-product

FIGURE 16.19 Infants are prone to spontaneous imitation of the behaviors they observe. Here a 13-month-old infant flosses her two teeth.

of intelligence and of having opportunities for observation. Instead, observational learning seems to require special psychological mechanisms.

This conclusion suggests, in turn, that the psychological mechanisms that enable humans to learn by observation are adaptations that have been shaped by natural selection because culture is beneficial (Figure 16.19). Of course, this need not be the case. Observational learning could be a by-product of some other adaptation that is unique to humans, such as language. But given the great importance of culture in human affairs, it is important to think about the possible adaptive advantages of culture.

Culture allows humans to exploit a wide range of environments using a universal set of mental mechanisms.

The archaeological record suggests that during the Pleistocene, humans occupied virtually all of Africa, Eurasia, and Australia. Modern hunter-gatherers developed an astounding variety of subsistence practices and social systems. Consider just a few examples. The Copper Eskimo lived in the high Arctic, spending their summers hunting near the mouth of the Mackenzie River and the long dark months of the winter living on the sea ice and hunting seals. Groups were small and heavily dependent on hunting. The !Xo lived in the central Kalahari Desert of Botswana, collecting seeds, tubers, and melons, hunting impala and gemsbok, enduring fierce heat, and living without surface water for months at a time. Their small, nomadic bands were linked together in large clusters organized along male kinship lines. The Chumash lived on the southern California coast, gathering shellfish and seeds and fishing the Pacific from great plank boats. They lived in large permanent villages with pronounced division of labor and extensive social stratification.

The fact that the !Xo could acquire the knowledge, tools, and skills necessary to survive the rigors of the Kalahari is not so surprising; many other species live there too. What is amazing is that the same brain that allowed the !Xo to survive in the Kalahari also permitted the Copper Eskimo to acquire the very different knowledge, tools, and skills necessary to live on the tundra and ice north of the Arctic Circle, and the Chumash to acquire the skills necessary to cope with life in crowded, hierarchical settlements. No other animal occupies a comparable range of habitats or utilizes a comparable range of subsistence techniques and social structures. For example, savanna baboons, the most widespread primate species, are limited to Africa and Arabia, and the diet, group size, and social systems of these far-flung baboon populations are much more similar to one another than the diet, group size, and social systems of human hunter-gatherers are.

Humans can live in a wider range of environments than other primates because culture allows us to accumulate better strategies for exploiting local environments much more rapidly than genetic inheritance can produce adaptive modifications. Animals like baboons adapt to different environments using various learning mechanisms. For example, they learn how to acquire and process the food they eat. Baboons in the lush wetlands of the Okavango Delta of Botswana learn how to harvest roots of water plants and how to hunt young antelope during the birth season. Baboons living in the harsh desert of nearby Namibia must learn how to find water and process desert foods. All such learning mechanisms require prior knowledge about the environment: where to search for food, what strategies can be used to process the food, which flavors are reinforcing, and so on. More detailed and more accurate knowledge allows more accu-

rate adaptation because it allows animals to avoid errors and acquire a more specialized adaptation.

In most animals, this knowledge is stored in the genes. Imagine that you captured
a group of baboons from the Okavango Delta and moved them to the Namibian
desert. It's a very good bet that the first few months would be tough for the baboons,
but after a relatively short time the transplanted group of baboons would probably be
quite similar to their neighbors. They would eat the same foods, have the same activity patterns, and use the same grooming techniques. They might even adjust the size
of their groups and the size of their social networks. The transplanted baboons would
become similar to the local baboons because they acquire a great deal of information
about how to be a baboon genetically; it is hardwired. To be sure, the transplanted
baboons would have to learn where things are, where to sleep, which foods are desirable, and which foods to avoid, but they would be able to do this without contact with
local baboons because they have the basic knowledge built in.

Human culture allows accurate adaptation to a wider range of environments
because *cumulative* cultural adaptation provides more accurate and more detailed
information about the local environment than genetic inher-
itance systems can provide. People are smart, but individual
humans can't figure out how to live in the Arctic, the Kalahari, or anywhere else without drawing on the knowledge of
local people. Think about being plunked down on an Arctic
beach with a pile of driftwood and seal skins and trying to
make a kayak (Figure 16.20). You already know a lot: what
a kayak looks like, roughly how big it is, and something
about its construction. Nonetheless, you would almost cer-
tainly fail. And, supposing you did make a passable kayak,
you would still have dozens of other skills to master before
you could make a contribution to the Inuit economy. The
Inuit could make kayaks, and do all the other things they
needed to do to stay alive in a challenging environment,
because they could make use of a vast pool of useful information stored in the minds of other people in their population.

FIGURE 16.20   The people of Nunivak Island in the Bering
Sea hunted seals from kayaks like this one.
These kayaks weighed less than 15 kg (less than about 30 lb) and
could be paddled at speeds of up to 11 km (7 miles) per hour.

The information contained in this pool is accurate and
adaptive because the combination of individual learning
and observational learning leads to rapid, cumulative adap-
tation. Even if most individuals blindly imitate the behavior of others, some individuals may occasionally come up with a better idea, and this will nudge traditions in an
adaptive direction. Observational learning preserves the many small nudges and
exposes the modified traditions to another round of nudging. This process generates
adapation more quickly than genetic inheritance does. The complexity of cultural traditions can explode to the limits of our capacity to learn them, far past our ability to
make careful, detailed decisions about them.

*Culture can lead to evolutionary outcomes not predicted by ordinary
evolutionary theory.*

The importance of culture in human affairs has led many anthropologists to conclude that evolutionary thinking has little to contribute to understanding human

behavior. They argue that because evolution shapes genetically determined behaviors, but not behaviors that are learned, culture is independent of biology. This argument is a manifestation of the nature–nurture controversy, and we explained why this reasoning is flawed at the beginning of the chapter. Although many anthropologists have rejected evolutionary thinking about culture, many evolutionists have made the opposite mistake. They reject the idea that culture makes any *fundamental* difference in the way that evolution has shaped human behavior and psychology. Some evolutionists argue that the genes underlying the psychological machinery that gives rise to human behavior were shaped by natural selection, so, at least in ancestral environments, the machinery must have led to fitness-enhancing behavior. If the adaptation doesn't enhance fitness in modern environments, that's because our evolved psychology is designed for life in a different kind of world.

We think both sides in this argument are wrong. We can't understand humans without understanding the complex interplay between biology and culture. This is because cumulative cultural evolution is rooted in a novel evolutionary trade-off between benefits and costs. Observational learning is beneficial because it allows human populations to accumulate vast reservoirs of adaptive information over many generations, leading to the cumulative cultural evolution of highly adaptive behaviors and technology. Because this process is much faster than genetic evolution, it allows human populations to evolve cultural adaptations to local environments: kayaks in the Arctic and blowguns in the Amazon. The ability to adjust rapidly to local conditions was highly adaptive for early humans because the Pleistocene was a time of extremely rapid fluctuations in world climates. However, the psychological mechanisms that create this benefit come with a built-in cost. Remember that the advantage of observational learning is that it avoids the need for all individuals to figure out everything for themselves. They can just do what others do. But to get the benefits of social learning, people have to be credulous, generally accepting that other people are doing things in a sensible and proper way.

This credulity opens up human minds to the spread of maladaptive beliefs and behaviors. If our neighbors believe that it's beneficial to bleed sick people and that it's a good idea to treat corn with lye, we believe that too. This is how we get wondrous adaptations like kayaks and blowguns. But we have little protection against the perpetuation of maladaptions that somehow arise. Even though the capacities that give rise to culture and shape its content must be (or at least must have been) adaptive on average, the behavior observed in any particular society at any particular time may reflect evolved maladaptations. Examples of these sorts of maladaptations are not hard to find.

Maladaptive beliefs can spread because culture is not acquired just from parents.

There are good reasons to expect maladaptive beliefs to spread. As you know, we acquire all our genes from our parents, but we acquire culturally transmitted beliefs and values from our parents, friends, teachers, religious figures, the media, and other sources. Biologist Richard Dawkins of Oxford University refers to culturally transmitted beliefs and values as **memes**. The logic of natural selection applies to memes in the same way that it does to genes. Memes compete for our memory and for our attention, and not all memes can survive. Some memes are more likely to survive and be transmitted than others. Memes are heritable, often passing from one individual to another without major change. As a result, some memes spread and others are lost.

Even though memes are subject to natural selection, it is not necessarily true that only memes that enhance our genetic fitness will spread. The rules of cultural transmission are different from the rules of genetic transmission, so the outcome of selection on memes can be different from the outcome of selection on genes. The basic rules of genetic transmission are simple. With some exceptions, every gene that an individual carries in her body is equally likely to be incorporated into her gametes, and the only way that those genes can be transmitted is through her offspring. Thus, only genes that increase reproductive success will spread. Cultural transmission is much more complicated. Memes are acquired and transmitted throughout an individual's life, and they can be acquired from grandparents, siblings, friends, coworkers, teachers, and even completely impersonal sources such as books, television, and now the Internet.

Genes are transmitted directly from parents to offspring, but memes may spread along many different pathways. This means that memes can spread even if they do not enhance reproductive fitness. If ideas about dangerous hobbies like rock climbing or heroin use spread from friend to friend, these ideas can persist even though they reduce survival and individual reproductive success (Figure 16.21). Beliefs about heaven and hell can spread from priest to parishioner, even if the priest is celibate. Moreover, cultural variants may accumulate and be transmitted within groups of people who form clans, fraternities, business firms, religious sects, or political parties. This process can generate groups that are defined by cultural values and traditions, not by genetic relatedness.

FIGURE 16.21 Cultural evolution may permit the spread of ideas and behaviors that do not contribute to reproductive success. Dangerous sports, such as rock climbing, may be examples of such behaviors.

Culture is part of human biology, but culture makes human evolution qualitatively different from that of other organisms.

The fact that culture can lead to outcomes not predicted by conventional evolutionary theory does not mean that human behavior has somehow transcended biology. The idea that culture is separate from biology is a popular misconception that cannot withstand scrutiny. Culture is generated from organic structures in the brain that were produced by the processes of evolution. However, cultural transmission leads to novel evolutionary processes. Thus, to understand the whole of human behavior, evolutionary theory must be modified to account for the complexities introduced by these poorly understood processes.

The fact that culture can lead to outcomes that would not be predicted by conventional evolutionary theory does not mean that ordinary evolutionary reasoning is useless. The fact that there are processes that lead to the spread of risky behaviors like rock climbing does not mean that these are the only processes that influence cultural behavior. Earlier in this chapter we saw that it is likely that many aspects of human psychology have been shaped by natural selection so that people learn to behave adaptively. We love our children, have strong aversions to mating with close relatives, and have an uncanny facility for learning language. There is every reason to suspect that these predispositions play an important role in determining which memes spread and which don't. As long as this is the case, ordinary evolutionary reasoning will be useful for understanding human behavior.

FURTHER READING

Barkow, J., L. Cosmides, and J. Tooby, eds. 1992. *The Adapted Mind, Evolutionary Psychology and the Generation of Culture.* Oxford University Press, New York.

Fragaszy, D. M., and S. Perry, eds. 2003. *The Biology of Traditions.* Cambridge University Press, Cambridge, England.

Richerson, P. J., and R. Boyd. 2004. *Not by Genes Alone: How Culture Transformed Human Evolution.* University of Chicago Press, Chicago.

Whiten, A., V. Horner, and S. Marshall-Pescini. 2003. Cultural panthropology. *Evolutionary Anthropology* 12: 92–105.

STUDY QUESTIONS

1. Much of the behavior of all primates is learned. Nonetheless, we have suggested many times that primate behavior has been shaped by natural selection. How can natural selection shape behaviors that are learned?

2. Many of the things that we do are consistent with general predictions derived from evolutionary theory. We love our children, help our relatives, and avoid sex with close kin. But there are also many aspects of the behavior of members of our own society that seem unlikely to increase individual fitness. What are some of these behaviors?

3. In some species of primates there seems to be an aversion to mating with close kin. The aversion seems to be stronger for females than for males. Why do you think this might be the case? Under what conditions would you expect this gender difference to disappear?

4. What evidence suggests that language is based on special-purpose cognitive mechanisms?

5. Human speech is composed of many words that can be rearranged to make different meanings. What are the advantages of this system?

6. The verb *to ape* means "to copy or imitate." Is its meaning consistent with what we now know about the learning processes of other primates?

7. Primatologists have documented many examples of behaviors that vary across populations, and some have concluded that this variation is a form of culture. Explain why this is or is not a reasonable conclusion.

8. Some things that we do seem to be maladaptive (think about skydiving, drug abuse, and collecting classic cars). Some people would argue that these behaviors provide evidence that natural selection has no important impact on modern humans. Is this a reasonable argument? Why or why not?

KEY TERMS

environment of evolutionary
   adaptedness/EEA
inbred matings
outbred matings
kibbutz

phonemes
grammar
syntax
social facilitation
observational learning

CHAPTER 17

HUMAN MATE CHOICE AND PARENTING

You should be convinced by now that every aspect of the human phenotype is the product of evolutionary processes. Over the last 10 million years, natural selection, mutation, and genetic drift have made us into large, nearly hairless, bipedal primates, with grasping hands and large brains. The same evolutionary processes have molded the psychological mechanisms that influence human behavior, causing us to behave differently from other primates in some contexts. There is simply no other explanation.

However, the fact that modern humans are the product of evolutionary processes does not necessarily mean that evolutionary theory will help us understand contemporary human behavior. Constraints on adaptation, which we discussed in Chapter 3, may have predominated in the evolution of human behavior, limiting the usefulness of adaptive reasoning. In Chapter 16, however, we saw that evolutionary theory has provided useful insights into certain aspects of human psychology, social organization, and culture. In this chapter we will present several more examples that show how evolutionary thinking can help us understand the day-to-day behavior of humans in modern societies.

In choosing these examples, we have focused on reproductive behavior because mating and parenting strongly affect fitness. The unfortunate person who chooses a mate that is lazy, infertile, or unfaithful is likely to have many fewer children than the person whose spouse is healthy, hardworking, and faithful. Neglectful parents who fail to provide adequate care for their offspring will raise fewer children than will attentive parents who carefully nurture their offspring. Because reproductive decisions are likely to have a marked effect on fitness, there is good reason to expect that our psychology has been shaped by natural selection to improve the chances of making good choices about who we mate with, who we marry, and how we raise our children. We do not have enough space to provide a comprehensive analysis of these topics. Instead, we focus on certain examples in which evolutionary theory provides novel and fundamental insights into human behavior and physiology.

THE PSYCHOLOGY OF HUMAN MATE PREFERENCES

Marry

Children—(if it Please God)—Constant companion, (& friend in old age) who will feel interested in one,—object *to be* beloved and played with. better than a dog anyhow.—Home, & someone to take care of house—Charms of music & female chit-chat.—These things good for one's health.—*but terrible loss of time.*—

My God, it is intolerable to think of spending one's whole life, like a neuter bee, working, working, & nothing after all.—No, no won't do.—Imagine living all one's day solitary in smoky dirty London house.—Only picture to yourself nice soft wife on a sofa with good fire, & books, & music perhaps—Compare this vision with the dingy reality of Grt. Marlbro St.

Marry—Mary—Marry Q.E.D.

Not Marry

Freedom to go where one liked—choice of Society & *little of it.*—Conversation of clever men at clubs—Not forced to visit relatives, & to bend in every trifle.—to have the expense & anxiety of children—perhaps quarrelling —**Loss of time.**—cannot read in the Evenings—fatness & idleness—Anxiety & responsibility—less money for books & c—if many children forced to gain one's bread.—(But then it is very bad for ones health to work too much)

Perhaps my wife wont like London; then the sentence is banishment & degradation into indolent, idle fool.

From p. 444 in F. Burkhardt and S. Smith, eds., 1986, *The Correspondence of Charles Darwin*, Vol. 2, 1837–1843, Cambridge University Press, Cambridge, England.

These are the thoughts of 29-year-old Charles Darwin, recently returned from his five-year voyage on the HMS *Beagle*. Soon after writing these words, Darwin married his cousin Emma, the daughter of Josiah Wedgwood, the progressive and immensely wealthy manufacturer of Wedgwood china (Figure 17.1). By all accounts, Charles and Emma were a devoted couple. Emma bore Charles 10 children and nursed him through countless bouts of illness. Charles toiled over his work and astutely managed his investments, parlaying his modest inheritance and his wife's more substantial one into a considerable fortune.

Darwin's frank reflections on advantages and disadvantages of marriage were very much those of a conventional, upper-class, Victorian gentleman. But people of every culture, class, and gender have faced the problem of choosing mates. Sometimes people choose their own mates, and other times parents arrange their children's marriages. But everywhere, people care about the kind of person they will marry.

Evolutionary theory generates some testable predictions about the psychology of human mate preferences.

For much of their evolutionary history, humans have lived in foraging societies. The adaptive challenges that men and women face in these kinds of societies are likely to have shaped their mating strategies. For women, this might have meant choosing men who would provide them with access to resources. Recall from Chapter 12 that there is considerable interdependence between men and women in foraging societies. Women mainly gather plant foods, and men are mainly responsible for hunting. Women's consumption exceeds their production for much of their reproductive life. Children do not begin to provide substantial amounts of their own food until they reach adolescence. Thus, for women, it might be important to choose a mate who will be a good provider.

Men's reproductive success depends largely on the fertility of their partners, so it is plausible that selection favored men who focused on this attribute. Women's fertility is highest when they are in their 20s and declines to zero when women reach menopause, at about 50 years of age (Figure 17.2). Thus, selection should have favored men who chose young and healthy mates. Because picture IDs were scarce in the Pleistocene, selection may have shaped men's psychology so that they are attracted to cues that reliably predict youth and health, such as smooth skin, good muscle tone, symmetrical features, and shiny hair.

For both men and women, it is important to find mates that they can get along with. Human children are dependent on their parents for a remarkably long time. Dur-

FIGURE 17.1 Charles Darwin courted and married his cousin Emma Wedgwood. This portrait was painted when Emma was 32, just after the birth of her first child.

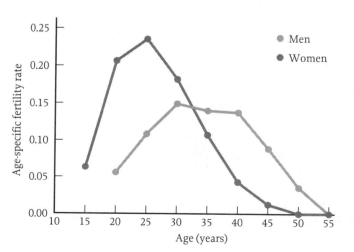

FIGURE 17.2 Age-specific fertility rates give the probability of producing a child at particular ages. !Kung women have their first child between the ages of 15 and 19 and the highest fertility rate in their 20s. Women's fertility falls to zero by age 50. !Kung men do not begin to reproduce until their early 20s, and their fertility rates are fairly stable in their 30s and 40s, dropping to low levels in their 50s.

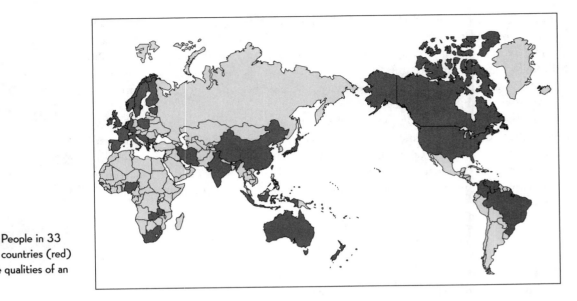

FIGURE 17.3 People in 33 countries (red) were surveyed about the qualities of an ideal mate.

ing this period, both parents provide food and shelter for their children. Because parental investment lasts for many years, adaptive thinking predicts that both men and women will value traits in their partners that help them sustain their relationships. Both are likely to value personal qualities like compatibility, agreeableness, reliability, and tolerance.

If evolution has shaped the psychology of human mating strategies, then we would expect to find common patterns across societies.

David Buss, a psychologist at the University of Texas, was among the first to test the evolutionary logic underlying human mating preferences and tactics. Buss enlisted colleagues in 33 countries to administer standardized questionnaires about the qualities of desirable mates to more than 10,000 men and women. Most of the data were collected in Western industrialized nations, and most samples represent university students in urban populations within those countries (Figure 17.3). In the questionnaires, people were asked to rate a number of traits of potential mates—good looks, good financial prospects, compatibility, and so on—according to their desirability. Respondents were also asked about their preferred age at marriage and the preferred age difference between themselves and their spouse.

People generally care most about the personal qualities of their mates.

Men and women around the world rate mutual attraction or love above all other traits (Table 17.1). The next most highly desired traits for both men and women are personal attributes, such as dependability, emotional stability and maturity, and a pleasing disposition. Good health is the fifth most highly rated trait for men and the seventh for women. Good financial prospect is the thirteenth most highly rated trait by men and the twelfth by women. Good looks are rated tenth by men and thirteenth by women. It is interesting, and somewhat surprising, that neither sex seems to value chastity highly. Perhaps this is because people were asked to evaluate the desirability of sexual experience before marriage (that is, virginity), not fidelity during their marriage.

TABLE 17.1   Men and women from more than 33 countries around the world (shown in Figure 17.3) were asked to rate the desirability of a variety of traits in prospective mates. The rankings of the values assigned to each trait, on average, are given here. Subjects were asked to rate each trait from 0 (irrelevant or unimportant) to 3 (indispensable). Thus, high ranks (low numbers) represent traits that were generally thought to be important. (From Table 4 in D. M. Buss et al., 1990, International preferences in selecting mates: A study of 37 cultures, *Journal of Cross-Cultural Psychology,* 21: 5–47.)

Trait	RANKING OF TRAIT BY: Males	Females
Mutual attraction/love	1	1
Dependable character	2	2
Emotional stability and maturity	3	3
Pleasing disposition	4	4
Good health	5	7
Education and intelligence	6	5
Sociability	7	6
Desire for home and children	8	8
Refinement, neatness	9	10
Good looks	10	13
Ambition and industriousness	11	9
Good cook and housekeeper	12	15
Good financial prospect	13	12
Similar education	14	11
Favorable social status or rating	15	14
Chastity*	16	18
Similar religious background	17	16
Similar political background	18	17

*Chastity was defined in this study as having no sexual experience before marriage.

Men and women show the differences in mate preferences predicted by parental investment theory.

Even though the ranking of the scores assigned to these traits is similar for men and women, there are consistent differences between men and women in how desirable each gender thinks these traits are. Buss found that people's sex had the greatest effect on their ratings of the following traits: "good financial prospect," "good looks," "good cook and housekeeper," "ambition and industriousness." As the evolutionary model predicts, women value good financial prospects and ambition more than men do, and men value good looks more than women do. Gender has a smaller and somewhat less uniform effect on ratings of chastity. In 23 populations, men value chastity significantly more than women do; in the remaining populations, men and women value chastity equally. There are no populations in which women value chastity significantly more than men do.

Men and women differ about the preferred ages of their partners.

Evolutionary reasoning suggests that men's mate preferences will be strongly influenced by the reproductive potential of prospective mates. Therefore, we would predict men to choose mates with high fertility or high reproductive value. By the same token, we would expect women to be less concerned about their partner's age than about their partner's ability to provide resources for them and their offspring.

A considerable amount of evidence suggests that men consistently seek and marry partners who are younger than they are and that women seek and marry partners somewhat older than themselves. Douglas Kenrick and Richard Keefe of the University of Arizona surveyed marriage records in two cities in the United States and in a small Philippine village, as well as personal advertisements in the United States, northern Europe, and India. In all of these cases, they found a similar pattern. As men get older, the age difference between them and their wives increases. Thus, young men marry women slightly younger than themselves, and older men marry partners considerably younger than themselves (Figure 17.4a). As women get older, there is little change in the age difference between them and their husbands (Figure 17.4b). Newspaper advertisements in which advertisers specify the range of ages for prospective mates demonstrate a very similar pattern. Henry Harpending of the University of Utah has found very similar patterns among the Herero, a pastoralist group in the northern Kalahari Desert of Botswana, in which marriages are unstable, divorce is common, and women have a considerable amount of financial independence.

Although men advertise for and marry progressively younger women, the actual age of their partners does not seem to fit the prediction that males will choose fertile mates. Older men seek and marry women who are considerably younger than they themselves are, but not young enough to produce children. Men's choices about who to date and who to marry may be driven by multiple factors, not just women's fertility. Older men may desire younger women, but they may also want to find someone who shares their taste in music, has similar goals in life, and so on. Furthermore, men's preferences and their marriages may reflect their own attractiveness in the mating market. Older men may want young women but know they will have to settle for partners closer to their own age. Together, the data taken from personal advertisements and from marriage records reflect individual desires tempered with reality.

Men and women vary about the preferred number of partners.

In addition to having different criteria for the ideal mate, men and women may also have different mating tactics. Because women devote nine months to each pregnancy and nurse their children for even longer, selection is likely to have favored a psychology that makes them cautious about involvement in sexual relationships that would expose them to the risks of pregnancy. (Of course, nowadays birth control reduces the risk of pregnancy for women, but effective methods of contraception are a recent innovation. Human mating tactics evolved in a world without such technology.) Women are likely to prefer stable, committed relationships with men who are willing and able to help care for them and their offspring. Because the costs of conception are borne mainly by women, men can afford to be more flexible in their mat-

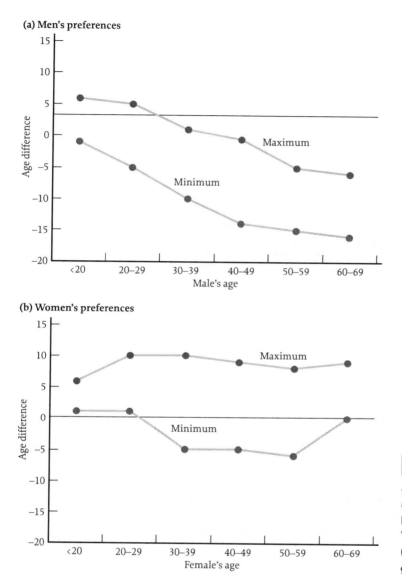

(a) Men's preferences

(b) Women's preferences

FIGURE 17.4 Mate preferences by sex. (a) In personal advertisements, all but the youngest men state preferences for women who are younger than themselves. As men get older, the age difference between themselves and preferred mates increases. (b) Women typically prefer men who are somewhat older than themselves, and these preferences remain the same as women get older.

ing tactics, and to have a psychology that makes them more open to mating opportunities that do not involve long-term commitments. However, we would expect men to form committed long-term relationships because children that receive care from both parents are more likely to thrive.

David Schmitt of Bradley University has coordinated a comprehensive cross-cultural study of human sexuality, sampling people, mainly university students, in 62 countries around the world. In this survey, people were asked about the traits that they valued in potential mates and were also asked about various aspects of their mating tactics. For example, they were asked the number of sexual partners they would like to have over various time intervals ranging from 6 months to 30 years. For all time intervals, men reported preferring a larger number of sexual partners than women did (Figure 17.5). This difference seems to be common cross-culturally (Figure 17.6), although the magnitude of the sex difference and the number of partners desired vary considerably.

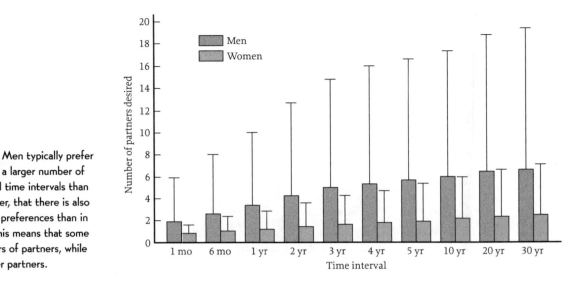

FIGURE 17.5 Men typically prefer a larger number of sexual partners across all time intervals than women do. Note, however, that there is also more variability in men's preferences than in women's preferences. This means that some men prefer large numbers of partners, while others prefer many fewer partners.

Differences in mating tactics may contribute to misunderstandings between men and women.

When you meet someone you're attracted to, you probably feel excitement and some degree of uncertainty. Some of this uncertainty arises because you are not sure whether the other person is as attracted to you as you are to him or her. And some of this uncertainty arises because you don't know what the other person's intentions are. Martie Haselton of the University of California Los Angeles, and David Buss, have pointed out that this uncertainty generates different kinds of problems for men and women. To understand the logic of their argument, let's think about what kinds of mistakes you could make in deciding whether someone was attracted to you. A false positive arises if you think the other person is attracted to you, when in fact that's not the case. A false negative occurs if you think the other person doesn't like you, when they

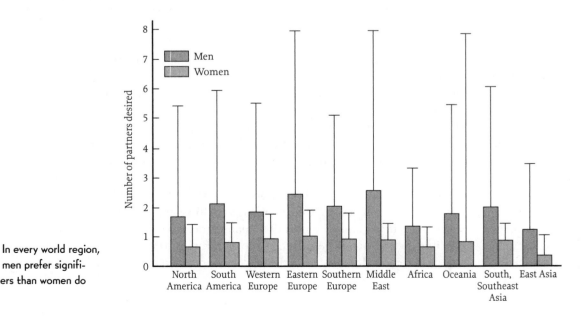

FIGURE 17.6 In every world region, men prefer significantly more sexual partners than women do over the next month.

really do. Both kinds of errors are costly: a false positive could lead you to make an overture that would be rejected ("Sorry, I need to wash my hair"); a false negative could prevent you from making any overture at all (and you will have nothing better to do than wash your hair).

Now think about the kinds of errors that can arise when there is uncertainty about the other person's intentions about the relationship. Haselton and Buss hypothesize that natural selection will predispose men and women to bias their judgments about new partners' sexual intentions and commitment in different ways. Women, who could become pregnant, are expected to be cautious about their partner's intentions, and as a result they will make more false negative errors than false positive errors. Put another way, evolutionary reasoning predicts that women are more likely to underestimate men's commitment than to overestimate it. Men, who are interested in pursuing both short-term and long-term relationships, are expected to minimize the chance of missing sexual opportunities, and as a result they will make more false positive errors than false negative errors. That is, they are likely to overestimate women's sexual interest more often than they underestimate it.

Haselton and Buss have conducted a number of different studies on college students in the United States to test this hypothesis. They have asked men and women to evaluate sexual intent and commitment in members of their own sex and the opposite sex; to imagine how they would interpret various kinds of signals directed to themselves (for example, held hands, declared love); and to recall instances when their own intentions were misunderstood by members of the opposite sex. The results conform to Haselton and Buss's predictions: men tend to overestimate women's sexual intent, and women tend to underestimate men's interest in commitment (Figure 17.7).

Culture predicts people's mate preferences better than gender does.

Both of the large cross-cultural data sets reveal considerable variation from country to country. Buss and his colleagues found that the country of residence has a greater effect than gender does on variation in all of the 18 traits in Table 17.1, except for "good financial prospect." This means that knowing where a person lives tells you more about what he or she values in a mate than knowing the person's gender does. Of the 18 traits, chastity (defined in Buss's study as no sexual experience before marriage) shows the greatest variability among populations. In Sweden, men rate chastity at 0.25, and women rate it at 0.28 on a scale of 0 (irrelevant) to 3 (indispensable). In contrast, Chinese men rate chastity

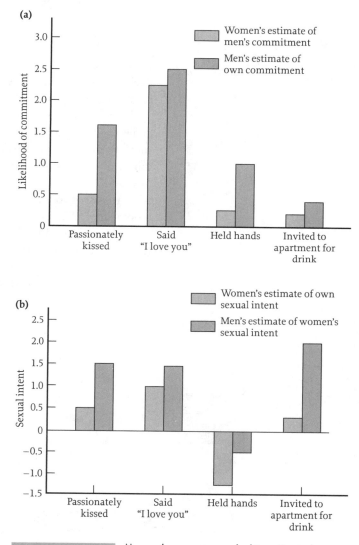

FIGURE 17.7 Men and women were asked to estimate how they would interpret particular courtship signals by members of the opposite sex and how they would rate the same signals by members of their own sex, using a scale from +3 (very likely) to −3 (very unlikely). (a) Men and women estimated the extent of commitment implied by a number of different courtship signals. Women tended to underestimate men's interest in commitment relative to men's own estimates of their interest in commitment. (b) Men and women estimated the likelihood of sexual intent implied by the same signals. Men tended to overestimate women's sexual intent relative to women's perceptions of their own intent.

TABLE 17.2	When men invest time, energy, or other resources in children, they may be enhancing their parenting effort or their mating effort.	
	Current mate is child's mother	Current mate is not child's mother
Man is child's father	Parenting effort + mating effort	Parenting effort
Man is not child's father	Mating Effort	Neither

2.54, and Chinese women rate it 2.61 (Figure 17.8). This means that there is more similarity between men and women from the same population than there is among members of each sex from different populations.

This result illustrates an important point: evolutionary explanations that invoke an evolved psychology and cultural explanations that are based on the social and cultural milieu are not mutually exclusive. The cross-cultural data suggest there are some uniformities in people's mate preferences that are the result of evolved psychological mechanisms. People everywhere want to marry kind, caring, trustworthy people. Men want to marry young women and women want to marry older men. But this is not the whole story. The cross-cultural data also suggest that human mate preferences are strongly influenced by the cultural and economic environment in which we live. Ultimately, culture also arises out of our evolved psychology, and the cultural variation in mate preferences that the cross-cultural data reveal must therefore also be explicable in evolutionary terms. However, the way our evolved psychology shapes the cul-

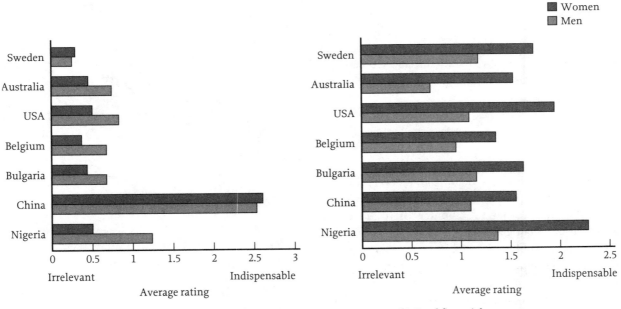

(a) Chastity

(b) Good financial prospect

FIGURE 17.8	Culture accounts for substantial variation in mate preferences. The average ratings given by men and women in several countries surveyed are shown for (a) the trait with the highest interpopulation variability ("chastity") and (b) the trait with the lowest interpopulation variability ("good financial prospect").

tures in which we live is complicated and poorly understood, and many interesting questions remain unresolved. Evolutionary theory does not yet explain, for example, why chastity is considered essential in China but undesirable in Sweden.

Evolutionary analyses of mate choice have generated considerable controversy over at least two different issues.

As we explained in Chapter 16, evolutionary analyses of human behavior generate considerable controversy. Work on human mate choice is no exception. Many critics have complained that evolutionary analyses simply reflect and reinforce Western cultural values, which celebrate women's youth and beauty and men's wealth and power. They argue that researchers are not studying evolved preferences, but rather are learning about cultural values and beliefs. In response, advocates of evolutionary analyses argue that the cross-cultural uniformity of mate preferences and mating tactics reflects evolved psychological predispositions that are modified, but not created, by culture.

Other critics have accepted the general logic of evolutionary reasoning but have questioned the methods used to assess mate preferences and mating tactics. Most of the early work was based on pencil-and-paper tests in which people, often undergraduates, were asked about their preferences and their personal experiences. These kinds of data may be biased in a number of ways. For example, cultural norms may lead men to exaggerate their sexual experience and women to understate their desire for sexual variety, even on anonymous surveys.

Moreover, for reasons that are not fully understood, results derived from "forced choice" tests, in which subjects are asked which of two alternatives they would choose, sometimes deviate from results in which subjects are asked to rate the same alternatives. Although this may seem like an arcane methodological issue, it may be important if different kinds of data generate different conclusions about the psychology underlying mating tactics.

This problem arises in studies of sex differences in jealousy. Buss and his colleagues have hypothesized that there will be sex differences in responses to emotional and sexual infidelity. Men, who are concerned about being cuckolded, will be more upset about their partners' sexual infidelity than about their emotional infidelity. On the other hand, women, who are concerned about access to resources for themselves and their offspring, will be more upset about their partners' emotional infidelity than about their sexual infidelity. When subjects are asked which form of infidelity would upset them more, men typically report that they would be more upset by sexual infidelity than emotional infidelity, and women report the opposite pattern. However, when Christine Harris of the University of California San Diego asked men and women *how much* they focused on each type of infidelity, these sex differences disappeared.

Harris suggests that the forced-choice paradigm provides a misleading picture of the sex differences underlying jealousy. It's possible, she argues, that men find sexual infidelity more upsetting than emotional infidelity in the forced-choice paradigm because they assume that their partners would not sleep with someone else unless they were emotionally involved with them; thus sexual infidelity is more upsetting because it implies both emotional and sexual betrayal. Similarly, women may be more upset by emotional infidelity than by sexual infidelity because they assume that if their partners are emotionally involved with someone else, they are also sleeping with them, but not vice versa. Although this explanation is cogent, we don't know if it is correct.

It is not yet clear whether sex differences in sexual jealousy are robust, or which type of methodology generates the most meaningful information. However, researchers are developing a battery of new methods that will allow them to investigate sexual jealousy and other aspects of mating preferences more fully.

SOME SOCIAL CONSEQUENCES OF MATE PREFERENCES

You might wonder how people's mate preferences influence their actual decisions and choices about marriage partners. In this section we describe the findings from one ethnographic study suggesting that these kinds of preferences actually influence people's behavior in social situations, and consequently shape the societies in which they live.

Kipsigis Bridewealth

Evolutionary theory explains marriage patterns among the Kipsigis, a group of East African pastoralists.

Among the Kipsigis, a group of Kalenjin-speaking people who live in the Rift Valley province of Kenya, women usually marry in their late teens (Figure 17.9), men usually marry for the first time when they are in their early 20s, and it is common for men to have several wives—a practice called **polygyny**. As in many other societies, the groom's father makes a **bridewealth** payment to the father of the bride at the time of marriage. The payment, tendered in livestock and cash, compensates the bride's family for the loss of her labor and gives the groom rights to her labor and the children she bears during her marriage. The amount of the payment is settled through protracted negotiations between the father of the groom and the father of the bride. The average bridewealth consists of six cows, six goats or sheep, and 800 Kenyan shillings. This is about one-third of the average man's cattle holdings, one-half of his goat and sheep herd, and two months' wages for men who hold salaried positions. Because men marry polygynously, there is competition over eligible women. Often the bride's father entertains several competing marriage offers before he chooses a groom for his daughter. The prospective bride and groom have little voice in the decisions their fathers make.

Anthropologist Monique Borgerhoff Mulder at the University of California Davis reasoned that Kipsigis bridewealth payments provide a concrete index of the qualities that each party values in prospective spouses. The groom's father is likely to prefer a bride who will bear his son many healthy children. His bridewealth offer is expected to reflect the potential reproductive value of the prospective bride. The groom's father is also expected to prefer that his son marry a woman who will devote her labor to his household. Kipsigis women who remain near their own family's households are likely to be called on to help their mothers with the harvest and to

FIGURE 17.9 These Kipsigis women are eligible for marriage. Their fathers will negotiate with the fathers of their prospective husbands over bridewealth. (Photograph courtesy of Monique Borgerhoff Mulder.)

assist their mothers in childbirth. Thus, the groom's father may prefer a woman whose natal family is distant from his son's household. The bride's father is likely to have a different perspective on the negotiations. Because wealthy men can provide their wives with larger plots of land to farm and more resources, we would expect the bride's father to prefer that his daughter marry a relatively wealthy man. At the same time, because the bride's family will be deprived of her labor and assistance if she moves far away from their land, the bride's father is likely to prefer a groom who lives nearby. The fathers of the bride and groom are expected to weigh the costs and benefits of prospective unions in their negotiations over bridewealth payments. For example, although the bride's father may prefer a high bridewealth payment, he may settle for a lower payment if the groom is particularly desirable. In order to determine whether these preferences affected bridewealth payments, Borgerhoff Mulder recorded the number of cows, sheep, and goats, as well as the amount of money, that each groom's family paid to the bride's family.

Plump women whose menarche occurred at an early age fetched the highest bridewealth payments.

Borgerhoff Mulder found that bridewealth increased as the bride's age at the time of **menarche** (her first menstruation) decreased (Figure 17.10). That is, the highest bridewealths were paid for the women who were youngest when they first menstruated. Among the Kipsigis, age at menarche is a reliable index of women's reproductive potential. Kipsigis women who reach menarche early have longer reproductive life spans, higher annual fertility, and higher survivorship among their offspring than do women who mature at later ages.

Borgerhoff Mulder wondered how a man assessed his prospective bride's reproductive potential, since men often do not know their bride's exact age, nor her age at reaching menarche. One way to be sure of a woman's ability to produce children would be to select one who had already demonstrated her fertility by becoming pregnant or

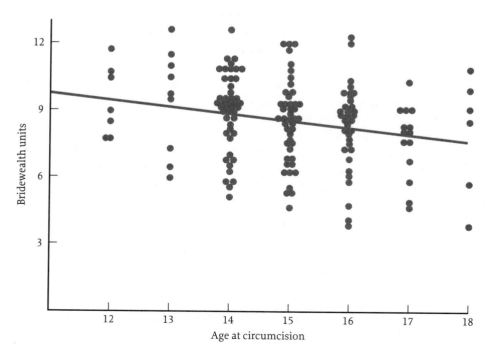

FIGURE 17.10 Kipsigis girls who mature early fetch larger bridewealth payments than older girls do. Among the Kipsigis, girls undergo circumcision (removal of the clitoris) within a year of menarche. The largest bridewealths were paid for the girls who underwent menarche and circumcision at the youngest ages. Bridewealth is transformed into standardized units to account for the fact that the value of livestock varies over time.

producing a child. However, bridewealths for such women were typically lower than bridewealths for women who had never conceived. Instead, bridewealth payments were associated with the physical attributes of women. The fathers of brides who were considered by the Kipsigis to be plump received significantly higher bridewealth payments than did the fathers of brides considered to be skinny. The plumpness of prospective brides may be a reliable correlate of the age at menarche, since menarcheal age is determined partly by body weight. Plumpness may also be valued because a woman's ability to conceive is determined partly by her nutritional status.

Bridewealth payments are also related to the distance between the bride's home and the groom's home; the farther she moves, the less likely she is to provide help to her mother, and the higher the bridewealth payment will be. However, there is no relationship between the wealth of the father of the groom and the bridewealth payment. The bride's father does not lower the bridewealth payment to secure a wealthy husband for his daughter. Although this finding was unexpected, Borgerhoff Mulder suggested that it may be related to the fact that differences in wealth among the Kipsigis are unstable over time. A wealthy man who has large livestock herds may become relatively poor if his herds are raided, decimated by disease, or diverted to pay for another wife. Although land is not subject to these vicissitudes, the Kipsigis traditionally have not held legal title to their lands.

Nyinba Polyandry

Polyandry is rare in humans and other mammals.

Because mammalian females are generally the limiting resource for males, males usually compete for access to females. As a result, among mammalian species polygyny is much more common than polyandry. As you may recall from Chapter 5, **polyandry** is a mating system in which one female is paired with two or more males. Polyandry is rare because, all other things being equal, males that share access to a single female produce fewer offspring than do males that maintain exclusive access to one or more females. The reproductive costs of polyandry may be somewhat reduced if brothers share access to a female—an arrangement called **fraternal polyandry**. Thus, in accordance with Hamilton's rule (see Chapter 8), it is plausible to assume that natural selection has shaped human psychology so that a man is more willing to care for his brother's offspring than for children who are unrelated to him.

Polyandrous marriage systems are as rare among human societies as they are in other mammalian species. Anthropologist George Peter Murdock compiled information about marriage practices in a sample of 862 societies around the world. In 83% of these societies, polygyny is the preferred form of marriage. In 16% of the societies, marriages are exclusively monogamous. Polyandry is practiced in only 0.5% of Murdock's sample.

Polyandrous marriage occurs in several societies in the Himalayas.

Although polyandry is generally rare among human societies, there are several societies in the highlands of the Himalayas in which fraternal polyandry is the preferred form of marriage. In these societies, several brothers marry one woman and establish a communal household. Because polyandry seems to limit a man's reproductive opportunities, we might ask why men tolerate polyandrous marriages. Nancy

Levine of the University of California Los Angeles studied one of these polyandrous societies: the Nyinba of northwestern Nepal (Figure 17.11). Her data shed some interesting light on this question.

The Nyinba live in four prosperous villages, nestled between 2850 and 3300 m (about 9500 and 11,000 ft) on gently sloping hillsides. Nyinba families support themselves through a combination of agriculture, herding, and long-distance trade. The Nyinba believe that marriages of three brothers are most desirable, allowing one husband to farm, another to herd livestock, and the third to engage in trade. In practice, however, all brothers marry jointly, no matter how many there are. The Nyinba are quite concerned with the paternity of their children. Women identify the fathers of each of their children, a task made easier by the fact that one or more of their husbands is often away from home for lengthy periods tending to family business. Although it is impossible to be certain

FIGURE 17.11 Polyandry is the preferred form of marriage among the Nyinba. In this family, three brothers are married to one woman. The Nyinba consider this to be the ideal number of cohusbands. (Photograph courtesy of Nancy Levine.)

how accurate these paternity assessments are, it is clear that the Nyinba place great stock in them. Men develop particularly close relationships with the children they have fathered, and fathers bequeath their share in the family's landholdings to their own sons.

Evolutionary theory helps explain why some polyandrous marriages are successful and others fail.

Polyandry is the ideal form of marriage among the Nyinba, but reality does not always conform to this ideal. Although all men marry jointly, some marriages break down when one or more of the brothers brings another wife into the household or leaves to set up an independent household. When households break up, each man receives a share of the estate and takes with him all the children he has fathered during the marriage. Levine reasoned that a comparison of marriages that remain intact and marriages that break up would provide clues about the kinds of problems that arise in polyandrous marriages. Together with one of us (J. B. S.), Levine has used her data to determine whether male decisions conform to predictions derived from evolutionary theory.

All other things being equal, the more men who are married to a single woman, the lower each man's reproductive success is likely to be. Thus we might expect marriages with many cohusbands to be less stable than marriages with fewer cohusbands. This turns out to be the case; few of the largest communal Nyinba marriages remained intact. Only 10% of the marriages that began with two cohusbands partitioned (split apart), but 58% of the marriages that began with four cohusbands did (Figure 17.12).

Some Nyinba marriages are arranged by parents; others are set up by the oldest brother. In either case, the wife is usually a few years younger than the oldest cohusband. In some marriages, the youngest cohusbands are considerably younger than their wives. Remember that Buss's cross-cultural data suggest that men prefer to marry younger women. Thus we might expect that men would be dissatisfied with marriages to women much older than themselves. In fact, the Nyinba men who were most junior to their wives were the ones most likely to initiate partitions. When these men

FIGURE 17.12 Among the Nyinba, marriages that contain more than three brothers are more likely to break up than marriages that include only two or three cohusbands. "Polyandrous" households are those that maintain intact polyandrous marriages. "Conjoint" households are those that added a second wife, which often effectively created two separate marriages within a single household. "Partitioned" households are those in which one or more men left the fraternal marriage and formed a new household.

remarried, they invariably chose women who were younger than themselves and who were younger than their first wives.

If the basic problem with polyandry is that it limits male reproductive opportunities, then we should expect males' satisfaction with their marriages to be linked to their reproductive performance. In most marriages, the oldest brother fathers the wife's first child. The second-oldest brother often fathers the second child, and so on. However, disparities in reproductive success among cohusbands often persist. A man's place in the birth order is directly related to his reproductive success, so the oldest brothers have more children than the youngest brothers have. Men's decisions to terminate their marriages are associated with their reproductive performance: men who remained in stable polyandrous marriages fathered an average of 0.1 children per year; men who terminated their marriages had produced, on average, only 0.04 children per year during the relationship.

Finally, kin selection theory would lead us to predict that close kinship among cohusbands would help stabilize polyandrous marriages because men should be more willing to invest in their brothers' children. We can test this prediction because there is a considerable amount of variation in the degrees of relatedness among cohusbands within households. Some households are composed entirely of full siblings. In others, the cohusbands may have multiple fathers, who are related themselves, and multiple mothers, who may also be related. The result is a complicated web of relationships among cohusbands. Contrary to predictions based on kin selection, there is no difference in the degree of relatedness among cohusbands in households that remained intact and households that dissolved. Moreover, when men remarried, they showed no inclination to align themselves with the cohusbands to whom they were more closely related.

Evolutionary theory explains certain aspects of polyandry but not others.

Polyandry is rare among human societies, as we would expect from an evolutionary perspective. When marriages dissolve, they seem to do so in ways that are consistent with predictions derived from evolutionary theory. Men leave marriages in which the women are much older, and they leave marriages when they have not fathered many children. In their decisions about whether to maintain their marriages, however, men seem to ignore kinship to their cohusbands—a surprising result, from an evolutionary perspective.

RAISING CHILDREN

Children are a lot of work. In addition to the maternal burdens of pregnancy and lactation, children need to be fed, carried, protected, clothed, and educated. In most human societies, this job is done mainly by parents. All this seems so normal and so obvious that it is easy to overlook the possibility that societies could be organized in many other ways. For example, babies could be bought and sold or traded back and forth like pets or domesticated animals. Such a system would have lots of practical advantages. It would be easy to adjust the size of your family, to select the ratio or order of boys and girls, and to regulate the spacing between children. Women who preferred to avoid pregnancy and delivery, or who were unable to bear children, could have a family just as easily as anyone else. Some people might even opt to skip the dubious pleasures of frequent diaper changes and midnight feedings, and acquire children who were already two or three years old. But this is not what happens. Instead, in virtually every society, most people raise their own children. It seems likely that people do this because their evolved psychology causes them to value their own children very differently from other people's children.

There is, however, considerable cross-cultural variation in human parenting behavior. In some societies, most men are devoted fathers; in others, men take little interest in children and rarely interact with their own offspring. In some societies, parents supervise their children's every waking moment; in others, children are reared mainly by older siblings and cousins. Moreover, some aspects of parenting behavior in some societies seem hard to reconcile with the idea that human psychology has been shaped by natural selection. There are cultures in which parents sometimes kill or physically abuse their own infant children, and cultures in which people regularly raise children who are not their own. Because such behaviors seem inconsistent with the idea that human behavior is controlled by evolved predispositions, their existence has been cited as evidence that evolutionary reasoning has little relevance to understanding modern human behavior.

In the remainder of this chapter we will consider data suggesting that observed patterns of parental investment, forms of neglect and abuse of children, and adoption are consistent with the idea that human behavior is influenced by evolved predispositions. Moreover, evolutionary reasoning can give fresh and useful insights about when and why such behaviors occur. However, we will also see that there are aspects of contemporary parenting behavior that evolutionary reasoning has not yet explained.

Parenting Effort and Mating Effort

Some human paternal investment is parenting effort, but some is mating effort.

Human children require care from their parents long after they are weaned. The lengthy period of parental investment means that some marriages will end before children are grown. Although death, separation, and divorce divide families, remarriage can create new families that include children from the partners' previous marriages and children from their present marriage. The theory of kin selection generally predicts that men and women will direct care selectively to kin, and this might lead them to favor genetic off-spring over stepchildren. At the same time, if men and women value their mates' invest-ment in their children, then care for children might also be a form of mating effort.

Kermyt Anderson, Hillard Kaplan, and Jane Lancaster have pointed out that, in humans, parental care may function as both parenting effort and mating effort. Thus, when husbands and wives invest in their genetic offspring, their efforts may enhance their inclusive fitness and the quality and durability of their marital relationship. Although parenting effort and mating are confounded when we think about husbands and wives investing in their joint progeny, it is possible to tease mating effort and par-enting effort apart, as we show in Table 17.2. As you can see, investment in stepchil-dren reflects mating effort but not parenting effort. On the other hand, investment in one's own offspring from a previous marriage reflects parenting effort but not mating effort. Investment in a mate's stepchildren from a previous relationship does not con-stitute parenting effort or mating effort.

Anderson and his colleagues interviewed a large number of men in Albuquerque, New Mexico, and asked them about their reproductive histories. They gathered infor-mation about a number of different measures of parental care, including whether men provided any financial support for children attending college and how much time they spent with children in the previous year. The data in Figure 17.13 show that both mat-ing effort and parenting effort seem to influence the extent of men's investment in chil-dren. Men are much more likely to provide money for their college-age children when they are still married to the mothers of those children than they are to provide money for their own children after the marriage has ended or for stepchildren. The magni-tude of the effects of mating effort and parenting effort seem to be about the same; men invest nearly as much in their stepchildren as they do in their own offspring from a previous relationship.

There is some evidence that similar patterns influence men in other societies. Anderson and his colleagues surveyed Xhosa high school students in Cape Town,

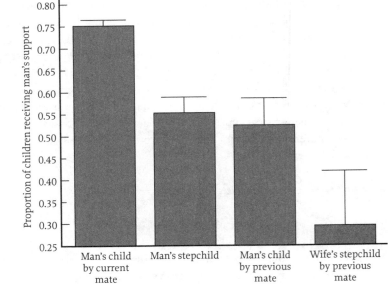

FIGURE 17.13 The proportion of children attend-ing college who receive support from men varies considerably. Men are significantly more likely to contribute to the costs of college for their own children when they are still with the child's mother than they are to contribute to the costs of college for their stepchildren. How-ever, men are equally likely to provide funds for stepchildren and their own children by a previous mate.

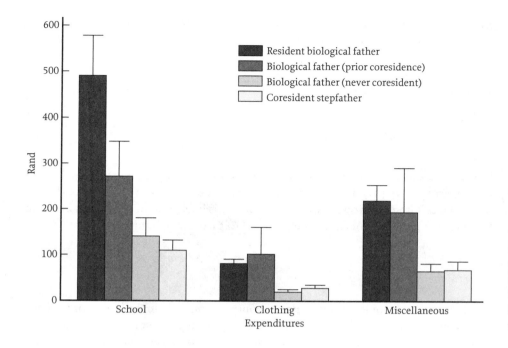

FIGURE 17.14 In South Africa, Xhosa men make bigger financial expenditures on behalf of their resident offspring than on behalf of stepchildren. Note that some children had never lived with their genetic fathers, while others had lived with them sometime in the past. Coresidence with genetic fathers has a sizable impact on the amount of investment children receive. At the time that these data were collected, one U.S. dollar was worth about 5 rand.

South Africa, and asked them about the amount and kinds of care they obtained from their fathers and stepfathers. These students spent more time with their resident genetic fathers than with their resident stepfathers, and they spent more time with their resident stepfathers than with nonresident genetic fathers (Figure 17.14). At the same time, the students generally received less financial support from their stepfathers than from their genetic fathers; they received the most support from resident genetic fathers.

Frank Marlowe of Harvard University has investigated the trade-off between mating effort and parenting effort among the Hadza, a foraging group in Tanzania. Marriages among the Hadza are relatively impermanent, so men may find themselves living with the mothers of their children or with women who have children from previous relationships. Hadza men hunt and bring food back to camp, where it is distributed. Although they are out of camp for about the same amounts of time, men who live with only biological offspring bring substantially more food back to camp than do men who live with at least one stepchild.

Hadza men also spend about 2% to 5% of every day caring directly for children. This care takes various forms: they may hold, clean, feed, comfort, or feed children; play with them; talk with them; and stay close to them (Figure 17.15). Marlowe predicted that men would provide more care for genetic offspring than for stepchildren, but he also predicted that men would make trade-offs between the extent of their parenting effort and that of their mating effort. In addition, Marlowe postulated that when men's mating opportunities were limited, they would invest more time in caring for their genetic offspring; and that when mating opportunities were abundant, men would increase mating effort and decrease parenting effort. As he expected, Marlowe found that Hadza men provide more care for their genetic offspring than for stepchildren, but they do spend some time caring for stepchildren. Caring for stepchildren might be a form of mating

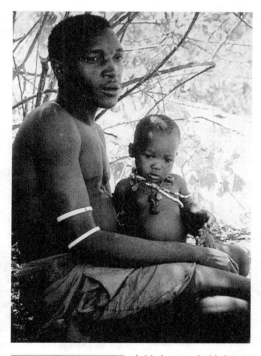

FIGURE 17.15 A Hadza man holds his child on his lap. Men provide more care for genetic offspring than for stepchildren, and they seem to balance mating effort against parenting effort. (Photo courtesy of Frank Marlowe.)

effort. Moreover, when men were living in larger camps with more eligible women, they provided less direct care for children.

Grandparental Care

Grandparents are closely related to their grandchildren and are often in a position to contribute to their care.

In human societies, men and women often live long enough to have grandchildren. Grandparents may play an active role in their grandchildren's lives, particularly if all their own children are grown. Grandparental care is likely to be a product of kin selection because grandparents are closely related to their grandchildren.

Uncertainty about paternity favors matrilateral biases in grandparental investment.

In humans, there is more certainty about maternity than about paternity. There is no doubt who the mother of a given infant is, but there is sometimes some uncertainty about the identity of the father. This asymmetry in certainty about parentage skews estimates of relatedness. Let's begin with the simplest case to review how we calculate relatedness between parents, offspring, and grandoffspring. The coefficient of relatedness (r) is 0.5 for women and their daughters, and 0.5 again for those daughters and their own daughters; so the relatedness between women and their daughter's children is equal to 0.5×0.5, or 0.25. For mothers of sons, however, the calculations need to take into account the probability, p, that the son is actually the father of his mate's children. When $p = 1$, there is no uncertainty about paternity; when $p < 1$, there is some uncertainty about who is the father. Thus the degree of relatedness between mothers and their son's children is devalued by p, or $0.5 \times 0.5p = 0.25p$. The same logic tells us that men are related to their sons and daughters by $0.5p$, to their daughters' children by $0.25p$, and to their sons' children by $0.25p^2$. Whenever $p < 1$, women will be more closely related to their children than their husbands are, and both parents will be more closely related to their daughters' children than to their sons' children.

This asymmetry in relatedness to grandchildren led Harald Euler and Barbara Weitzel of the University of Kassel to predict that there would be matrilateral biases in grandparental investment. Euler and Weitzel surveyed nearly 2000 German adults and asked them how much care they received from their grandparents (Figure 17.16). In this population, both maternal grandparents provide more care than their paternal counterparts do. And on both sides of the family, grandmothers provide more care for children than grandfathers do. However, maternal

FIGURE 17.16 In Germany, maternal grandparents provide more care on average than paternal grandparents, perhaps because parents are more confident of their daughters' maternity than their sons' paternity. Adults were asked to rate the amount of care that they received from each of their grandparents on a seven-point scale. High scores correspond to higher amounts of care. Here the mean and the standard deviations are plotted.

grandfathers provide significantly more care than paternal grandmothers do, even though both are related to their grandchildren by $0.25p$. Of course, the matrilateral bias in care for grandchildren might arise if there were a tendency for children to live closer to their maternal grandparents than to their paternal grandparents. Euler and Weitzel's data indicate that this is not the case, however. Moreover, the pattern held when the authors controlled for grandparents' age and availability.

Discriminative Parental Solicitude

Evolutionary theory predicts that parents should terminate investment in offspring if their prospects are poor.

Parents' ability to invest in their offspring is limited, so investment in one offspring limits their ability to invest in other offspring. If a child's prospects for survival are poor or the costs of raising a particular child are very high, then investment will not enhance parental fitness. Thus, natural selection is expected to favor mechanisms that cause parents to adjust investment in offspring in relation to the offspring's impact on parental fitness. Before birth, maternal physiology is expected to terminate pregnancies when fetal prospects are poor or the costs of carrying the fetus to term threaten maternal health. After birth, we expect parental psychology to be sensitive to the child's condition, the parents' economic circumstances, and the parents' alternative opportunities to pass on their genetic material. This phenomenon has been labeled **discriminative parental solicitude** by psychologists Martin Daly and Margo Wilson of McMaster University in Ontario, Canada.

Prenatal Investment

Selection sometimes favors the termination of pregnancy when either the mother or the fetus is in poor condition.

The costs of pregnancy must be weighed against the potential benefits. For women, every pregnancy is a costly investment. Pregnancy lasts nine months, and during their pregnancies, women need more food and work somewhat less efficiently. Childbirth is also a major source of mortality among women. The magnitude of these costs, and their impact on the mother's future reproductive success, will depend partly on the mother's condition at conception. Women who are in poor health or badly nourished will be less able to meet the demands of pregnancy and will take longer to recover from their pregnancies than will healthy, well-nourished women.

The fitness benefit that the mother will gain depends largely on the quality of the fetus that she carries. If the fetus is sickly or suffers from a genetic defect, it will be unlikely to survive. If the mother is in poor condition, she may be unable to provide the resources that her fetus or infant needs to survive. In such cases, the costs of the pregnancy will outweigh the benefits. Thus we would expect natural selection to favor physiological mechanisms that terminate a pregnancy when there is something wrong with the fetus or the mother is in very poor condition.

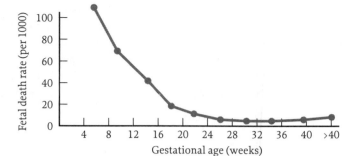

FIGURE 17.17 Most fetal deaths occur during the first trimester of pregnancy.

In some cases, miscarriages appear to provide a maternal mechanism for maintaining quality control over pregnancy.

It has been estimated that only 22% of all conceptions are carried to term. The rest are miscarried, usually before the twelfth week of pregnancy (Figure 17.17). In the majority of cases, miscarriages are associated with overt chromosomal abnormalities in the fetus. There are good reasons to expect that natural selection acting on mothers would favor miscarriages under these circumstances.

Most people think of miscarriages as pathologies—maladaptive and unpredictable aberrations that cause the fetus to die and the pregnancy to be terminated. For those who suffer miscarriages, the loss of a fetus is often deeply distressing. In such cases, parents may never know why their fetus died or whether their next one is likely to survive. As upsetting as miscarriages are for parents, there is good reason to believe that some of the mechanisms that produce miscarriages may be adaptive responses that have been favored by natural selection over the course of human history.

There is conflict between mother and fetus over whether a given pregnancy should be sustained.

To this point we have considered miscarriages from the point of view of selection acting on the mother. The picture looks different from the perspective of the fetus. As we explained in Chapter 7, the fetus has a greater interest in its own survival (and a weaker interest in any future sibling's survival) than does its mother. Thus there will be a certain scope for conflict between the mother and her fetus over whether a given pregnancy should continue. Natural selection will favor genes expressed in the fetus that prevent those spontaneous abortions that are induced by genes expressed in the mother. The fetus plays an active role in promoting its own survival.

In humans, pregnancy is maintained by the production of **luteinizing hormone** (**LH**) by the anterior pituitary gland. Luteinizing hormone, in turn, stimulates the production of another hormone, **progesterone**, by the **corpus luteum**, a mass of endocrine cells formed in the mother's ovary after ovulation. Progesterone inhibits uterine contractions that would terminate the pregnancy.

From very early in pregnancy, the fetus influences the levels of progesterone in its mother's bloodstream. Initially the fetus releases **human chorionic gonadotropin** (**hCG**), which stimulates the production of progesterone by the mother's corpus luteum, directly into the mother's bloodstream. By the eighth week of pregnancy, however, the fetus can produce enough progesterone to sustain the pregnancy, even if the corpus luteum is removed from the mother. Thus, the eight-week-old fetus is able to manipulate the maternal endocrine system to enhance its own viability (Figure 17.18). It seems quite plausible that the ability of the fetus to manipulate the level of progesterone in its mother's bloodstream has been favored by natural selection because this ability allows the fetus to protect itself from premature termination of the pregnancy.

Infanticide

Cross-cultural analyses indicate that infanticide occurs when a child is unlikely to survive, when parents cannot care for the child, or when the child is not sired by the mother's husband.

Children have been deliberately killed, fatally neglected, or abandoned by their parents through recorded history and across the world's cultures. It is tempting to dismiss infanticide by parents as a pathological side effect of modern life. After all, a child is a parent's main vehicle for perpetuating his or her own genetic material. However, evolutionary analyses suggest that parents who kill their own children may, under some circumstances, have higher fitness than parents who do not do so.

Daly and Wilson used the Human Relations Area Files, a vast compendium of ethnographic information from societies around the world, to compile a list of the reasons why parents commit infanticide. They based their study on a standard, randomly selected sample of 60 societies that represent traditional societies around the world. In 39 of these societies, infanticide is mentioned in ethnographic accounts, and in 35 of the societies Daly and Wilson found information about the circumstances under which infanticide occurs. There are three main classes of reasons why parents commit infanticide: (1) the child is seriously ill or deformed, (2) the parents' circumstances do not allow them to raise the child, or (3) the child is not sired by the mother's husband (Table 17.3).

In 21 societies, children are killed if they are born with major deformities or if they are very ill. In traditional societies, children with major deformities or serious illnesses require substantial amounts of care and impose a considerable burden on their families. They are unlikely to survive, and if they do, they are unlikely to be able to support themselves, marry, or produce children of their own. Thus it is plausible that selection has shaped human psychology so that we are predisposed to terminate investment in such children and to reserve resources for healthy children.

In some societies, children are killed when the parents' present circumstances make it too difficult or dangerous for them to raise the children. This includes cases in which births are too closely spaced, twins are born, the mother has died, there is no male present to support the children, or the mother is unmarried. It is easy to see why these factors might make it very difficult to raise children. Twins, for example, strain a mother's abilities to nurse her children and to provide adequate care for them. Moreover, twins often are born prematurely and are of below-average birth weight, making them less likely to survive than single infants. In traditional societies, it is not always possible to obtain substitutes for breast milk. This problem dooms some children whose mothers die when they are very young. If a child's father dies before it is born or when it is an infant, its mother may have great difficulty supporting herself and her older children. The child's presence might also reduce her chances of remarrying and producing additional children in the future. When circumstances are not favorable, parents who attempt to rear children may squander precious resources that might better be reserved for older children or for children born at more favorable times.

FIGURE 17.18 Just eight weeks after conception, the human fetus is able to produce enough progesterone to sustain pregnancy.

TABLE 17.3   In a representative cross-cultural sample of societies, the rationales for infanticide are consistent with predictions derived from evolutionary theory. Parents commit infanticide mainly when the child is unlikely to thrive, when their own circumstances make it difficult to raise the child, or when the child was not fathered by the mother's spouse. (Data from Table 3.1 in M. Daly and M. Wilson, 1988, *Homicide,* Aldine de Gruyter, New York.)

Rationale	Number of Societies
Child is of poor quality	
Deformed or ill	21
Parents' circumstances do not allow them to raise child	
Twins born	14
Children too closely spaced or numerous	11
No male support for child	6
Mother died	6
Mother unmarried	14
Economic hardship	3
Born in wrong season	1
Quarrel with husband	1
Paternity is not assigned to wife's husband	
Adulterous conception	15
Nontribal sire	3
Sired by mother's previous husband	2
Other reasons	15

In 20 societies, infanticide occurs when a child is sired during an extramarital relationship, by a previous husband, or by a member of a different tribe who is not married to the mother. Recall from Chapter 8 that the theory of kin selection predicts that altruism will be restricted to kin. According to this theory, males should not be predisposed to support other men's children.

Before you condemn those who kill their children, keep in mind that the options for parents in traditional societies are very different from the options available to people in our own society, who have access to modern health care systems, social services, and so on. Decisions by parents to kill their children are often reluctant responses to the painful realities of life. Whether these considerations are sufficient to absolve the parents in your eyes depends, of course, on your moral beliefs.

Adoption

In many societies, children are adopted and raised by adults other than their biological parents.

Adoption is the flip side of infanticide. In some regions of the world, particularly Oceania and the Arctic, a substantial fraction of all children are raised in adoptive households. Adoption can be thought of as a form of altruism because it takes considerable time, energy, and resources to raise children. In other animal species, including other primates, voluntary extended care of others' offspring is uncommon. There are, however, examples of *in*voluntary extended care: some species of parasitic birds, such as cuckoos, routinely lay their eggs in other birds' nests, tricking the unwitting hosts into rearing cuckoo young as their own (Figure 17.19). The fact that we label such behavior **nest parasitism** reflects the fact that this is a form of exploitation, enhancing the fitness of the parasitic cuckoo at the expense of its host. In human societies, there is no need to trick adoptive parents into caring for children, since they are typically eager to assume responsibility for other people's children.

ADOPTION IN OCEANIA

Adoption is very common in the societies of the Pacific Islands, and the pattern is consistent with the predictions of evolutionary theory.

At first glance, adoption seems inconsistent with evolutionary theory, which predicts that people should be reluctant to invest time and energy in unrelated children. This apparent

FIGURE 17.19   Cuckoos lay their eggs in the nests of other species of birds. The hosts unwittingly rear the alien chicks as their own.

inconsistency prompted Marshall Sahlins, a cultural anthropologist at the University of Chicago, to cite adoption as an example of a human behavior that contradicts the logic of evolutionary theory. In *The Use and Abuse of Biology*, Sahlins pointed out that adoption is very common in the societies of the Pacific Islands. In fact, it is so common that the majority of households in many of these island societies include at least one adopted child. According to Sahlins, such widespread altruism toward nonkin shows that evolutionary reasoning does not apply to contemporary humans, and demonstrates that human societies are free to invent almost any social arrangement.

Sahlins's challenge prompted one of us (J. B. S.) to take a closer look at the pattern of adoption in a number of the societies of Oceania. The data tell a very interesting story. Adoption seems to provide an adaptive means for birth parents to regulate the sizes of their families and to enhance the quality of care they give to each of their offspring. Moreover, many of the features of adoption transactions in Oceania are consistent with predictions derived from kin selection theory:

- Adoptive parents are usually close kin, such as grandparents, aunts, or uncles (Figure 17.20). Close kin participate in adoptive transactions much more often than would be expected if children were adopted at random, without respect to kinship.
- Natural parents give up children when they cannot afford to raise them, and they rarely give up firstborn children for adoption.
- Adoptive parents generally have no dependent children; they are usually childless or the parents of grown children, but sometimes they are simply wealthy enough to be able to raise an additional child.
- Natural parents are often reluctant to give up their children for adoption, and regret the need to do so.

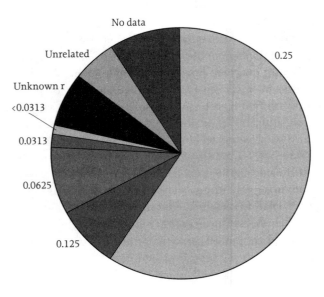

FIGURE 17.20 People in Oceania adopt mainly kin. Information about the numbers of adoptive parents and their relationships with their adoptive children in a number of communities in Oceania have been collected by ethnographers. The numbers here represent the degree of relatedness between the child and its adoptive parents. Most adoptions involve close kin ($r \le .25$), such as aunts, uncles, and grandparents.

- Natural parents maintain contact with their children after adoption, and terminate adoptions if children are neglected, mistreated, or unhappy.
- Natural parents prefer to have their children adopted by well-to-do individuals who can provide adequately for the children's daily needs or bestow property on them.
- Sometimes asymmetries in investment exist between natural and adoptive children; adopted children often inherit less property from their adoptive parents than biological offspring do.

The same pattern characterizes adoptions in some traditional societies elsewhere.

A number of of the same features characterize adoption in the North American Arctic, where many children are adopted. Moreover, adoption transactions in Oceania and the North American Arctic bear a striking similarity to the more temporary fosterage arrangements that are common in West Africa. In each of these cases, birth parents seem to act in ways that increase the health, security, and welfare of their children, and care for children is preferentially delegated to close kin.

Adoption transactions seem to fit predictions derived from the theory of kin selection, but this does not mean that we have fully explained human adoption transactions. Not all adoption transactions in Oceania fit the evolutionary model. We have not accounted for the fact that adoption is more common in some societies than in others, or that there are some societies, including our own, in which adoption is not restricted to relatives. It is to this problem that we now turn.

ADOPTION IN INDUSTRIALIZED SOCIETIES

In contemporary industrial societies, adoption often involves strangers.

As you read the preceding description of adoption in the traditional societies of Oceania, you may have been struck by how different these transactions are from adoptions

TABLE 17.4   The patterns of adoption in the United States and Oceania show both similarities and differences.

Feature	Oceania	United States
Economic difficulties figure in the adoption decision.	Yes	Yes
Adoptive parents are usually childless or wealthy enough to raise another child.	Yes	Yes
Children are adopted by close kin.	Usually	Sometimes*
Biological parents often regret the need for adoption.	Yes	Yes
Legal authority for the child is transferred exclusively to the adoptive parents.	No	Yes
The identities of the natural parents are known to the adoptee.	Yes	No
Contact is maintained between biological parents and child after adoption.	Yes	No
Biological parents want children to be adopted by well-to-do people.	Yes	Yes
Asymmetries exist in the care of adoptive children and biological children.	Yes	?

*In the United States from 1952 to 1971, approximately one-fourth of adoptions involved kin, another fourth involved stepparents, and one-half involved unrelated individuals.

in the United States. In the United States and in other industrialized nations, adoption is often a formal, legal process involving strangers. But as you compare the features of adoption transactions in Oceania and the United States in Table 17.4, you will see that there are similarities as well as differences between them.

In Oceania and in the United States, children are given up for adoption mainly when their parents are unable to raise them, and they are frequently adopted by people who have no dependent children of their own or by people who can afford to raise additional children. In both Oceania and the United States, biological parents often give up their children with considerable reluctance and hope to place their children in homes where the children's prospects will be improved.

The main difference between adoption in Oceania and in the United States is that in Oceania, adoption is a relatively informal, open transaction between close kin, while in the United States, adoption is often a formal, legal transaction between strangers. The anonymity of the U.S. model has a number of ramifications. When the identity of the biological parents is not disclosed to the adoptive parents or the adopted child, contact between biological parents and their children is broken. In Oceania, adopted children's interests are protected by their biological parents, who maintain contact with them and reserve the right to terminate the adoption if the children are mistreated or unhappy. In the United States, government agencies are responsible for protecting the interests of adopted children. In recent years, some of these differences have been eroded as open adoptions have become more common, and the courts have given adoptees the right to find out the identities of their birth parents.

The different patterns of adoption in Oceania and the United States may result from the same basic evolved psychological motivations.

Overall, the similarities in adoption seem to be related to people's motivations about children; the differences are related to how the transactions are organized in each culture. In Oceania and the United States, people seem to share concerns about their children. We are deeply concerned about the welfare of our own children, and many people have deep desires to raise children. These feelings are likely to be the product of evolved psychological predispositions that motivate us to cherish and protect children. Although people in Oceania and the United States may have very similar feelings about children, the adoption process is clearly different. Nepotism (favoring relatives over nonrelatives) is a central element in adoption transactions in Oceania but not in the United States. People in Oceania rely on their families to help them find homes for their children and to obtain children; people in the United States turn to adoption agencies, private attorneys, and strangers.

We are not sure why kinship plays such a fundamental role in adoption transactions in Oceania but not in industrialized societies like the United States and Canada. We can speculate that this difference is due to differences in the availability of children who are eligible for adoption, or to the tendency of family members to be dispersed geographically. However, nepotism generally seems to play a more important role in the societies of Oceania than it does in industrialized societies.

IS HUMAN EVOLUTION OVER?

This question is often raised by students in our courses, and it seems a sensible question to consider as we come to the end of the story of human evolution. As we have seen, modern humans are the product of millions of years of evolutionary change. Of course, so are cockroaches, peacocks, and orchids. All of the organisms that we see around us, including people, are the products of evolution, but they are not finished products. They are simply works in progress.

In one sense, however, human evolution is over. Because cultural change is much faster than genetic change, most of the changes in human societies since at least the origin of agriculture, almost 10 kya, have been the result of cultural, not genetic, evolution. Most of the evolution of human behavior and human societies is not driven by natural selection and the other processes of organic evolution; rather, it is driven by learning and other psychological mechanisms that shape cultural evolution. However, this fact does not mean that evolutionary theory or human evolutionary history is irrelevant to understanding contemporary human behavior. Natural selection has shaped the physiological mechanisms and psychological machinery that govern learning and other mechanisms of cultural change, and an understanding of human evolution can provide important insights into human nature and the behavior of modern peoples.

FURTHER READING

Barrett, L., R. I. M. Dunbar, and J. Lycett. 2002. *Human Evolutionary Psychology.* Princeton University Press, Princeton, NJ.

Betzig, L., M. Borgerhoff Mulder, and P. Turke, eds. 1988. *Human Reproductive Behavior*. Cambridge University Press, Cambridge, England.

Buss, D. 1994. *The Evolution of Desire*. Basic Books, New York.

Daly, M., and M. Wilson. 1988. *Homicide*. Aldine de Gruyter, Hawthorne, NY.

Silk, J. B. 1990. Human adoption in evolutionary perspective. *Human Nature* 1: 25–52.

STUDY QUESTIONS

1. In Chapter 7 we said that the reproductive success of most male primates depends on the number of females with which they mate. Here we discussed Buss's argument that a man's reproductive success will depend mainly on the health and fertility of his mate. Why are humans different from most primates? Among what other primate species should we expect males to attend to the physical characteristics of females when choosing mates?

2. Why should men value fidelity in prospective mates more than women should?

3. In Buss's cross-cultural survey, what was the most important attribute in a mate for both men and women? Does this result falsify his evolutionary reasoning?

4. Are Borgerhoff Mulder's observations about the Kipsigis consistent with Buss's cross-cultural results? Explain why or why not.

5. Explain why polyandry is so rare among mammalian species. Some bird species are polyandrous. What kinds of behaviors would you expect to find among females in these species?

6. Explain why individual organisms may sometimes increase their fitness by killing their own offspring. What does your reasoning predict about the contexts in which infanticide will occur?

7. Newborn babies attract an incredible amount of attention. Complete strangers stop to chuck them under the chin, coo at them, and comment on how cute they are. If natural selection has favored discriminative parental solicitude, as the data on infanticide seem to suggest, how can you explain the unselective attraction to newborn infants?

8. Why is adoption altruistic from an evolutionary perspective? How can adopting other people's babies be adaptive?

KEY TERMS

polygyny

bridewealth

menarche

polyandry

fraternal polyandry

discriminative parental solicitude

luteinizing hormone/LH

progesterone

corpus luteum

human chorionic Gonadotropin/hCG

Hooff, 1989, Functional aspects of reconciliation among captive long-tailed macaques (Macaca fasicularis), American Journal of Primatology 19:39–51; 8.15: Joan B. Silk; 8.16a: From Table 1 in J.A. Johnson, 1987, Dominance rank in juvenile olive baboons, Papio anubis: the influence of gender, size, maternal rank and orphaning, Animal Behaviour 35:1694–1708; 8.16b: Joan B. Silk; 8.17: Joan B. Silk; 8.18: From Figure 1 in R. M. Seyfarth and D. L. Cheney, 1984, Grooming, alliances, and reciprocal altruism in vervet monkeys, Nature 308:541–543; 8.19: From Figure 2 in F. B. M. de Waal, 1997, The chimpanzee's service economy: Food for grooming, Evolution & Human Behavior 18:375–386.

CHAPTER 9

9.0: Courtesy of Susan Perry; 9.1: Cover: Time Life/Getty Images; Photo: AP/Wide World Photos; 9.2: W. Perry Conway/Corbis; 9.3: Joan B. Silk; 9.4: Gallo Images/Corbis; 9.5: Yann Arthus-Bertrand/Corbis; 9.6a :Joan B. Silk; 9.6b: Courtesy of Susan Perry; 9.7: Wolfgang Kohler, The Mentality of Apes. Routledge & Kegan Paul, Ltd., London, 1927. Reproduced with permission from the publisher; 9.8a: © Steve Bloom; 9.8b: Photograph courtesy of Tetsuro Matsuzawa; 9.9a–c: Redrawn from p. 109 in S.J. Jones, R. D. Martin, and D. A. Pilbeam, 1992, The Cambridge Encyclopedia of Human Evolution, Cambridge University Press, Cambridge; 9.10: From figures 1a and 1c in Reader, S.M., & Laland, K.N. 2002. Social intelligence, innovation, and enhanced brain size in primates. Proc. Nat. Acad. Sci.,99:4436-4441; 9.11: From Figure 2 in Byrne, R.W. and Corp, N. 2004. Neocortex size predicts deception rate in primates. Proc. R. Soc. Lond. B 271: 1693-1699; 9.12: Kevin Schafer/Corbis; 9.13: Robert Boyd and Joan B. Silk; 9.14: Joan B. Silk; 9.15a: Joan B. Silk; 9.15b: Courtesy of Susan Perry; 9.17: Courtesy of E. Menzel; 9.18: Courtesy of the Goodall Institute; 9.19: Photo courtesy of the Cognitive Evolution Group, University of Louisiana at Lafayette.

Part III: Bipedal footprints dating from approx. 3.5 mya discovered in Laetoli, Tanzania. (John Reader, 1999/Science Photo Library/Photo Researchers, Inc.).

CHAPTER 10

10.1a-b: Figure from pp. 38–39 in R. J. G. Savage and M. R. Long, 1986, Mammal Evolution, Facts on File and the British Museum (Natural History), Oxford, England; 10.2: From Figure 5.3 in R. D. Martin, 1990, Primate Origins and Evolution: A Phylogenetic Reconstruction, Princeton University Press, Princeton, NJ; 10.3: © Art Wolfe/artwolfe.com; 10.5: Adapted from Zachos, J. et al., Trends, rhythms, and aberrations in global climate 65 mya to present, Science, 292:688 2001; 10.7: From p. 200 in S. J. Jones, R. D. Martin, and D. A. Pilbeam, 1992, The Cambridge Encyclopedia of Human Evolution,

Cambridge University Press, Cambridge; 10.8: Sargis 2002, Science 298:1564, November; 10.9: From J. G. Fleagle, 1998, Primate Adaptation and Evolution, 2nd Ed., Academic Press, San Diego, p. 353; 10.10a–b: From Figure 3 in K. D. Rose, 1994/5, The earliest primates, Evolutionary Anthropology 3:159–173; 10.11: From Figure 11.9 in J. G. Fleagle, 1988, Primate Adaptation and Evolution, Academic Press, San Diego; 10.12: From Figure 12.5 in J. G. Fleagle, 1988, Primate Adaptation and Evolution, Academic Press, San Diego; 10.13: From Figure 12.6 in J. G. Fleagle, 1988, Primate Adaptation and Evolution, Academic Press, San Diego; 10.14a–c: From Figure 1.10 in G. Conroy, 1990, Primate Evolution, W. W. Norton, New York; 10.15: From Figure 12.13 in J. G. Fleagle, 1988, Primate Adaptation and Evolution, Academic Press, San Diego; 10.16: From Figure 14.11 in J. G. Fleagle, 1998, Primate Adaptation and Evolution, 2nd Ed., Academic Press, San Diego; 10.17: Robert Boyd; 10.18a–c: From Figure 2 in R. D. Martin, 1993, Primate origins: Plugging the gaps, Nature 363:223–234;10.20: Christophe Ratier/NHPA.UK; 10.21: Photograph courtesy of Laura MacLatchy. 10.22: From Figure 13.7 in J. G. Fleagle, 1988, Primate Adaptation and Evolution, Academic Press, San Diego. 10.24: From Figure 2.23 in R. D. Martin, 1990, Primate Origins and Evolution: A Phylogenetic Reconstruction, Princeton University Press, Princeton, NJ; 10.25: Photo courtesy of Salvador Moya-Sola. Reproduced with permission of Nature, 379: 156-159.

CHAPTER 11

11.0: Courtesy M.P.F.T. 11.1: Robert Boyd; 11.2: B. Senut et al./C.R. Acad. Sci. Paris, Sciences de la Terre et des planetes/ Earth and Planetary Sciences 332 (2001) 141; 11.3: © M.P.F.T. Photo courtesy of Michel Brunet; 11.4: From Figure 1 in T. D. White, D. C. Johanson, and W. H. Kimbel, 1981, Australopithecus africanus: Its phyletic position reconsidered. South African Journal of Science 77:445–470; 11.5: © National Museum of Kenya; 11.6: From Figure 1 in M. G. Leakey, C. S. Feibel, I. McDougall, and A. Walker, 1995, New four-million-year-old hominid species from Kanapoi and Allia Bay, Kenya, Nature 376:565–571; 11.7: © Institute of Human Origins/ Nanci Kahn; 11.8: John Reader/Science Photo Library/Photo Researchers, Inc; 11.9: © 1999 David L. Brill; 11.10: Courtesy of Richard Klein; 11.11a–c: © 1981 Luba Dmytryk Gudz/Brill Atlanta; 11.12: From Figures 20.15 and 20.20 in L. Aeillo and C. Dean, 1990, An Introduction to Evolutionary Human Anatomy, Academic Press, New York; 11.14: © 1981 Luba Dmytryk Gudz/Brill Atlanta; 11.15: © 1999 John Reader; 11.16: Joan B. Silk; 11.17: Courtesy of Richard Klein; 11.18: From Cean, C. et al. Nature 2001, 414:695, Figure in AustralopithecineGrowthDean.eps; 11:19: © 1999 David L. Brill; 11.20: Courtesy of Alan Walker; 11.21: © National Museum of Kenya; 11.24: © National Museum of Kenya; 11.25a–c: From p. 80 in R. Lewin, 1989, Human Evolution, Blackwell Scientific, Boston; 11.27: Lee Berger, University of Witswatersrand; 11.28: From Figure 1 in A. Sillen, 1992, Strontium-calcium ratios (Sr/Ca) of Australopithecus robustus and associated fauna from Swartkrans, Journal of Human Evolution 23:495–516; 11.29: © Wolfgang Kaehler, www.wkaehlerphoto.com; 11.30: Meave Leakey; 11.34: Robert Boyd; 11.36a–b: Joan B. Silk; 11.37a–b: Joan B. Silk; 11.38: Joan B. Silk; 11.39: From Figure 3.1 in R. I. M. Dunbar, 1988, Primate Social Systems, Cornell University Press, Ithaca, NY; 11.40a-b: Courtesy of Craig Stanford; 11.41: From Figure 1 in C. Stanford, J. Wallis, H. Matama, and J. Goodall, 1994, Patterns of predation by chimpanzees on red colobus monkeys at Gombe National Park, 1982–1991, American Journal of Physical Anthropology 94:213–228; 11.42: Robert Boyd; 11.43: Courtesy of William McGrew; 11.44: Adapted from Table 13 in C. Boesch and H. Boesch, 1989, Hunting behavior of wild chimpanzees in the Tai National Park, American Journal of Physical Anthropology 78: 547–573; 11.45: Courtesy of Craig Stanford.

CHAPTER 12

12.0: Peter Johnson/Corbis; 12.1: From p. 113 in K. Schick and N. Tooth, 1993, Making Silent Stones Speak, Simon and Schuster, New York; 12.2: Redrawn from p. 141 in K. Schick and N. Tooth, 1993, Making Silent Stones Speak, Simon and Schuster, New York; 12.4: Courtesy of Kim Hill; 12.:5 Courtesy of Nicholas Blurton Jones;12.9: Francesco d'Errico; 12.10: From Figure 6.1 in R. Potts, 1988, Early Hominid Activities in Olduvai, Aldine de Gruyter, New York; 12.11: From Figure 2 in R. Potts, 1984, Home bases and early hominids, American Scientist 72:338–347; 12.12: From Figure 3 in R. Potts, 1884, Home bases and early hominids, American Scientist 72:338–347; 12.13: © Art Wolfe/artwolfe.com; 12.14a–c: National Museum of Natural History, Smithsonian Institution, Washington, DC; 12.15a–b: © Y. Arthus-Bertrand/Peter Arnold, Inc.; 12.16: Robert Boyd and Joan B. Silk; 12.17: Joan B. Silk; 12.18: Robert Boyd; 12.19: Robert Boyd; 12.20: Drawing by Christian Gurney from Figure 2 in Henry T. Bunn and Ellen M. Kroll, 1986, Systematic butchery by Plio/Pleistocene homonids at Olduvai Gorge, Tanzania, Current Anthropology, 27:432–452; 12.21: Courtesy of Robert Bailey; 12.23: From Figure 4 in R. Potts, 1984, Home bases and early hominids, American Scientist, 72:338–347.

CHAPTER 13

13.0: Photo courtesy Prof. Peter Brown, The University of New England, Armidale, Australia. Permission also granted by Nature Publishing Group (http://www.nature.com); 13.1: Redrawn from Updike, Neil D. 1995. Mammalian migration and climate over the last seven million years. In Paleoclimate and Evolution, With Emphasis on Human Origins, E.S. Vrba, G.H. Denton, T.C.Partridge and L.H.Burckle, eds. New Haven, Yale University Press; 13.3: David Lordkipanidze; 13.:5 © Alan Walker; 13.6: Photograph courtesy of Alan Walker, reprinted with permission of the National Museums of Kenya; 13.8: From p. 232 in K. Schick and N. Tooth, 1993, Making Silent Stones Speak, Simon and Schuster, New York; 13.10: National Museum of Kenya; 13.11: National Museum of

Kenya; 13.12: From Figure 17 in C. Stringer and C. Gamble, 1993, In Search of the Neanderthals, Thames & Hudson, New York; 13.14: National Anthropological Archive; 13.16: From p. 224 in S. Jones, R. Martin, and D. Pilbeam, 1992, The Cambridge Encyclopedia of Human Evolution, Cambridge University Press, Cambridge; 13.17: R. Potts, Smithsonian Institution; 13.21: Courtesy of Richard Klein; 13.23: Photo courtesy Prof. Peter Brown, The University of New England, Armidale, Australia. Permission also granted by Nature Publishing Group (http://www.nature.com); 13.24: Javier Trueba/Madrid Scientific Films; 13.25: From Figure 1, Greenland Ice-Core Project, 1993, Climate instability during the last interglacial period recorded in the GRIP ice core, Nature 364:203–207; 13.28a-b: From Figure 34 in C. Stringer and C. Gamble, 1993, In Search of the Neanderthals, Thames & Hudson, New York; 13.29: From Figure 3.2 in C. Stringer, 1984, Adaptation in the Pleistocene, pp.55–83 in Hominid Evolution and Community Ecology, ed. by R. Foley, Academic Press, New York; 13.30a: © BIOS/Peter Arnold, Inc.; 13.30b: Maurizio Lanini/Corbis; 13.31: ©Martin Harvey; 13.32: © Erik Trinkaus; 13.33: Joan B. Silk; 13.34: Eric Delson; 13.35: Photograph by Michael Day.

CHAPTER 14

14.0: © Jean Clottes/DRAC Rhône-Alpes; 14.4: Courtesy of Science; 14.5: © Jean-Michel Labat/AUSCAPE International; 14.6: From Figure 5.6 in F. Bordes, 1968, La Paleolithique dans le monde, Hachette, Paris; 14.7: From Figure 7.9 in R. Klein, 1989, The Human Career, University of Chicago Press, Chicago; 14.8: From Figure 34.8 in O. Soffer, 1989, The Middle to Upper Paleolithic transition on the Russian Plain, pp. 714–742 in The Human Revolution, ed. by P. Mellars and C. Stringer, Princeton University Press, Princeton, NJ; 14.10: From Figure 13.4 in P. Mellars, 1996, The Neanderthal Legacy, Princeton University Press, Princeton, NJ; 14.11: © Jean Clottes/DRAC Rhône-Alpes; 14.12: Ulmer Museum, Ulm, Germany; 14.20: Housed in National Museum of Ethiopia, Addis Ababa. Photo © 2001 David L. Brill\Brill, Atlanta; 14.21: From Figure 15 in P. Mellars, 1989, Major issues in the emergence of modern humans, Current Anthropology, 30:349–385; 14.22: S. McBrearty and A. Brooks; 14.23: © Chip Clark: Museum of Natural History, Smithsonian; 14.24: © Centre for Development Studies, University of Bergen.

Part IV: Footprint on the moon from the Apollo landing (NASA).

CHAPTER 15

15.0: Ariel Skelley/Corbis; 15.1a-c: From Figure 20.12 in W. Bodmer and L. L. Cavalli-Sforza, 1976, Genetics, Evolution, and Man, W. H. Freeman, New York; 15.2: AP/Wide World Photos. 15.3a: George Long/Sports Illustrated; 15.3b: Richard Mackson/Sports Illustrated; 15.4: Adapted from p. 4 of M. Gopnik and M. B. Crago, 1991, Familial aggregation of a developmental language disorder, Cognition 39:1–50; 15.5a-b: Courtesy of Marion I. Barnhart, Wayne State University Medical School, Detroit, MI; 15.7: From Figures 2.14.1B and 2.14.9 in L. L. Cavalli-Sforza, P. Menozzi, and A. Piazza, 1994, The History and Geography of Human Genes, Princeton University Press, Princeton, NJ; 15.8: Sarah Errington/Panos Pictures; 15.9: From Figure 100 in G. Flatz, 1987, The genetics of lactose digestion in humans, Advances in Human Genetics 16:60; 15.10: © Jean Higgins/Unicorn Stock; 15.11: From Figure 2.3.3 in L. L. Cavalli-Sforza, P. Menozzi, and A. Piazza, 1994, The History and Geography of Human Genes, Princeton University Press, Princeton, NJ; 15.14: From Figure 1 (p. 241) in D. Hatl, 1980, Principles of Population Genetics, Sinauer, Sunderland, MA; 15.15: © John W. McDonough; 15.16: From Figure 19.12 in W. F. Bodmer and L. L. Cavalli-Sforza, 1976, Genetics, Evolution, and Man, Freeman, New York; 15.18: From Figure 16.6 in G. A. Harrison, J. M. Tanner, D. R. Pilbeam, and P. T. Baker, 1988, Human Biology: An Introduction to Human Evolution, Variation, Growth, and Adaptability, 3rd ed., Oxford Science Publications, Oxford; 15.19: From Figure 2.11.1 in L. L. Cavalli-Sforza, P. Menozzi, and A. Piazza, 1994, The History and Geography of Human Genes, Princeton University Press, Princeton, NJ; 15.20: From Figure 2.13.4 in L. L. Cavalli-Sforza, P. Menozzi, and A. Piazza, 1994, The History and Geography of Human Genes, Princeton University Press, Princeton, NJ; 15.21a–b: From Figures 2.2.3 and 2.3.3 in L. L. Cavalli-Sforza, P. Menozzi, and A. Piazza, 1994, The History and Geography of Human Genes, Princeton University Press, Princeton, NJ.

CHAPTER 16

16.0: © Perry van Duijnhoven; 16.1: © Stephen Dalton/Photo Researchers, Inc.; 16.2: © Joe Cavanaugh/DDB Stock Photo; 16.3: Oil painting by Martin Pate. Courtesy Cultural Resources, National Park Service; 16.4: From Figure 6.6 in W. H. Durham, 1992, Coevolution, Stanford University Press, Stanford, CA; 16.5: Anup Shah/Nature Picture Library; 16.6a: From Table 12.6 in A. P. Wolf, 1995, Sexual Attraction and Childhood Association, Stanford University Press, Stanford, CA; 16.6b: From Tables 11.1, 11.2, and 11.3 in A.P. Wolf, 1995, Sexual Attraction and Childhood Association, Stanford University Press, Stanford, CA; 16.7: Premaphotos Wildlife; 16.8: Dr. Ronald H. Cohn/The Gorilla Foundation; 16.9: Steve Winters/Courtesy of the Language Research Center; 16.10: Adapted from Table 71 in J Needham, 1988, Science and Civilization in China, vol. 4, pt. 3, Cambridge University Press, Cambridge, UK; 16.11a–b: From Figures 929 and 943 in J. Needham, 1988, Science and Civilization in China, vol. 4, pt. 3, Cambridge University Press, Cambridge, UK; 16.12: Courtesy of Susan Perry; 16.13: © Kennosuke Tsuda/Nature Production, Tokyo; 16.14: Behavioral Ecology Research Group, University of Oxford; 16.15: © Pete Oxford/Minden Pictures; 16.16: Courtesy of William C. McGrew; 16.17: Anup Shah/Nature Picture Library; 16.18: Photograph by Gaku Ohashi, Primate Research Institute, Kyoto University; 16.19: Robert Boyd; 16.20: Corbis; 16.21: © Kennan Harvey.

CHAPTER 17

17.0: The Marriage Contract, Jan Jozef II Horemans, 1768. Rockoxhouse, Antwerp (inv. nr. 77.9); 17.1: English Heritage Photo Library/G. P. Darwin on behalf of Darwin Heirlooms Trust; 17.2: From Tables 7.1 and 13.3 in N. Howell, 1979, Demography of the Dobe !Kung, Academic Press, New York; 17.3: From Figure 6.10 in J. Wood, 1994, Dynamics of Human Reproduction, Aldine de Gruyter, New York 17.4a-b: Redrawn from Kenrick & Keefe, 1997; 17.5. Redrawn from Table 2 in Schmitt et al. 2003; 17.6: Redrawn from Table 3 in Schmitt et al. 2003; 17.7a-b: Data redrawn from Haselton and Buss 2000; 17.8: From Tables 2 and 6 in D. Buss, 1989, Sex differences in human mate preferences: Evolutionary hypotheses tested in 37 cultures, Behavioral and Brain Sciences 12:1–49; 17.9: Photograph courtesy of Monique Borgerhoff Mulder; 17.10: From Figure 3.2 in M. Borgerhoff Mulder, 1988, Kipsigis bridewealth payments, pp. 65–82 in Human Reproductive Behavior, ed. by L. Betzig, M. Borgerhoff Mulder, and P. Turke, Cambridge University Press, Cambridge; 17.11: Photograph courtesy of Nancy Levine; 17.12: From N. L. Levine and J. B. Silk, 1997, When polyandry fails: Sources of instability in polyandrous marriages, Current Anthropology 38:375–398; 17.13: From Table 2 in Anderson et al. 1999. Evolution and Human Behavior 20:405-431; 17.14: From Figure 2 in Anderson et al. 1999. Evolution and Human Behavior 20:433-451;17.15: Courtesy of Frank Marlowe; 17.16: From Table 1 in Euler & Weitzel, 1996; 17.18: Photograph by Lennart Nilsson/Albert Bonniers Forlag AB, Behold Man, Little, Brown and Company; 17.19: Stephen Dalton/Photo Researchers, Inc.; 17.20: Adapted from Table III in J. B. Silk, 1980, Adoption in Oceania, American Anthropologist 82:799–820.

EPILOGUE

1: Courtesy of the National Portrait Gallery, London.

APPENDIX

1: From Figure B.1.b–c in G. Conroy, 1990, Primate Evolution, W. W. Norton, New York.